ADVANCES
IN LABORATORY
AUTOMATION
ROBOTICS

Edited by:

Janet R. Strimaitis
and
Gerald L. Hawk

Volume 4

Zymark Corporation
Zymark Center
Hopkinton, MA USA

Zymark Corporation   Hopkinton, MA USA

Zymark Corporation

Zymark Center
Hopkinton, MA 01748 USA   ISBN 0-931565-03-0
(617) 435-9501
Telex: 174 104
Telefax: (617) 626-8652

Current Printing(last digit)

10 9 8 7 6 5 4 3 2 1

PRINTED IN THE UNITED STATES OF AMERICA

Zymark, Zymate and EasyLab are registered trademarks,
PyTechnology and CONFIRM are trademarks of the Zymark Corporation.

PREFACE

This volume contains selected papers presented at the Fifth International Symposium on Laboratory Robotics-1987 held at the Boston Park Plaza Hotel, Boston, MA, USA, October 18-21, 1987. These papers cover a broad interdisciplinary range of topics on the application of robotic technology to laboratory automation. We are indebted to the authors for these contributed papers and their patience in producing this book. Also, we want to thank them for reviewing the final preparation of their manuscript.

The editors wish to thank Christine O'Neil, Karen Hughes, Michelle Alger and Therese Shannon for their valuable assistance at all stages in the preparation of this volume. Also, we wish to thank Jan Wittmer for the cover design.

This is Volume 4 of a series on Laboratory Robotics and we hope you find it stimulating as well as providing you with a review of current applications.

Janet R. Strimaitis

Gerald L. Hawk

CONTENTS

v

Microbiology

Biotechnology

vii

Advanced Technology

AUTOMATION OF HIGH PERFORMANCE LIQUID CHROMATOGRAPHY ANALYSES USING A ZYMATE LABORATORY ROBOT

C.N. Peck, K.M. Lehr, N.E. Lutenske
The Dow Chemical Company
Analytical & Environmental Chemistry Research Laboratory
Health & Environmental Sciences
1803 Building
Midland, Michigan 48674

ABSTRACT

An automated system based on a Zymate Laboratory Robot (Zymark Corporation, Hopkinton, MA) has been developed for sample preparation and high performance liquid chromatography (HPLC) analyses. This versatile system has been used to analyze samples from two very different, complex matrices - paperboard extracts and bird feed.

The first HPLC application developed for the robot involved analysis of paperboard extracts for a primary amine ranging in concentration from 50 to 200 ng/mL in solution. This was achieved by the preparation of a time-dependent, pre-column detrivative followed by HPLC analysis. Automation of this application reduced the analyst's time involvement from 16 hours to 1 hour for 50 samples and provided good precision (2.6% at 26.8 ng/mL and 2.2% at 121.4 ng/mL at the 95% confidence level) by providing exact timing and execution.

The robotic system was programmed for the extraction/HPLC analysis of an herbicide from bird feed using many of the same unit operations developed in the first application. Automation of this analysis reduced the analyst's time involvement by 85%. Use of serialized programming provided uniform sample handling and reduced the time required to obtain the result for the first sample from approximately 6 hours to 55 minutes for 15 samples and from 110 minutes to 55 minutes for 1 sample. The precision for this analysis was 2.6% at 47.05 mg/L and 2.5% at 121.4 mg/L at the 95% confidence level.

Innovative technology in these applications included the use of puncturable foil caps and septum caps as alternatives to screw-capping sample tubes, the construction of a liquid-dispensing hand equipped with a vented, double needle, and the invention of an "intelligent" cannula which allows recovery from head-on collisions.

INTRODUCTION

High performance liquid chromatography (HPLC) analyses are performed on large numbers of samples with complex matrices in the Analytical and Environmental Chemistry group of The Dow Chemical Company. Two areas providing routine samples are food-packaging component evaluation and avian toxicity studies. Many of the samples require extensive preparation or derivatization operations before the HPLC analysis can be performed.

Food-packaging component evaluations begin by extracting polymers or other materials used in food packages with solvents that are designated as food simulants.[1] The extracts are then analyzed to determine if any components of the food package have migrated into the food simulant. This type of study provides information about materials that may become indirect food additives at trace levels. This information is then used to make decisions about use of a particular material for food-packaging applications.

Avian toxicity studies are performed to determine the effect of agricultural chemicals in their diet on wildlife in the areas where the chemicals are used. An integral part of these studies is measuring the concentration of the test compound in the bird feed to determine the stability and uniformity of the test compound in the feed matrix.

A laboratory robotics system was designed to perform sample preparation and HPLC analyses on samples from a food-packaging evaluation and an avian toxicity study. The food-packaging evaluation application involved analysis of aqueous and ethanolic paperboard extracts for a primary amine. The robotic system was used to prepare a pre-column fluorescent derivative of the amine and inject the sample for HPLC analysis. The same robotic system was then used to extract an herbicide from bird feed, store a portion of the extract, and inject the sample for the HPLC analysis. This report describes the development of this flexible automated system for sample preparation coupled with HPLC analysis.

EXPERIMENTAL

Equipment

A Zymate I Laboratory Robot equipped with a general purpose hand, liquid-dispensing hands, master laboratory station (MLS), centrifuge, capper, vortex mixer, power and event controller (PEC), sample conditioning station, and a balance interface was used for these applications.

Other equipment used in these procedures included an LDC III constametric pump (Laboratory Data Control, Riviera Beach, FL), a Perkin-Elmer LS-4 fluorescence detector (Perkin-Elmer Corporation, Norwalk, CT), an LDC III variable wavelength detector, a Mettler AE-163 balance (Mettler Instrument Corporation, Hightstown, NJ), and a Hewlett-Packard 3357 laboratory data system (Hewlett-Packard Corp., Sunnyvale, CA).

Pre-column Derivatization/HPLC Analysis

The analyst begins the analysis by placing test tubes containing a measured aliquot of the test solution in the rack. The liquid chromatograph is turned on and allowed to equilibrate while the robot prepares the first sample. The robot moves the tube from the rack to the liquid dispensing nozzle, adds the derivatizing reagent and a diluent, mixes the sample, and returns the tube to the rack. The liquid dispensing hand is then used to sip the extract from the tube into the HPLC injector station. The hand is washed and returned to the parking station. Since the HPLC ten minute run time was longer than the three minutes required to prepare a sample for analysis, the robot prepared each sample immediately prior to the injection. The robot would begin the next sample just before the previous run had finished to provide exact timing and uniform sample handling. The unit operations for this analysis are summarized in Table 1.

TABLE 1. Unit Operations Program for Pre-Column Derivatization/HPLC Analysis.

Step	Performer	Operation
1	analyst	fill solvent bottles, put tubes containing measured amount of samples in rack, enter # of samples, start automated procedure
2	robot with PEC	turn on pump
3	robot with GPH	take tube from rack to liquid dispensing nozzle
4	MLS	add derivatizing agent and diluent
5	robot with GPH	move tube to vortex
6	vortex and PEC	mix sample
7	robot with GPH	return tube to rack
8	robot with LDH	place LDH in sample tube
9	MLS	sip sample into HPLC injector loop
10	HPLC injector	inject onto column
11	MLS	wash cannula
12	robot	wait for HPLC run
13	robot	return to step 2 for next sample
14	PEC	switch solvent reservoir bottles
15	PEC	turn pump off

GPH= General Purpose Hand; PEC= Power and Event Controller: LDH= Liquid Dispensing Hand;
MLS= Master Laboratory Station

Bird Feed Extraction/Analysis

The analyst begins this analysis by weighing approximately 5 g of bird feed sample into a tared 50 mL centrifuge tube which is sealed with a open top cap with a silicone septum. The liquid chromatograph is turned on and allowed to equilibrate while the robot prepares the first sample. The centrifuge tube containing the feed is placed in the vortex station and held in place with an air actuator. The robot uses a liquid-dispensing hand equipped with a vented outer needle to pierce the septum in the cap and add solvent to the bird feed in the tube. The tube is mixed for 20 minutes in the vortex station to extract the feed and then transferred to the centrifuge. The tube is centrifuged for 3 minutes and returned to the vortex station. An aliquot of the extract is transferred to a tared dilution tube using the needle hand and the MLS. Dilution solvent is then added to the extract. The diluted sample is mixed by drawing the solution in and out of the cannula, using the MLS, and sample is then injected into the HPLC. The unit operations for this analysis have been summarized in Table 2.

Many of the unit operation programs developed for the pre-column derivatization/HPLC analysis program were used as the foundation for the bird feed extraction/HPLC analysis program. This program was written to insure that each sample and standard has verifiable processing during extraction, dilution, and injection. The program was serialized (Figure 1) to minimize the time between HPLC runs and reduce the time required to obtain results from the first analysis. Serialization was achieved by using the vortex and HPLC run times to tare tubes and prepare subsequent samples.

TABLE 2. Unit Operations Program for Birdfeed Extraction/HPLC Analysis.

Step	Performer	Operation
1	analyst	fill solvent bottles, put tubes containing standard solution and samples in rack, enter run parameters, start automated procedure
2	robot with PEC	turn on pump; analyze standards
3	robot with GPH	take samples tube from rack and place in vortex station
4	robot with LDH2 and MLD	add extraction solvent
5	vortex and PEC	vortex sample
6	robot with GPH	tare dilution tubes (after first sample only)
7	robot with GPH	place sample tube in centrifuge
8	centrifuge	centrifuge sample
9	robot with GPH	take sample out of centrifuge and place in vortex station
10	robot with LDH2	sip aliquot of extract from centrifuge tube
11	robot with GPH	place dilution tube in balance and weigh aliquot
12	robot with LDH and MLS	mix sample and fill loop
13	HPLC injector	inject sample onto column
14	robot with GPH	repeat steps 3-5 for next sample
15	HPLC injector	make second injection;
16		repeat steps 6-14 for remaining samples; analyze standards
17	robot with PEC	switch solvent valve to wash column

PEC= power and event controller; GPH= general purpose hand with grippers; LDH2= liquid dispensing hand with vented needle; LDH= liquid dispensing hand with 6" cannula; MLS= master laboratory station

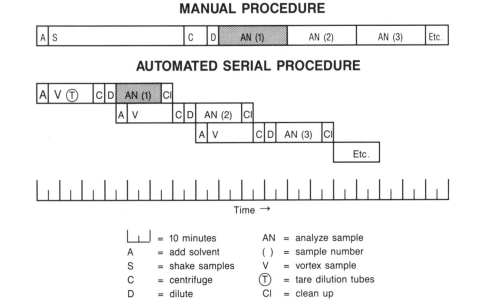

Figure 1. Serialization of Bird Feed Extraction/HPLC Analysis Replaces Shaking with the Vortex Mixing and Reduces Time Required to Obtain Results from First Sample by 55 Minutes.

RESULTS

The automated system for sample preparation/HPLC analysis was successful in reducing analyst time and providing reproducible, reliable numbers for both preparation of a fluorescent derivative of a primary amine in paperboard extracts and extraction of an herbicide from bird feed.

The precision at the 95% confidence level was 4.5% at 26.8 ng/mL and 2.2% at 214.2 ng/mL for the pre-column derivatization/HPLC analysis. The results from the analysis have been summarized in Table 3.

TABLE 3.   Precision Study of Fluorescing Derivative of Primary Amine at 26 ng/mL and 214 ng/mL Nominal Concentration.

Analyzed Concentration (ng/mL)	Analyzed Concentration (ng/mL)
26.01	216.35
26.38	211.18
26.76	212.03
26.33	212.30
26.93	212.97
26.84	216.44
27.36	214.85
27.79	217.44
26.8 $\pm$ 4.5%	214.2 $\pm$ 2.2%

The precision at the 95% confidence level was 2.6% at 47.05 mg/L and 2.5% at 121.4 mg/L. The results have been summarized in Table 4.

TABLE 4. Precision Study of Herbicide Standards Analyzed by Robotic System at 47 mg/L and 121 mg/L nominal concentration.

Concentration(mg/L)	Concentration(mg/L)
45.9	121.8
47.6	122.8
46.2	119.7
47.1	121.0
47.7	118.5
47.0	121.5
47.6	121.9
47.3	123.6
46.7	122.6
47.4	120.6
47.05 ± 2.6%	121.4 ± 2.5%

DISCUSSION

Automation of sample preparation coupled with HPLC analysis led to the development of several innovative ideas for solving problems encountered during the analyses. Use of centrifuge tubes and test tubes, which both have rounded bottoms, resulted in poor reproducibility in many screw-capping operations because the rounded bottom of the tube would move in the capper. Raising the jaws on the capper improved reproducibility in capping centrifuge tubes but made it difficult to use 3 dram autosampler vials in the analysis.

Elimination of screw capping for the tubes with rounded bottoms was achieved using two different approaches in the two applications. The pre-column derivatization/HPLC analysis used disposable culture tubes with an aluminum foil cover taped over the tube. The foil cover prevented contamination or evaporation of the sample prior to analysis and was easily punctured by the liquid dispensing nozzle during the analysis (Figure 2).

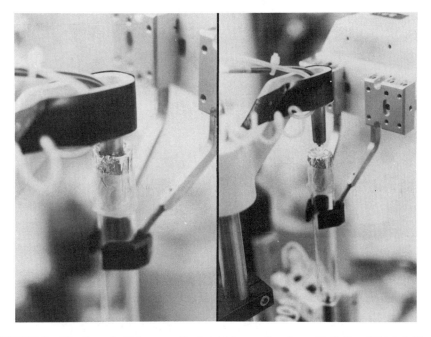

FIGURE 2. The Sample Tubes are Sealed with an Aluminum Foil Cap Which is Easily Punctured by the Liquid-dispensing Nozzle.

The bird feed extraction/HPLC analysis used an open top cap with a silicone septum which was pierced with a double vented needle. Design of this needle and cap allowed the introduction and withdrawal of solvent to and from the centrifuge tube without affecting the pressure (Figure 3).

Another problem developed during the use of a 6" cannula to sip solvent from test tubes when the test tube or other glassware was out of alignment relative to the robot. The cannula would collide with the object, bend, dispense the solvent on the table top and disrupt the analysis. The robot would continue the analysis with the bent cannula until the analyst returned and intervened.

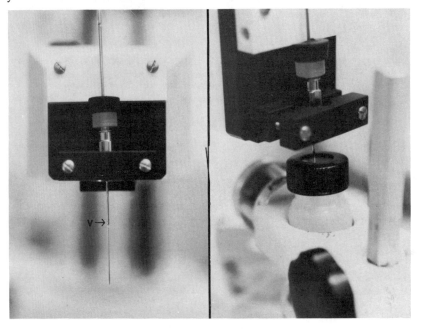

Figure 3.   The Vented (V) Double Needle Pierces the Septum Cap and Allows Introduction or Removal of Solvent Without Affecting Pressure.

This problem was eliminated with the development of a new bend resistant cannula hand (Figure 4). The block supporting the cannula was drilled out to allow the cannula to slide vertically if it came into contact with the test tube, rack or other object. A magnetic reed switch mounted on the top of the hand opened when the cannula was in the up position and the signal was relayed to an electrical input on the PEC. Corrective action was then programmed to reposition the cannula and repeat the procedure.

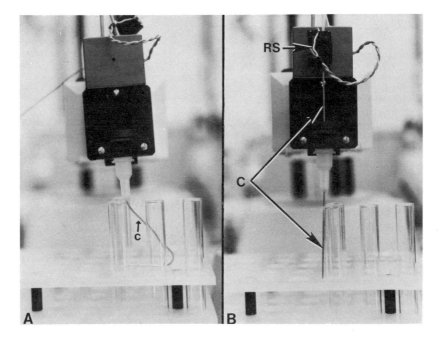

Figure 4. A. The Fixed Cannula (C) Bends When it Comes in Contact With the Rack. B. The Lehr Cannula (C) Slides Away From the Object in its Path and Does Not Bend. The Output From Magnetic Reed Switch (RS) is Relayed to the Power and Event Controller to Signal an Error Condition Exists.

CONCLUSIONS

Development of this robotic system has provided flexibility for handling two different types of sample preparations coupled with HPLC analysis. It has reduced tedium and time required for the analyst to process large numbers of samples.

The uniform sample history, precise timing, and ability to document the sample preparation procedure provide valuable tools necessary for good laboratory practices.

The modular design of the program software allows modification of these programs for other HPLC applications with different sample origins.

ACKNOWLEDGEMENTS

The authors wish to thank David Williams for the photography, Bruce Kropscott and Tim Lickly for their valuable suggestions and guidance in this project, and Linda Roy for preparation of this manuscript.

REFERENCES

1. "FDA Guidelines for Chemistry and Technology Requirements of Inderect Food Additive Petitions" Bureau of Foods, Food and Drug Administration, Department of Health, Education and Welfare, Washington, D.C. 20204, 1976.

GENERIC SAMPLE PREPARATION SYSTEM FOR AUTOMATION OF PESTICIDE RESIDUE ANALYSIS

I. Laws and R. N. Jones
Residues and Environmental Chemistry Section
ICI Plant Protection Division
Jealotts Hill Research Station
Bracknell, Berkshire
ENGLAND, RGl2 6EY

ABSTRACT

Generation of crop residue and environmental fate data is an important part of both the development of a new pesticide and the support for existing products. The development process spans a number of years and generates a large number of samples, from soil to animal tissue, all requiring analysis to low levels, typically 10 ppb. In our laboratory, which services ICI's worldwide interest in agrochemicals, the demand for this type of trace level analysis has increased dramatically over the last five years.

Pesticide residue methods vary greatly in detail, but many can be broken down into a series of similar physical processes- eg. extraction, liquid-liquid partition, solid phase clean-up followed by GLC or HPLC determination. The sample preparation phase of pesticide residue analysis therefore represented an ideal target for automation, provided the equipment used was flexible enough to meet the rapidly changing demands for different analysis.

A Zymark Laboratory Automation System was purchased to meet this need and has been developed to provide a generic sample preparation system for pesticide residues requiring GLC analysis from a wide variety of sample matrices. It is intended to extend the system to perform preparation of samples requiring analysis by HPLC in the near future.

The design, development, and performance of the system will be discussed.

INTRODUCTION

The registration of pesticides around the world, in combination with the development of many different products, is becoming more complex and expensive, requiring more detailed and extensive data submissions. This data demand has been reflected in the increased workload now being placed on ICI's plant protection division's (PPD) residue laboratories at Jealotts Hill in the UK. A number of factors have contributed to the larger workload:

1. The residue laboratories are responsible for providing environmental fate and residue data worldwide. Expansion of the business has seen the number of analyses performed in the laboratories rise by 100% in less than four years.

2. The cost of each analysis has risen with people, consumables, and laboratory space all becoming more expensive.

3. To compound the problems listed above, residue chemistry has become more complex with a number of specialized requirements being introduced over the past few years, e.g. the EEC directive on water quality requiring analytical methods for pesticides in water to levels of 0.1ug/L (100 ppt). Such demands require complex methods and can involve large numbers of samples.

Against this background of rising demands and costs, but not resources, it was clear that we needed to examine carefully the way in which we performed our analysis. Following a review of the methods used by the residue laboratories a two-fold approach to increasing efficiency has been developed. These areas are summarized on the following page.

a) **To automate existing methods and techniques.** The residue chemistry laboratories have vast experience in conventional residue chemistry, and it was clearly important to develop and make full use of this valuable resource.

b) **To develop or adapt new techniques for use in environmental analysis**- e.g. immunoassay and super critical fluid chromatography, both of which have the potential to reduce the amount of time-consuming sample clean-up and derivitization required prior to analysis of a sample.

This paper describes the development of an automated system capable of applying existing techniques to increase throughput of samples in our residue laboratories.

SYSTEM SPECIFICATION

Examination of most chemical assays, including pesticide residue chemistry, reveals three familiar areas which describe the typical phases in the method used (sample preparation, analysis/determination, data capture and reporting). The proportion of time taken by each step is dependent on the type of assay. With the use of autosamplers on chromatographic instruments and the advent of computer data capture and reporting, the sample preparation phase of residue chemistry has become the rate limiting step in any analysis. It consumes up to 80% of an analyst's working time. This phase of the analytical process was therefore an important target for automation. The most important criteria for a successful system are listed below:

1) Accuracy and Precision - Any system must produce of a quality at least equivalent to those of a human analyst.

2) Flexibility - This laboratory supports a large number of compounds. Any automated system would have to be easily adapted to a range of methods.

3) Reliability - All work carried out by the laboratory is performed to important deadlines; any automated system would have to be reliable to enable it to be used confidently for important work.

4) Any automated equipment would need to be able to operate unattended, preferably overnight, if large gains in productivity were to be made.

5) The equipment must be safe in operation including the use of volatile solvents and radio-labelled samples.

An initial examination of the methods used in the laboratories revealed a huge variety in solvents, extraction times, chromatographic clean-up conditions etc. and the use of one system to cover a number of these looked unlikely. If, however, the physical processes used during an analysis were considered, a series of tasks emerged which were common to almost all of the methods examined. These processes include:

-Weighing Of Sample

-Addition Of Extraction Solvent

-Extraction By Maceration

-Liquid - Liquid Partition

-Solid Phase Clean-Up

-Concentration Of Extract

-Dissolution Of Extract

-Transfer To Chromatography Vial

If a system able to perform all of these steps could be constructed, then a generic residue chemistry tool able to meet the flexibility requirements of the laboratory would be available. In order to develop such a system, a typical method which could be directly transferred to an automated system was chosen. The method chosen covered residue analysis for "Karate", a novel pyrethroid insecticide currently under development by PPD, for use on a wide variety of crops around the world. As a result of this wide application, the project was expected to generate large numbers of samples and therefore presented a good target for automation. The structure of PP321 and a flow scheme for its analysis are shown in Figures 1 and 2.

KARATE

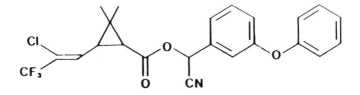

CODE NUMBER : 321
Novel Pyrethroid Insecticide
Active at Low Rates
Low Environmental Impact

FIGURE 1. Structure of "Karate"

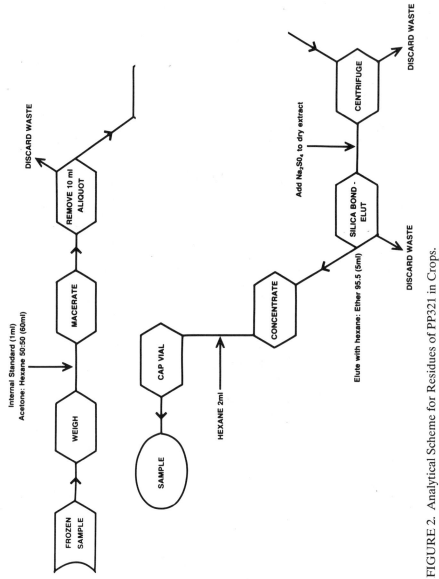

FIGURE 2. Analytical Scheme for Residues of PP321 in Crops.

In early 1986 a Zymark Laboratory Automation System was purchased to automate the determination of "Karate" residues, with a view to later expanding the capabilities of the system to a range of other compounds.

SYSTEM DEVELOPMENT

The system components were placed on the table to provide the key analytical processes in defined areas of the table. Figure 3 shows a schematic layout of the robot table. The close proximity of modules required in the same physical process (e.g. vortex and centrifuge for liquid-liquid partitions) enabled faster operation of the system by minimizing robot travel time. The software to run the system was also developed in a modular way to provide a series of physical processes which could be combined in any sequence with a range of solvents and other variables to build up a wide variety of methods. This modular or generic approach was followed to support rapid transfer of methods to the automated system and minimum down time between applications.

RESULTS

The programming and validation work for the development of the first automated assay for residues of "Karate" required approximately five months to complete. The resulting system is able to process eight samples during a working day or up to 16 samples when running overnight (an analyst would normally prepare 10 samples in a normal working day). The system therefore represented a significant potential increase in analytical resources.

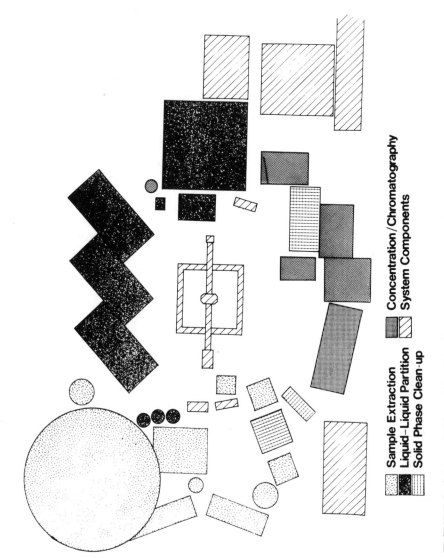

Sample Extraction
Liquid–Liquid Partition
Solid Phase Clean-up

Concentration/Chromatography
System Components

FIGURE 3. Schematic Plan of Residue Chemistry System.

Validation of PP321 Assay

It was clearly important to establish that the assays performed by the robot gave results of a satisfactory standard which were comparable with those obtained by human analysts. The first stage in this procedure was to process samples fortified at a known level with the analyte and internal standard. The results of two validation runs are shown in Table 1 and demonstrate satisfactory performance with excellent precision and accuracy. The criteria used within our laboratories for acceptance of data require internal standard recoveries of $100\pm30\%$ and discrimination between the analyte and internal standard through the method of <7%.

TABLE 1. Control Apple Fortified at 0.1 mg/kg with PP321 and Internal Standard.

Sample No.	Internal Standard Recovery %	Corrected Residue (mg/kg)
1	106	0.100
2	108	0.102
3	107	0.102
4	105	0.100
5	75	0.104
6	98	0.103
7	83	0.102
8	80	0.105
9	83	0.106
Mean	95	0.102
Std Deviation	12	0.002

The validation of the system was continued by assessing recovery of analyte over the range of residues typically found in samples. Control samples were fortified with levels of "Karate" ranging from .01 ppm (the usual limit of determination of the method) to 1.0 ppm. The robot system was used to add internal standard at the relevant level. The results of this study are shown in Table 2. No bias was detected across the range of concentrations examined, with the precision and accuracy of the data being satisfactory. No carryover of residues was detected between samples.

The final stage of validation, a direct comparison of human and robot generated results, is shown in Table 3. No significant difference between the results was found, with the slight variation in reported residue being due to non-homogeneous samples. All of the residue is associated with the peel which forms <1% of the sample. Slight differences in the distribution of peel in the prepared sample taken for analysis gives rise the variation of result seen in Table 3.

Similar validation packages have been generated for the other assays transferred to the automated system. All have provided satisfactory data with no bias between human and robot prepared samples.

TABLE 2. Control Apple Fortified over the Range 0.01 - 1.0 mg/kg with PP321 (internal standard added by robot).

Sample No.	Fortification level (mg/kg)	Internal Standard Recovery %	Corrected Residue (mg/kg)
1	0.01	71	0.013
2		46	0.013
3	0.05	84	0.051
4		71	0.052
5	0.10	80	0.105
6		83	0.106
7	1.0	108	1.06
8		112	1.03

TABLE 3. Comparison of Human and Robot Generated Data (samples are apples and pears).

Sample No.	Robot Int. Std. Recovery %	Robot Residue (mg/kg)	Human Int. Std. Recovery %	Human Residue (mg/kg)
1	83	0.10	119	0.10
2	84	0.11	127	0.12
3	83	0.09	111	0.07
4	81	0.08	127	0.07
5	88	0.08	127	0.09

Development of Additional Assays

The modular design of the system has significantly reduced the development time required for transfer of new assays to the system. Methods of analysis for five compounds have now been developed on the system in times ranging from as little as one week for an assay similar to that for "Karate" to six weeks for a complex HPLC based assay. These times are significantly less than the five months required to develop the first method.

Routine Use

The system has been used to process over 700 samples in a period of approximately one year. By taking full advantage of the modular layout of the system, it is possible to run a complex assay overnight and then run a simple assay during the working day by simply replacing sample racks and inserting of new software. Down time between complex assays is less than one week, including validation time for the new assay. The mechanical reliability of the equipment has been excellent, with trouble free routine operation for periods of up to four weeks.

DISCUSSION

By using a generic approach, a system capable of automating a wide range of pesticide residue chemistry methods has been developed. This generic approach has also enabled rapid transfer of methods to the automated system and reduced down time between applications to a minimum. The system has further demonstrated the ability to perform reliably when operated nightly for periods of up to four weeks. It is estimated that, with a full range of methods, the system will provide analytical resources equivalent to two man years per year of effort. It is intended to expand the capability of the system to include chromatographic analysis immediately following the preparation of the sample, which in conjunction with computer data capture and reporting, will provide fully automated sample analysis.

AUTOMATION OF DRUGS OF ABUSE TESTING WITH FISHER'S MAXX 5[tm] ROBOT & GC/MS ANALYSIS

Chauder Li, John Potucek and Harold Edelstein
Fisher Scientific Company Chemical Manufacturing Division
1 Reagent Lane
Fair Lawn, New Jersey 07410

ABSTRACT

Three major factors in the current testing procedures to confirm the presence of drugs of abuse justify robotic automation. These are: (1) increasing numbers of specimens demand higher sample throughput procedures, (2) higher cost and time-consuming sample preparation require a more rapid and cost-effective process, (3) the importance of precise scientific and legal documentation.

In this paper, we present two recent developments in the testing of drugs of abuse. We have developed a new solid phase extraction procedure to prepare urinary samples and analyze these for cocaine metabolite derivative by GC/MS. Based on this manual procedure, a Fisher Scientific Maxx 5 robotic system was built and installed. This system is designed to perform sample preparation of the cocaine metabolite, benzoylecgonine, in urine specimens and prepare these for GC/MS testing.

INTRODUCTION

Since drugs of abuse have become a major problem in society and the workplace in recent years, the demand for testing to identify the usage of these illegal substances has increased dramatically. There is a critical need and a legal requirement for an accurate, rapid, and low-cost confirming test such as a Standard Operating Procedure for each drug following a positive screening trial. Total automation of the drugs of abuse testing program appears to provide an ideal solution for this need. This program, in general, should include three elements: automated sample preparation with a laboratory robot, automated analytical measurement with an autosampler, and computerized data reduction and documentation. Currently, the U.S. Army drugs of abuse testing laboratories and certain commercial laboratories are involved in the development of this type of system. Fisher Scientific Co. is collaborating with these laboratories to develop an automated system for the sample preparation of urine specimens prior to GC/MS analysis. This communication is a progress report on the project.

Testing of urinary samples is the most common procedure employed in a drugs of abuse testing program. To confirm the existence of cocaine in a urine specimen, the identification of its predominate metabolite, benzoylecgonine, by GC/MS analysis is usually performed. In this paper, we present the results obtained from two areas:

1. The development of a new sample preparation methodology for the cocaine metabolite, benzoylecgonine, and the GC/MS analysis of this analyte,

2. The design and the installation of a laboratory robotic system to automate this new sample preparation method.

URINALYSIS TESTING OF COCAINE METABOLITE BY GC/MS

Chemistry of Testing Procedure

The testing for the presence of drugs of abuse is first accomplished by a screening method such as thin layer chromatography (TLC) , enzyme multiplied immunoassay technique (EMIT) , or radioimmunoassay (RIA). Samples indicating a positive result should then be confirmed by a second specific and unambiguous technique. GC/MS is accepted as the method of choice for this confirmation.[1] According to a Standard Operating Procedure supplied by U.S. Army drugs of abuse testing laboratory, the confirmatory testing of cocaine by GC/MS involves three steps: 1. liquid/liquid extraction of the major metabolite of cocaine, benzoylecgonine, from urine specimen, 2. treatment of the isolated benzoylecgonine to form an alkylated derivative and subsequent liquid/liquid extraction of the derivative, 3. GC/MS analysis of the isolated drug derivative. This multiple liquid/liquid extraction method is not ideal for a large testing program because it is time-consuming and labor intensive.

Solid Phase Extraction

The first step in the design of an automated sample preparation procedure is the development of a simple and efficient manual procedure which can be automated by a laboratory robot. We have achieved this goal by converting the multiple liquid/liquid extraction process to the solid phase extraction method. Thus, benzoylecgonine was extracted from urine samples by a PrepSep[tm] C_{18} solid phase extraction column (Fisher Scientific Co.). The extract can be selectively removed from the C_{18} column and converted to an alkylated derivative. This derivative is then further purified by adsorption onto and subsequent removal from a PrepSep C_1 solid phase extraction column (Fisher Scientific Co.). Using a commercial vacuum manifold, the sample preparation of twelve urine samples can be performed simultaneously. This new solid phase extraction procedure provides a rapid and reliable method for the detection of the cocaine metabolite in urine by GC/MS. It is currently being validated in a commercial laboratory for large scale testing in a drugs of abuse program.

Gas Chromatography/Mass Spectrometry

This new solid phase extraction method was employed to prepare urine samples known to contain three different concentration levels of benzolyecgonine respectively: 60, 150, and 300 ng/mL. Deuterated benzoylecgonine was added to the urine specimen as an internal standard. The isolated alkylated derivative was analyzed by GC/MS on an HP 5890 GC/5970 MSD instrument with a GC capillary column (HP 5, 5% diphenyl/95% dimethyl polysiloxane, 12.5M x 0.2 mM x 0.33 uM). Quantitation of the analytes was obtained in a Selective Ion Monitoring (SIM) mode at the mass ratio of 224/227. Our data indicated that the percentage recovery of the alkylated benzoylecgonine ranged from 91.70% to 99.92% using the deuterated molecule as the internal standard. The precision of the sample preparation, expressed as coefficient of variation (CV), ranged from 2.2% to 3.6%.

MAXX 5 ROBOTIC SYSTEM

System Design

The primary goal in this project was to develop an automated system which (1) performed the testing of cocaine metabolite in urine with the same or better accuracy and precision as the manual solid phase extraction procedure, and (2) could be operated routinely by personnel without extensive experience in robotic training. Based on this concept, a Fisher Scientific Maxx 5 robotic system was built and installed. The system was designed as an integral unit with all the components assembled on modern Contempra^{tm} laboratory furniture. The robotic modules were located around the benchtop and the various accessories were stored in the lower cabinets. A schematic of bench layout is

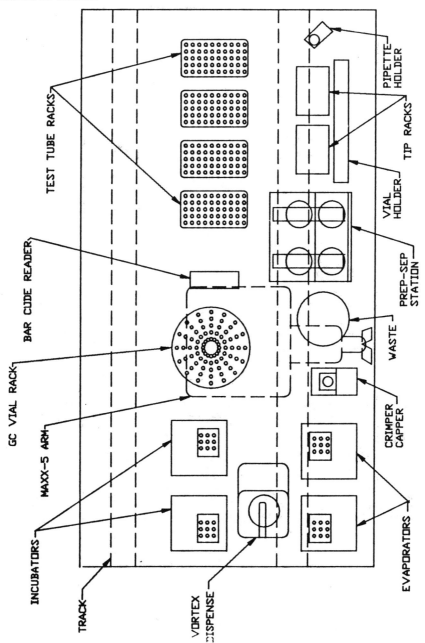

FIGURE 1. Maxx-5 Cocaine Method Table Layout.

shown in Figure 1 which includes a robotic arm on track, PrepSep stations, a Barcode reader, a Crimp capper, Evaporators module, Incubators module, Vortex dispenser with nozzles, pipette tip holder, and racks for test tubes, pipette tips, and vials. The cabinets under the bench top stores the system controller, two units of Cavro^{tm} liquid dispenser module, air compressor and air manifold unit, vacuum pump, waste container, and the electrical and plumbing systems. The robotic arm is mounted on an overhead linear track (Figure 2) with the capability to reach a work area of three by seven feet horizontal and two feet vertical.

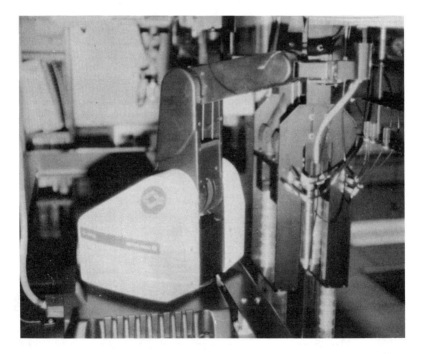

FIGURE 2. Maxx 5 Robotic Arm.

System Operation

The Maxx 5 Robotic system is controlled directly by an IBM PC or compatible computer. This system is operated by a menu-driven process. Figure 3 shows the Main Menu. A Maxx 5 robotic program consists of several components; these are paths, appliances, pallets, I/O switches, delays, and logic statements. A "path" is made of a series of steps taught to the robot by the user with a joystick. Each step is memorized by pressing the space bar. "Appliances" are subroutines generated by the user for the control of the robotic modules. "Pallets" are programs defining locations in a multiple vessel holder such as a test tube rack; they are programmed by recording four locations using the joystick. To create a subprogram, such as a path or a pallet, a user simply follows the steps listed on the menu screen shown in Figure 4. A typical Maxx 5 program is listed Table 1.

```
                         MAIN MENU

              Joystick                (Adjust Joystick)
              Create Test a Path      (Manual Control)
              Name Accessories        (Assign Names to I/O)
              Edit                    (Any File)
              Verify syntax           (Check a Program)
              Run                     (A Program)
              Library                 (Copy/Delete/Rename)
              Home Robot
              Free arm

              Quit                    (Return to DOS)
```

FIGURE 3. Main Menu Screen.

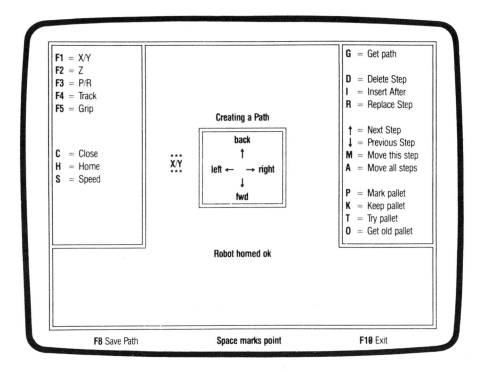

FIGURE 4. Creating a Path Screen.

TABLE 1. An Example of a Maxx 5 Program.

Command	Action
VAR N	Declares variables
Use initial	Appliance - Subprogram sets all switches off
Home	Homes robot
N = 1	Counter
On vacuum	Switch - turns vacuum on
Use C_{18}	Appliance - loads and conditions PrepSep C_{18} column
Delay 5	Robot waits 5 seconds
Outrack sample N	Pallet - sample N taken out of test tube rack
To TBar	Path - sample taken to barcode reader
Use Barread	Appliance - barcode in read
Revto TBar	Path - reverse path taken to test tube rack
Inrack sample N	Pallet - sample returned to test tube rack
Off vacuum	Switch - turns vacuum off

TABLE 2. Procedure and Modules for Automated Cocaine Analysis.

Experimental Procedures	Maxx 5 Robotic Modules
1. Load and condition PrepSep C_{18} column[2]	Maxx 5 arm PrepSep station Cavro liquid dispenser Module 1
2. Read barcode number of urine specimen	Maxx 5 arm Barcode reader
3. Pipette urine sample to PrepSep column	Maxx 5 arm pipette holder
4. Solid phase extraction of urine sample	PrepSep station Cavro liquid dispenser Module 1
5. Evaporate and dry the extract at 60^0C under N_2	Evaporators module
6. Derivatization of benzoylecgonine	Cavro liquid dispenser Module 2 Incubators module
7. Hydrolysis of the derivative reaction mixture	Vortex dispenser with nozzles Cavro liquid dispenser Module 2
8. Solid phase extraction alkylated benzoylecgonine by PrepSep C_1 column	PrepSep station of Cavro liquid dispenser Module 1
9. Crimp vials containing purified alkylated benzolyecgonine	Crimp capper
10. Read barcode number of crimped vials	Barcode reader
11. Load vials in GC/MS autosampler tray	GC vial tray

AUTOMATED SAMPLE PREPARATION OF URINARY COCAINE SPECIMEN

The experimental procedures and the Maxx 5 robotic modules designed to carry out the automated sample preparation of urinary cocaine specimens are listed sequentially in Table 2.

Method Summary

To perform this automated sample preparation of urinary cocaine samples on a routine basis, we have written a Maxx 5 robotic program which consisted of three sections of subprograms.   Program 1 carries out experimental procedures from step 1 to step 5. Program 2 executes the procedures of step 6 and 7; program 3 completes the remaining procedures from step 8 to step 11.   After the robot completes the sample preparation, laboratory staff will manually load a GC autosampler tray for the further analytical measurement. Several innovative engineering designs are noteworthy here. For instance, Figure 5 displays a PrepSep station which consists of four column dispensers and a dual column extraction station, all built as a single module. The column will be loaded onto the extraction station automatically without the robotic arm. This design increases the sample throughput tremendously. A barcode reader uses laser light to scan the barcode number and store it directly in the PC computer. Figure 6 shows a crimp capper which holds the cap with vacuum and crimps the cap onto the GC vial with air pressure. The Cavro liquid dispenser module has a capability of employing up to 8 syringe units to deliver liquid from 10 uL to 100 mL.   Figure 7 displays evaporator modules for drying liquid samples at elevated temperature under a nitrogen stream.

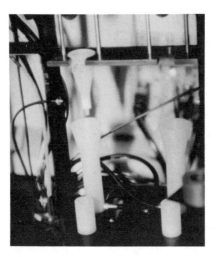

FIGURE 5. PrepSep Station.

FIGURE 6. Crimp Capper.

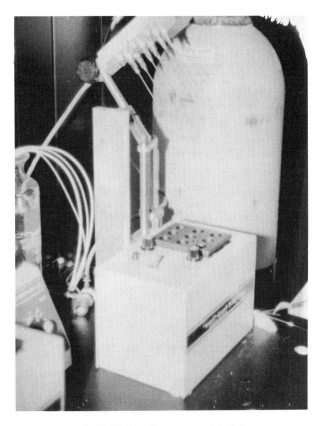

FIGURE 7. Evaporator Module.

CONCLUSION

As an ongoing research effort to develop new sample preparation methodologies for analytical laboratories engaged in the analyses of drugs of abuse and also environmental pollutants, we have presented some of our recent laboratory developments in this paper. We have successfully developed a new solid phase extraction procedure for the sample preparation of urinary cocaine metabolite, benzoylecgonine, and performed GC/MS analysis of this analyte. Further, a Maxx 5 robotic system has been designed and constructed based on this manual sample preparation method. This system consists of several innovative engineering-designed robotic modules such as PrepSep station, Cavro liquid dispenser module, barcode reader, crimp capper, and evaporator module. This Maxx 5 robotic system will shortly be routinely performing sample preparation in the testing of urinary cocaine specimens in a commercial testing program.

REFERENCES

1.   John Jewell, "The Testing of Drugs of Abuse in the Military", paper presented in the Conference of Testing for Drugs of Abuse in Toronto, Canada, January 26-27, 1987.

2.   C. Li, J. Potucek, H. Edelstein, "Automated Method Development of Liquid Solid Extraction", Advances in Laboratory Automation - Robotics 1986, J. Strimaitis and G. L. Hawk, ed. (Zymark Corporation, Inc., Hopkinton, MA, 1986), pp 451-465.

Maxx 5, PrepSep, and Contempra are registered trademarks of Fisher Scientific Company. Cavro is the trademark of Cavro Scientific Instruments, Inc.

TRACE LEVEL ANALYSIS OF HERBICIDES PERFORMED ON A NEW ROBOTIC SAMPLE PREPARATION SYSTEM

Peyton C. Beals, William Wildman, and Patricia Timmoney
Waters Chromatography Division
Millipore Corporation
34 Maple St.
Milford, MA 01757

ABSTRACT

The analysis and quantitation of very low levels of herbicides has gained increasing importance. The fact that these compounds, even in low parts per billion concentrations, may have a profound effect on living organisms and the environment, has required researchers to seek greater sensitivity from their analytical methods. One means of obtaining higher sensitivity is to enrich the sample through the use of a small packed bed. This method of trace enrichment employing a small solid phase extraction column has gained rather broad acceptance. However, even this form of concentration suffers the disadvantage of being labor intensive and producing results which may vary significantly due to erratic flow rates and volumes.

This paper presents the automated trace enrichment of herbicides performed on a new, easily configured, and space efficient robotic system. This system will be described and the chromatographic results of the analysis will be discussed in terms of reproducibility, sensitivity, linearity and recovery.

INTRODUCTION

The analysis and quantification of trace level ground water contaminants has always presented certain specific and difficult problems. These problems range from sample collection and transport to method sensitivity.

One trend has continued throughout the history of ground water analysis in general and specifically with herbicide contamination of ground water - the requirement to detect and quantitate increasingly lower concentrations. The need to detect herbicide concentrations at parts per billion and even parts per trillion levels has been driven by the realization that these compounds can have significant environmental impact at very low concentrations. It has also been demonstrated that these compounds, once in the water table, can be effectively transported to every corner of a given ecosystem. These two factors combined dictate that the presence of herbicides and also pesticides in ground water must be detected early so that concentration trends can be monitored and sources may be identified and controlled.

The burden of this detection falls on the shoulders of various laboratories in both the public and private sectors. These labs are faced with an increasing work load comprised of samples which must be examined more rigorously than ever before. Typically, these laboratories are compelled to employ new techniques and technologies along with larger sample volumes to meet the requirements of more stringent standards. Unfortunately, unproven techniques and larger sample volumes can often run counter to the researcher's desire to generate better data on a given sample and to do this for larger numbers of samples.

Historically, trace levels of organics in water have been isolated by means of liquid-liquid extraction. Distillation or evaporation and reconstitution have also been employed when circumstances were advantageous to such techniques. However, these techniques all suffer, to a greater or lesser extent, from variability due to transfer loss, inaccuracies in volumetric delivery, inadequate solvent purity, and sample volatility. Also, large sample volumes often render these techniques impractical.

One other technique has gained wide acceptance, during the past decade, as applied to trace analysis of ground water. That technique is solid phase extraction (SPE). A small device filled with a bed of chromatographic packing material is utilized to preconcentrate contaminants by passing the entire ground water sample across it. Then the contaminants are eluted off the SPE column by a much smaller volume, thus affecting a concentration effect. This paper presents such a method which has been fully automated using a new robotic sample preparation device, the Waters MilliLab^{tm} Workstation.

EXPERIMENTAL

Equipment and Materials

The Waters MilliLab Workstation is a self-contained automated sample preparation device. Capabilities inherent in the standard MilliLab Workstation configuration include liquid handling, microfiltration, solid phase extraction, dilution, evaporation, reagent or standard addition, and sampler transfer. Two additional MilliLab Workstation accessories, the HPLC Injector Accessory and Multiple Intake Accessory, were also employed in this present work. The MilliLab Workstation was interfaced to an HPLC system comprised of a Model 600 Multisolvent Delivery System, a Model 481 UV Wavelength Detector, and a RESOLVE^{tm} C_{18}-5u column. Samples were concentrated on C_{18} Sep-Pak Plus^{tm} extraction cartridges. Data was collected and results computed by a Model 840 Data and Control Station. No additional modifications to the MilliLab

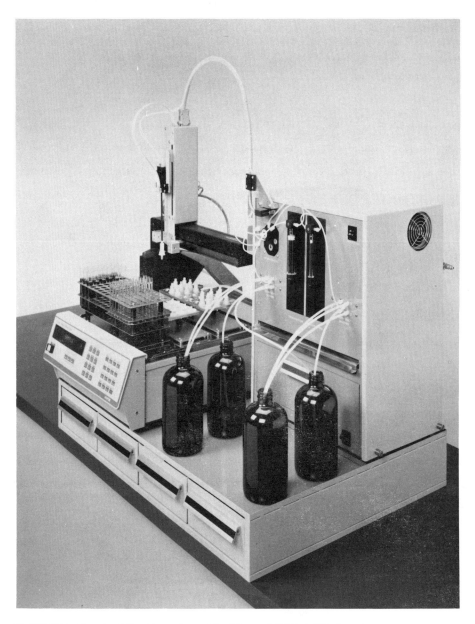

FIGURE 1. Standard Configuration of the Waters MilliLab Workstation.

Workstations were necessary to perform this work. (All HPLC instrumentation is from Waters Chromatography Division, Millipore Corporation, Milford, MA).

Quantitive grade standards of 2,4-dichlorophenoxyacetic acid (2,4D), 2,4,5-trichlorophenoxyacetic acid (2,4,5T), and 2-(2,4,5-trichlorophenoxy) proprionic acid (2,4,5 TP) Acid were utilized (PolyScience Corporation, Niles, IL.) and weights were taken on a Model A 200 S analytical balance (Sartorius, Brinkman Instrument Co., Div. of Xybron, Westbury, N.Y.). The acetonitrile and methanol were of analytical grade (J.T. Baker, Phillipsburg, N.J.) Water of 1 mega-Ohm purity was supplied by a Milli-R/Q Water Purification System (Millipore Corp., Bedford, MA).

The Waters MilliLab Workstation (Figure 1) is comprised of three main modules: the Base Module, the Fluidics Module, and the Transport Module. The standard system allows a total of six solvents to be delivered by two syringe pumps. The addition of the Multiple Intake Accessory allows up to fifteen solvents or, as in the case of this paper, sample per syringe pump. All fluid handling and all movement or utilization of disposable devices is done through the use of the Multi-Function Probe (Figure 2). This probe is equipped with an expandable tip constructed of Kalrez[tm] fluoroelastomer which expands when inserted into a female Luer fitting. This forms a seal which allows the probe to move the devices and pass fluids through them at relatively high pressures.

BLADDER

FIGURE 2. Detail of Multi-Funtion Probe Tip.

Procedure

A twenty three step method (Figure 3) was written to instruct the MilliLab to process each sample as follows:

Wash the probe with methanol/acetonitrile (70/30)

Precondition the Sep-Pak Plus cartridge by passing 4 mL of the Methanol-Acetonitrile mixture and 6 mL of 2% Acetic Acid across a C_{18} Sep-Pak Plus solid phase extraction cartridge.

Prime the fluidic system and probe with the sample.

Re-attach the cartridge and pass a specified volume (1000 mL) of sample across the cartridge.

Purge excess fluid (water) from cartridge with gas (air).

Elute and collect the herbicide fraction with methanol-acetonitrile mixture.

Purge residual sample from cartridge with gas (air).

Dispose of the Sep-Pak Plus Cartridge into the solid waste container.

Transfer 100 uL of sample to the HPLC Injector Accessory.

Inject 20 uL of sample into the HPLC system.

Instruct the data station to begin data collection.

It should be noted that ten steps (SELECTs and REPLACEs) in the method program are required only to instruct the workstation to attach and detach the SPE cartridge. If these are disregarded, a nearly one to one correlation exists between the MilliLab Workstation pre-programed step routines and manual chemical operations.

Samples were prepared by making serial dilutions of a 10 parts per million solution of 2,4-D, 2,4,5-T and 2,4,5-TP in water. It was necessary to acidify this solution with acetic acid to enhance solubility and retain the compounds in their acid forms. Sample concentrations prepared and subsequently analyzed were 200 parts per trillion, 20 parts per billion, 100 parts per billion, and 500 parts per billion.

MilliLab Method Worksheet

METHOD DESCRIPTION			
Method to Prepare	Trace Enrichment	METHOD DESCRIPTION	
Saved in file #	5	Tube Set 2	43
Element Rack 1	C18 Sep-Pak Plus	Tube Set 3	0
Element Rack 2		Tube Set 4	0
Auxiliary GasPressure	5 psi	Tube Set 5	0
Reagent Reservoirs 7 ___ 8 ___		Tube Set 6	0
9 ___ 10 ___			

Pump 1 — Syringe 5000 ul, Solvent 33 2% HOAC, Solvent 34 MeOH-ACN, Solvent 3
Pump 2 — Syringe 1000 ul, Solvent 1 Water, Solvent 2, Solvent 3

PARAMETERS

STEP TYPE	ELEMENT E-RACK (A)	SYRINGE (B)	VOLUME (C)	COUNTS (D)	SPEED (E)	SOLVENT (F)	FROM (G)	FROM HT. (H)	TO (I)	TO HEIGHT (J)	PORT (K)	DIRECTION (L)	DELAY DWELL (M)
1 WASH	0	1	5000	2	6	34							
2 SELECT	1												
3 WASH	1	1	5000	2	15	33							
4 REPLACE													
5 ELUTE		1	5000	3	6	99			11	0			
6 SELECT	1												
7 ELUTE		1	5000	200	15	99			11	0			
8 REPLACE													
9 VALVE									11	0	6		15
10 SELECT	1												
11 VALVE									11	0	6		30
12 REPLACE													
13 WASH	0	1	5000	3	6	34							
14 SELECT	1												
15 ELUTE		2	1000	1	15	1			2	0			
16 REPLACE													
17 VALVE									11	0	6		15
18 SELECT	1												
19 VALVE									2	0	6		30
20 REPLACE													
21 WASH	0	1	5000	2	6	34							
22 SAMPLE		2	100	1	15	1	2	0	12	0			
23 INJECT													
24													
25													

Letters in parentheses should be used to cross reference which STEPS require which of the above PARAMETERS.

WASH (A,B,C,D,E,F)   SELECT (A)   VALVE (I,J,K,M)
SAMPLE (B,C,D,E,F,G,H,I,J)   REPLACE No Parameters   WISP (L)
ELUTE (B,C,D,E,F,I,J)   DISPOSE No Parameters   INJECT (M)

FIGURE 3. MilliLab Worksheet Showing Entire Method Program.

RESULTS

Previous to this present work, it had been experimentally determined that the minimum detectable limit of this method, with the available equipment, was approximately 100 parts per billion. This implies that a reasonable minimum sample concentration to analyze would be 200 parts per trillion. This assumes a one thousand fold increase in concentration performed through solid phase extraction. Further, it had already been determined that concentration of 10 parts per million yielded adequate quantitation without secondary concentration. The above facts were used to set the experimental range and the original standard concentration.

The experimental results for precision and recoveries are presented in Tables 1 and 2. Examples of the typical chromatography and improvement of signal to noise, due to enrichment are presented in Figures 4 and 5. These figures show the original 500 ppb sample and the subsequent 500 ppm enriched sample. Note should be taken of the change in the milli-Volt scale between the two chromatograms.

Blanks of 2% acetic acid and methanol-acetonitrile are not presented but were run as controls. These blanks were chromatographed directly after having been passed through a solid phase extraction cartridge. The water did not generate any artifact peaks. The methanol-acetonitrile mixture did, occasionally, generate some small peaks after having passed through a cartridge. Two of these peaks eluted closely to the 2,4-D peak. However, near baseline resolution was achieved. A simple linear regression of the peak areas generated by the various magnitudes of concentration yielded a correlation coefficient of nines to at least four decimal places for all three compounds.

TABLE 1. Per Cent Coefficients of Variation Obtained from Automated Trace Enrichment Method.

Concentration	2, 4,-D	2, 4, 5-T	2, 4, 5-TP
200 ppb	15.87%	13.20%	16.65%
20 ppm	3.28%	2.77%	3.03%
100 ppm	2.98%	2.41%	2.55%
500 ppm	1.45%	.72%	.74%

TABLE 2. Recoveries Obtained from Automated Trace Enrichment Method.

Concentration	2, 4,-D	2, 4, 5-T	2, 4, 5-TP
200 ppb	193.2%	125.9%	115.4%
20 ppm	93.7%	89.9%	92.0%
100 ppm	107.1%	104.5%	99.5%
500 ppm	107.9%	104.2%	100.5%

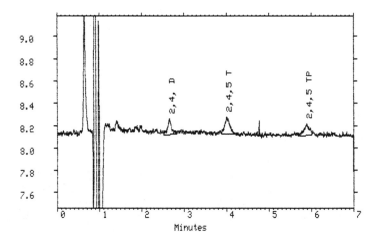

FIGURE 4. Chromatogram of 500 ppb Sample Before Enrichment.

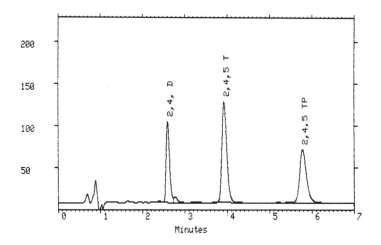

FIGURE 5. Chromatogram of 500 ppb Sample After Enrichment (theoretical concentration is 500 ppm.)

DISCUSSION

Each sample took slightly over two hours to be automatically processed by the workstation. While this may seem to be an extended period of time, it should be remembered that this method was performed without manual intervention. Approximately thirty minutes of set up was required prior to sample processing. In the final assessment, thirty minutes of manual labor resulted in over twelve hours of automated sample preparation and data collection. It should also be noted that no attempt was made to manually replicate this work, primarily because time and resources would not allow such a labor intensive study.

Since no manual enrichment was performed, no comparison between the automated technique can be made. However, method precision, the aspect which most benefits from automation, can be compared between the dilute and enriched samples. It can be seen that the trend is exactly what would be predicted.[1] The samples in the ppb range generated double digit per cent coefficients of variation. The analysis of the ppm concentration enriched samples yielded per cent coefficients of variation ten to twenty times superior and improved with increased concentration. This is not surprising, but is still worthy of mention.

Due to the many orders of magnitude encompassed in this study, linearity of the method was nearly perfect. The concentration range of the analysis was such that relatively large variances at certain data points did not calculate as significant. It is assumed that if this technique were applied to a reduced target concentration range, the correlation coefficient would suffer to some degree. The present work suggests, however, that the linearity would still remain highly adequate.

As the broad concentration range enhanced the linearity of the study, it appears to have reduced the reliability of recovery data. Previous work on similar techniques has indicated that there is no concentration dependency.[2] Yet this study indicates a trend of high recoveries at the extreme ends of the concentration range and slightly depressed recoveries for intermediate concentrations. This trend can be partially explained by two related factors. First, due to the exceedingly low area counts of the lower concentrations, the integration parameters of the data system were optimized to detect these peaks. This change was made after the single point calibration curve had been established. This could cause these peaks to appear to be disproportionately large. Second, the high concentration. Samples were ten to fifty times stronger than the standard concentration. It may be that the data station and detector could not generate a totally accurate calibration with this discrepancy in concentrations. These high concentration samples were also integrated using the enhanced integration parameters. It is believed that the recoveries of the 20 ppb sample enhanced to 20 ppm are representative of the method. The average recovery for all three compounds, at this concentration level, was almost 92%. Further work will be done to determine that there is no dependency between recovery and concentration.

This present study did not perform a comparison between recovery and sample volume. Previous work by other researchers indicates a relationship exists.[2] It appears that recoveries decrease as the volume of sample to be enriched is increased. This, along with the results of this study, implies that the best possible results will be obtained from this enrichment approach when the HPLC and data systems are optimized to analyze the narrowest acceptable concentration range at the lowest acceptable stable sensitivity.

SUMMARY

This paper indicates that dramatic enhancements in sensitivity and thereby precision and accuracy can be achieved for ground water analysis through the enrichment of samples on solid phase extraction cartridges. Further, this work has demonstrated that this process can be easily, rapidly and totally automated with great success by employing the Waters MilliLab Workstation.

This study has shown that with very little manual effort, extensive sample preparation can be performed and large amounts of data collected. This data is of a high quality not previously available through other manual methods. The fact that this entire method could be automated allowed for the more efficient use of that most precious of all resources, time.

ACKNOWLEDGEMENTS

The authors would like to thank Gary Fallick, Director of the MilliLab Venture, for the time to complete this work. We would also like to thank Harold Pogue and McKim Beckwith for the tools to do this work. Finally, we would like to thank all our fellow workers for the patience they exercised towards us during this study.

REFERENCES

1. "Sample Preparation Techniques In Environmental Analysis," in Sample Preparation Technology, G.L. Hawk and J.N. Little. eds, Zymark Corp. Hopkinton, Ma., 1982, pp 14-19.

2. Wells, M.J.M., "General Procedures for the Development of Adsorption Trapping Methods used in Herbicide Residue Analysis", Presented at Second Annual International Symposium on Sample Preparation and Isolation Using Bonded Silicas, Procedings published by Analytichem International Inc., Harbor City,, Ca., Copyright 1985, pp 63-68.

3. Ouellette, R.P., King, J.A., Chemical Week Pesticides Register, McGraw Hill, New York, NY., 1977, pp 19-89, 172, 285.

AUTOMATION OF USP DISSOLUTION APPARATUS I, THE BASKET METHOD

James P. McCarthy
ICI Pharmaceuticals Group
Concord Pike and Murphy Road
Wilmington, DE 19897

ABSTRACT

An automated method has been developed for USP Apparatus I dissolution testing. The U.S. Pharmacopeia describes two methods of pharmaceutical tablet dissolution testing. Apparatus I dissolves the tablet or capsule inside a 40-mesh screen basket. Apparatus II uses a paddle to effect dissolution.

The two major obstacles in automating apparatus I were how to repeatedly attach and remove the baskets to and from the spindles and how to sample the dissolved tablet solutions at the precise time. They were overcome by using magnets with plastic guides to attach the baskets to the spindles and by interfacing an Electronically Controlled Dissolution Sampling System available from Van-Kel. Samples can be taken simultaneously from all six vessels at intervals as short as 5 minutes apart. This feature is very useful when dissolution profile testing is performed.

The program can be run with quantitation by UV analysis after the last sample is taken, or with quantitation by HPLC performed manually after all runs are completed. Total time required to perform a dissolution test by the robot is slightly longer than the time required for a manual dissolution. However, the robot can work 23 hours out of each day while manual dissolutions can be performed for less than 8 hours each day. Accuracy and precision of the robot results are excellent. The apparatus also includes a safety system designed to detect water spills and turn off electricity to prevent an electrical hazard.

INTRODUCTION

Dissolution testing is the measurement of the rate at which a drug in a solid dosage form dissolves. In 1970, the USP adopted a generalized dissolution test to measure dissolution rates.[1] The apparatus utilizes a 40 mesh screen basket containing the tablet or capsule rotated in a vessel filled with dissolution media. A second apparatus was later added which uses a paddle to stir the media with the tablet or capsule lying in the bottom of the vessel.[2] Dissolution testing is one method of determining the adequacy of drug formulations. It is also used in Quality Assurance programs to determine lot-to-lot equivalence. A reproducible method is therefore critical to make accurate judgements on the formulation.[3-6]

One way to perform a test reproducibly is to automate the procedure with robotics. In addition to reproducibility, another reason to automate dissolution testing is to save analyst time. A great deal of time in the test is spent doing menial tasks or simply waiting to withdraw samples from the vessels. These tasks are completed by the automated dissolution system without human involvement, allowing the analyst to do other more complex tasks. Sustained action formulations require samples to be taken over periods as long as 24 hours. Since most research and development labs do not have second or third shifts, automation is necessary. The robot performs the same tasks as a manual dissolution test, reproducibly and consistently. By using robotics, variability associated with technique is greatly reduced. For all of these reasons, USP Apparatus II, the paddle method, has been successfully automated using robotics by many people including this lab.[7-11]

Now USP Apparatus I, the basket method, has also been automated. Up to 72 tablets can be tested in one continuous run - i.e. twelve dissolution tests with six tablets dissolved in each test. This article describes the fully automated dissolution of pharmaceutical dosages using USP Apparatus I, the basket method.

PROGRAMMING

The programming used is a seven-tier hierarchy utilizing phrases to describe positions the robot occupies. Programming the dissolution procedure was conducted in a manner to maximize the number of applicable products and to duplicate the USP procedure. An overview of the program is shown in Figure 1. Different drugs and formulations require different dissolution parameters such as volume of media, type of media, number of sampling intervals, time of samplings, and spindle rotation speed. Variables have been created in the program to allow these parameters to be easily set to whatever is specified in the method.

The sub-program "INITIALIZE" sets the dissolution parameters which are recalled later in the program. Also, tubing used for the sampling process is purged with deionized water to remove any air bubbles. Air bubbles in the tubing increase pressure in the syringes and sampling lines which can cause inaccurate volumes to be drawn and dispensed. The syringes are always partially filled with deionized water to prevent air from entering the tubing.

In the sub-program "PREPARE VESSELS," the media is added by a Master-flex pump. By overfilling the vessels with media and siphoning back the excess, the correct volume is dispensed to each vessel. If needed, modifiers such as buffers or acids are then added. In "TEST VESSELS," the sampling probe (long sipper) withdraws a sample from each vessel and reads the absorbance using the UV/VIS spectrophotometer. An absorbance reading of

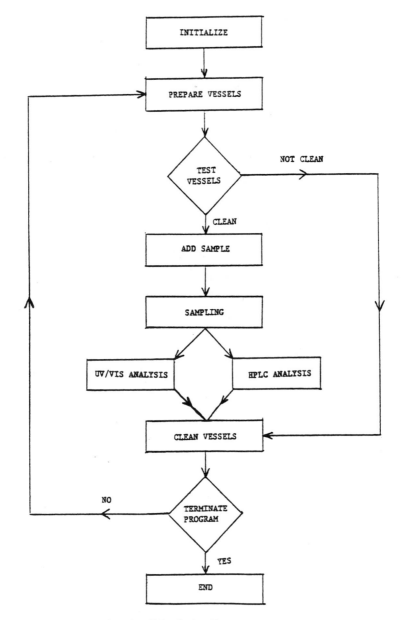

FIGURE 1. Flow Chart of Basket Dissolution Program.

fresh media is made as a reference before the vessels are tested. If the absorbance of a vessel is greater than the reference by a preset value, it is presumed to be contaminated. The vessel is then cleaned, refilled and retested. The absorbance of each vessel is also used as the background and is subtracted from the sample absorbance in the quantitation of samples.

"ADD SAMPLE" picks up the tablet cup containing the tablet and pours it into a specially constructed basket. The basket is then placed on the spindle using a magnet to attach it. This is repeated until all six baskets are attached. Rotation of the spindles is started and the spindles are then lowered into the vessels. When the baskets are fully lowered, a timer marks that time as the beginning of the dissolution. "SAMPLING" is done by the Electronically Controlled Dissolution Sampling System (ECDS) available from Van-Kel. Samples from all six vessels are taken simultaneously and transferred to test tubes. UV quantitation is performed by the robot after the last sampling. Quantitation by HPLC is performed manually after the run is complete.

In the sub-program "CLEAN VESSELS," the spindles are raised to allow the robot arm access to the baskets. Each basket is serially removed and cleaned. After all six baskets are finished, the vessels are cleaned using a high pressure hot water spray. During the spraying, a pump is used to remove the used media and the rinse water.

After each dissolution test, the program determines if more samples remain to be tested using the sub-program "TERMINATE PROGRAM". If more samples are to be tested, the program recycles to line number 1, "PREPARE VESSELS". If no more samples remain, then the program turns off the equipment and ends.

ROBOTIC SYSTEM

The cornerstone of this automated dissolution system is a Zymate I Laboratory Robot. Interfaced to it are a dissolution tester, a UV/VIS spectrophotometer, and the ECDS. All of this equipment is interfaced through the power and event controllers (PEC). The equipment and bench layout used in this system are shown in Figure 2.

Interfacing this equipment was vital to successfully automating the USP basket apparatus dissolution procedure. Control of the Van-Kel dissolution tester allows the robot to set rotation speed for the paddles or baskets (spindles). The robot also controls raising and lowering the spindles, and monitors bath temperature through this interface. Quantitation of the dissolved drug is accomplished by either the UV/VIS spectrophotometer or by HPLC. A modified flow-through cell in the spectrophotometer is connected to the sampling probe by the Master Lab Station (MLS). Absorbance readings of the sample and standard solutions are sent from the spectrophotometer to the robot controller through an analog/digital (A/D) input. Calculations are then done and a report is printed with all of the absorbances and the time that the sample was taken as well as the calculated percent drug dissolved. HPLC analysis is currently performed manually. Samples requiring HPLC analysis are stored in test tubes by the robot.

Since all six samples are started at once by lowering the baskets into the filled vessels, a sampling device capable of withdrawing six samples simultaneously was required. The Van-Kel ECDS sampler consists of a crossbar manifold with sampling probes attached to it, a 12-channel pump, and a fraction collector (Figure 3). As the sampling probes are lowered, the pump starts transferring solution through the lines and valves and back into the vessel. Flushing the tubing with the sample solution assures that an accurate sample is taken. Once the tubes have been flushed, the valves open to pump the sample solution into test tubes in the fraction collector. After the sample has been taken, the pump

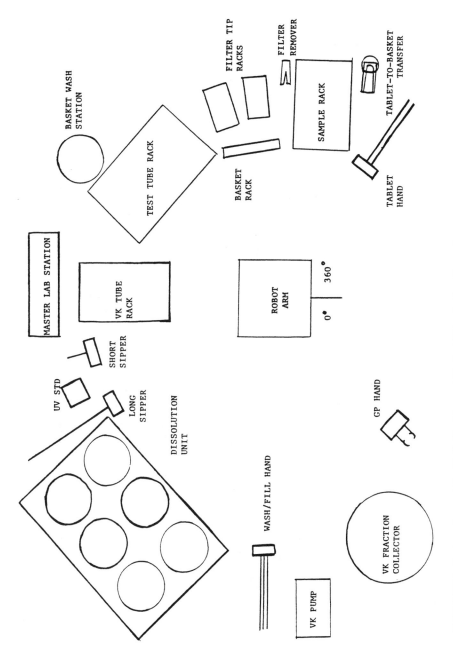

FIGURE 2. System Layout for Both Paddle and Basket Dissolution Procedures.

FIGURE 3. Van-Kel Electronically Controlled Dissolution Sampling System.

reverses and purges the lines of liquid using air. The sampling probes are mounted to a motorized crossbar allowing them to be lowered into the vessel only during sampling. Leaving the sample probes in the vessels during the dissolution can increase the dissolution rate of the drug and thus is not recommended.[12,13] The fraction collector has been modified with a hinge and an air actuated cylinder to swing it away allowing the robot arm access to the filled test tubes.

A "tablet-to-basket transfer station" has been developed for placing the tablet into the dissolution basket quickly and reproducibly (Figure 4). A funnel is used to channel the tablet into the dissolution basket as it sits on a stand. A groove in the stand guides the basket directly under the funnel while the tablet hand is placing it on the stand. A cup containing the tablet is then picked up by the same hand and poured into the funnel. After dropping the empty cup into a storage bucket, the dissolution basket is picked up and attached to the spindle. Modifications to the baskets and spindles were necessary to assure consistent attachment. The basket has been modified by attaching a steel washer to the top. A ring-shaped magnet filled with a beveled plastic disk is attached to the spindle (Figure 5) to allow repeated attachment and removal of the basket. The disk is used as a guide when attaching the basket to the spindle. The basket is consistently on center because of the beveled insert. After each dissolution is completed, the baskets are washed in a two-liter plastic bottle fitted with a drain in the bottom (Figure 6). A stream of hot water and pressurized air sprayed down onto the baskets combine to effectively clean the baskets. The two-liter polyethylene bottle contains the wash water and excess spraying.

A safety system designed to prevent water spills and electrical hazards has been incorporated into the robot layout. It is designed to detect water spills and disrupt electricity to all of the water pumps, circulators, and solenoid valves. The solenoid valves control the flow of water into the system. When electricity is cut off, the valves for the

FIGURE 4. The Tablet-to-Basket Transfer Station.

FIGURE 5. Modified Spindle for Basket.

vessel wash hand, the basket wash station, and the dissolution media reservoir close, stopping the flow of water into the system. When electricity is cut off to the circulator and Master-Flex pumps, all water movement within the system stops. This combination keeps water spills to negligible amounts. The electricity is also cut off to these units to eliminate any potential hazard from water contacting electricity.

The location of each piece of equipment in the system was critical for a successful application. The robot arm moves much slower than a human. Therefore, movement of the arm during the dissolution test had to be kept at a minimum in order to maximize efficiency. In this application, equipment used together in various parts of the test are grouped near each other. Figure 2 shows the layout of the dissolution system. For taking samples from basket method dissolutions, the general-purpose hand, Van-Kel fraction collector, sampling pump, and a tube rack are all located within a small area. To add the

FIGURE 6. Basket Wash Station.

samples to the vessels, the tablet hand, tablet rack, basket rack, and tablet-to-basket transfer station are all located together. The sampling probes, UV/VIS standard, MLS, and UV/VIS spectrophotometer are grouped together to reduce the sample tubing between them. A smaller volume of sample can be drawn therefore reducing the time necessary for withdrawal and transfer. Reducing the amount of movement shortens the time to do a dissolution test and therefore improves the overall efficiency of the application.

VALIDATION OF SAMPLING

Sampling the dissolved drug solution contained in the vessels is one of the critical steps of the dissolution test. Quantitating the samples using the spectrophotometer is another critical step. Experiments were devised to show if dilution or loss of drug occurs during sampling or quantitation. To do this, aliquots of a standard solution were placed in each of the six vessels and sampled by the robot. The solutions sampled from each vessel were then compared to the original standard solution using the robot interfaced UV/VIS spectrophotometer. The mean recovery from the six vessels was 99.9% of the standard. The recoveries ranged from 99.8% to 100.2% with a percent relative standard deviation (% RSD) of 0.16. It is evident that no loss of drug or dilution and no error with quantitation occurs.

Another concern with the sampling technique was sample carryover by the filters on the sampling probes. It is not possible for the robot to change filters between tests during an automated run. After each complete automated run, the filters can be manually changed. It is recommended that the sampling lines be flushed to remove particulate matter that may have adhered to the surface of the filter.[14] The lines and filters of the ECDS sampler are back-flushed after each sampling interval with a small volume of sample to remove particulates and then flushed with air to remove any remaining solution from the lines and filters. To test the effectiveness of flushing the lines and filters, twelve dissolution tests were conducted in the normal manner. A blank dissolution test was then done without tablets to determine how much contamination occurred, if any. Essentially no drug (less than 1%) was quantitated for all six vessels in the blank dissolution test.

VALIDATION OF AUTOMATED DISSOLUTION TEST

Dissolution tests using the USP calibrator tablets, Prednisone and Salicylic Acid, were conducted on the robotic system using both the automated procedure and the manual procedure. Since the two procedures are significantly different in many areas, it was necessary to compare them on the same equipment. The same bath, vessels, and dissolution controller were used. Different spindles and baskets, as well as sampling and quantitating techniques, were used in the comparison since they are different in the actual procedures. All of the automated and manual procedure results shown in Table 1 are within USP specifications. Standard deviations are consistently higher for the automated procedure. This could be caused by irregularities in the modified spindles and baskets. The modified spindles and baskets show a very slight off center rotation, although within USP specifications. Eccentricity of the basket is not a serious problem, however it could be responsible for the higher standard deviation of the automated procedure results.[15] Disturbances in the circulation of the media have been known to cause variable results.[16] Overall, the results in Table 1 are satisfactory, showing good correlation between the automated and manual procedures.

TABLE 1. Comparison of Robot and Manual Dissolution Results using USP Calibrator Tablets.

Prednisone (50 RPM)	Mean	S.D.
Robot	13.44	3.48
Manual	13.24	1.98
Prednisone (100 RPM)		
Robot	44.53	2.01
Manual	44.16	1.57
Salicylic Acid (50 RPM)		
Robot	17.94	0.82
Manual	17.97	0.57
Salicylic Acid (100 RPM)		
Robot	27.23	1.05
Manual	28.68	0.93

CONCLUSION

The automation of USP Apparatus I dissolution testing has been successfully accomplished. All of the steps in the test are completed by the robot so that multiple tests can be done without human involvement. Applications other than a single sampling at 30 minutes are also possible. The ability to perform multiple samplings is already built into the program; it just was not utilized here.

The robot procedure described in this paper follows the USP methodology. It also adheres to the guidelines set forth in the "Handbook Of Dissolution Testing" by William A. Hanson.[17] Most importantly, the robot performs the test consistently and reproducibly.

Twelve tests can be performed by the robot in a single automated run with very little analyst time. At most, a person can perform seven 30-minute tests in a typical workday. This robotic system is now being used routinely for both Apparatus I and Apparatus II type dissolutions.

ACKNOWLEDGMENTS

I wish to thank Norm Wiggins for many helpful discussions and Adam Cunningham and Chuck Hartman for fabricating many custom parts.

REFERENCES

1. The United States Pharmacopeia, l8th rev. , (Mack Publishing Co. , Easton, PA, 1970), pp. 934.

2. The United States Pharmacopeia, 5th supplement USP XIX, (Mack Publishing Co. , Easton, PA, 1979), pp. 221.

3. B.E. Cabana and R. O'Neill, "FDA's Report on Drug Dissolution" Pharm. Forum, 71-75 (1980).

4. W.A. Hanson, Handbook of Dissolution Testing, (Pharmaceutical Technology Pub. , Springfield, OR, 1982) pp. 2.

5. D.C. Cox, et al., "Guidelines for Dissolution Testing," Pharm. Tech. 2(4), 41-53 (April 1978).

6. J.C. Wahlich, "The Automation of Dissolution Testing," Pharm. Tech. 4(9), 92-101 (September 1980).

7. L.M. Sattler, T.J. Saboe, and T.F. Dolan, "Automated Dissolution Testing," Zymark Application Note AP305, (Zymark Corp. , Hopkinton, MA, Nov. 1984) .

8. L.J. Kostek, B.A. Brown, and J.E. Curley, "Fully Automated Dissolution Testing," in Advances in Laboratory Automation Robotics 1985, J.R. Strimaitis and G.L. Hawk, eds., (Zymark Corp. , Hopkinton, MA, 1985), pp. 701-720.

9. J.J. Fett, J.J. Buletza, and E.C. Lewis, "Automation of HPLC and Flow Injection Analysis Dissolution Methods through use of the Zymate Laboratory Automation System," in Advances in Laboratory Automation Robotics 1986, J.R. Strimaitis and G.L. Hawk, eds., (Zymark Corp. , Hopkinton, MA, 1986), pp. 153-165.

10. B.J. Compton and O.N. Hinsvark, "A Review of Automated Dissolution Testing," Pharm. Tech. 10(8), 28-36 (August 1986).

11. A.N. Papas, et. al., "Evaluation of Robot Drug Dissolution Measurements," Anal. Chem. 57(7), 1408-1411 (June 1985).

12. W.A. Hanson, Handbook of Dissolution Testing, (Pharmaceutical Technology Pub., Springfield, OR, 1982) p. 85.

13. C.E. Wells, "Effect of Sampling Probe Size on Dissolution of Tableted Drug Samples,"J. Pharm. Sci. 70(2), 233 (Nov. 1980).

14. W.A. Hanson, Handbook of Dissolution Testing, (Pharmaceutical Technology Pub., Springfield, OR, 1982) p.86.

15. W.A. Hanson, "Solving the Puzzle of Random Variables in Dissolution Testing," Pharm. Tech. 11 (6), 24-31 (June 1987).

16. W.A. Hanson, Handbook of Dissolution Testing, (Pharmaceutical Technology Pub., Springfield, OR, 1982) p. 85.

17. W.A. Hanson, "Automation of Dissolution Testing," in Handbook of Dissolution Testing, (Pharmaceutical Technology Pub., Springfield, OR, 1982), pp 125-149.

ROBOTIC HPLC ANALYSIS OF SOLID DOSAGE FORMS

William A. Davidson and Kathryn Lam
Boehringer Ingelheim Pharmaceuticals, Inc.
Ridgefield, CT 06877

ABSTRACT

A robotic system used to perform HPLC assay and content uniformity tests on solid dosage forms is described. The system uses only gravimetric data to determine results and has the capability to perform multiple products during a single robotic run. A validation protocol is outlined that separates the validation process into an overall system validation and into individual product validation.

A Laboratory Information Management System is described that networks the robot with a HP-Vectra^{tm} personal computer and a HP laboratory data system to make decisions on chromatographic results, and to perform data reduction and report generation.

INTRODUCTION

The use of laboratory robots in the pharmaceutical industry has been widely accepted.[1,2,3] Many topics have been covered - special applications, justification of system purchases, problems associated with "roboticizing" validated manual methods, continuous validation just to name a few. Our system was purchased in June of 1986 to perform testing on pre-IND, and NDA dosage forms only up to approval stage. Many of these products never reach NDA status, but the testing required is still quite involved. Unlike a system in a QC laboratory that can be dedicated to one or two products, our robot needed to be very flexible with the ability to test many different products without an extensive time lag between revalidation for each product. Along with the need to be flexible we wanted the ability to analyze two or more products during one robotic run. This was dictated by our type of sample load, consisting of different products that become due at the same time, however the amount of testing for each product may not justify using the robot.

This paper describes our approach to robotic method validation. The details of how we interfaced the robot to a PC and a Laboratory Data System in order to perform real time decisions on chromatographic data and to generate reports are also outlined.

EXPERIMENTAL

Robotic System

The equipment interfaced to the robot is listed in Table 1. Figure 1 is a schematic of the bench layout.

TABLE 1. Equipment Interfaced to the Zymate II System.

Zymark^{tm} Corporation (Hopkinton, Massachusetts)

  Zymate II Robot
  General Purpose Hand
  Syringe Hand
  Computer Module/with Disc Drive (V3 software,180K memory)
  Interface (Z-845)
  Monitor
  Printer
  Power and Event Controller (PEC)
  Capping Station
  Vortex Station
  Analytical Instrument Interface
  Balance Interface

Mettler Instruments Corporation (Highstown, New Jersey)
  AE-160 Electronic Balance, with Option 011 Data
  Interface

Sonicor Instrument Corporation (Copiague, New York)
  SC-200 Ultrasonic Bath

Cole-Palmer Instrument Corporation (Chicago, Illinois)
  Masterflex^{tm} Solvent Pump, Model 7014

Hewlett Packard Corporation (Palo Alto, California)
  HP Vectra^{tm} Personal Computer, 20 Mb Hard Disc Drive,
  1.2 Mb Floppy Disc Drive

  HP-3350A Laboratory Data System; A-600 CPU,
  RTE-A Operating system, Revision 4.0

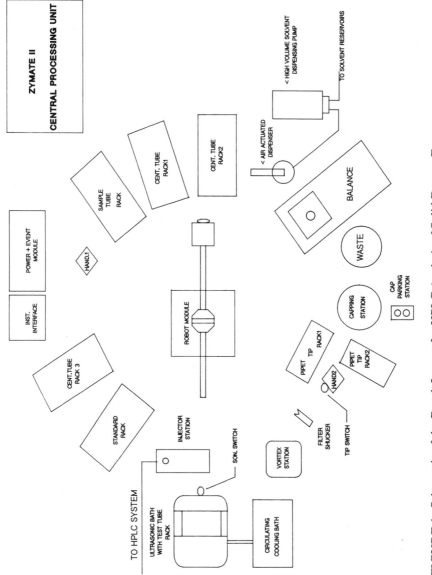

FIGURE 1. Schematic of the Bench Layout for HPLC Analysis of Solid Dosage Forms

High Performance Liquid Chromatography System

The HPLC system equipment is listed in Table 2. It currently has the capability to switch between two isocratic methods, however with an upgraded solvent controller and column switching valve, five different methods will eventually be able to be performed during a single robotic run. Figure 2 gives an overview of the entire system.

TABLE 2. High Performance Liquid Chromatography System.

Millipore Corporation, Waters Chromatography Division
(Milford, Massachusetts)

   Model 510 HPLC Pump
   Model 60057 Automated Switching Valve

Kratos Analytical (Ramsey, New Jersey)

   Spectroflow^{tm} 783 Absorbance Detector

Autochrom Corporation (Milford, Massachusetts)

   Model 111 OPG/S, One Pump Gradient Controller

Hewlett Packard Corporation (Palo Alto, California)

   18652 A/D Converter
   3390A Integrator

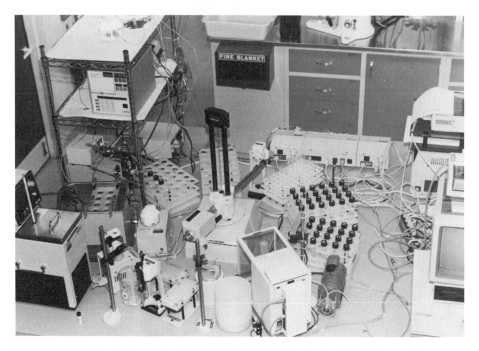

FIGURE 2. Robotic System for Multi-Method HPLC Analysis of Solid Dosage Forms.

Sample Preparation Scheme

Our system automates the procedure outlined in Table 3. This is a general method description, with the degree of serialization dependant on the length of the HPLC run. If the samples or standards require dilutions, these are done using one mL pipet tips and adding the diluent to a dilution tube on the balance.

The procedure's accuracy and speed is increased by using only gravimetric data to calculate results. The solvent dispensing system is not only faster than a syringe driven one, but it is also easier to validate and maintain.

TABLE 3. General Sample Preparation Description.

Step	Action
1	Place one tablet in disposable test tube
2	Pour tablet into 50 mL centrifuge in balance
3	Dispense approximately 25 g of solvent into centrifuge tube
4	Sonicate for 5 minutes
5	Vortex for 30 seconds
6	Dispense filtered sample into injector station
7	Inject 10 uL

TABLE 4. Error Control Routines.

Type	Function
Input Switches	
a. Tip Switch	Confirms that pipet tip with filter is attached.
b. Sonicator Switch	Confirms proper capper operation. Two missed confirmations in sequence results in termination of the program.
Gravimetric	All composite, tablet, and solvent weights are assigned minimum values. If the weight received from the balance falls below the minimum, appropriate action is taken. If the problem re-occurs consistently the program may be terminated.
CONFIRM	Used in the injection program to verify that the pipet tip was not removed during the filter tip shucking routine.

System Reliability

System reliability is always a concern for an automated instrument. Table 4 outlines the major error control routines programed into the EasyLab[tm] programs.

CONFIRM[tm] techniques are also used throughout the programming to check capper and vortex operation as well as to verify the presence of tubes, caps, etc. Error control should be considered a dynamic process, continually improving as the operators gain more experience.

VALIDATION

The major concern when using any automated system such as the robot, is validation of the system.[4] It is critical that all parameters that affect the outcome of the analysis are identified and validated. The validation scheme should be documented and able to be repeated without any procedural questions.

There are essentially three written documents that have to be prepared. An overall system validation report, individual product validation reports, and a maintenance and calibration logbook. A brief overview of how each is prepared follows.

System Validation

The two areas identified as critical to overall system validation were programming and balance operation. The entire robotic system is basically a computer program that moves. Once something is fixed in the programming it doesn't change unless a part of the system physically breaks down. Even when this happens, the programming is not at fault. To reduce the amount of work required to validate the robotic system, the programs were split into two groups, core programs and specific application programs. The core programs are those which will not change no matter what the application is. An example of this type of program would be PUT.TUBE.IN.BALANCE or GET.TUBE.FROM.RACK. Unless you move the balance or the rack, these programs will always do the same thing. These programs should only need validation once. It should not be necessary to revalidate these programs simply because you change from Product 1 to Product 2. The analysis procedures may be entirely different, but getting a tube from the same rack or placing it in the same balance will always be the same.

The other category of programs, specific application programs, will change. These programs are usually the top 2 levels of programs. They control how long and in what order things are done. If a change in dilution is necessary, just change one of the application programs. The core programs are then referenced from the validation report for each individual application.

The validation report for the core programs contains the following:

- Overview

- Instrumentation and stations

- Balance calibration

- Algorithms and variable description

- Program listing

- Schematic of table top

- Details of the PEC hookups

- Spatial positions

The validation report for the specific application contains:

- Description of top and second level programs

- Variable description

- A program listing flowchart

Once the initial report for the overall system is finished, future reports for the specific applications will be much easier to generate.

Balance Calibration

Calibration of an analytical balance used in a robotic system has been discussed by Haller et al.[5] Class S-1 weights (Fisher Standard Weights, Fisher Scientific, Springfield, NJ, or equivalent) in the weight ranges used in the analysis are weighed 20 times. The mean, range, and %RSD are determined. The acceptance criteria are a %RSD less than 0.3% and a mean within the accuracy range of the balance. Table 5 shows results from a typical weight validation. This data serves to calibrate the balance along with the validation of data transfer between the balance and the robot CPU.

TABLE 5. Balance Calibration Summary.

Standard	Weight(x_{20})	Range	%RSD
100 mg	100.1 mg	99.3-100.8 mg	0.290
200 mg	199.9 mg	199.2-200.9 mg	0.150
1 g	1.000 g	0.9992-1.001 g	0.030
10 g	10.000 g	9.9993-10.0010 g	0.006
20 g	20.000 g	19.9997-20.0004 g	0.002

PROCEDURE VALIDATION

Along with the validation of the programming specific for each application as mentioned above, the following is required for the validation report for each product.

Weight Transfer Validation

Since all our results are based on gravimetric data, the verification that all weight transfers are accurate is crucial to the success of each application. Using tared centrifuge and sample tubes, a modified version of the application is run with delays at all transfer steps so that the tubes can be manually re-weighed. Ten "samples" are prepared. Table 6 details the data from a typical run. The quality of the data is determined by the lack of bias (positive or negative) and the absolute percentage difference of less than one percent for powder and tablet weights and 0.05 % for solvent weights over 1 gram.

TABLE 6. Weight Transfer Data.

Powder Weights			Solvent Weights		
External balance mg	System balance mg	% Diff.	External balance g	System balance g	% Diff.
233.3	232.6	0.30	25.5360	25.5353	0.003
235.0	232.8	0.94	25.6974	25.6969	0.002
234.9	233.3	0.68	25.7539	25.7579	0.016
235.5	235.6	0.04	25.8541	25.8573	0.012
235.4	238.6	1.34	25.8555	25.8580	0.010
239.0	238.5	0.21	25.8735	25.8736	0.000
237.8	237.2	0.25	25.9354	25.9363	0.003
233.3	234.5	0.51	25.9485	25.9488	0.001
231.9	232.9	0.43	25.9708	25.9740	0.012
233.1	232.6	0.21	26.0117	26.0137	0.008
		Avg.= 0.49%			Avg.= 0.007%

Chemistry Validation

Our department has set up assay method validation guidelines based on FDA requirements. Since the robotic procedures generally vary the on-column injection amounts and the extraction scheme but not the chromatography, we must only perform tests showing detector response linearity, recovery of active ingredient, and comparison to manual method.

Detector Response Linearity

The response of the standard is determined at 5 evenly spaced levels (one sample weighing with serial dilutions) over the range of 50-150% of the assay level. This is done in triplicate with two injections at each level. Linear regression analysis is performed, the acceptance criteria is a correlation coefficient greater than 0.999 and a bias of less than 2.0% for each analysis. Table 7 shows the results from a typical linearity determination.

TABLE 7. Typical Assay Linearity Results.

Standard %	Amount Injected (ug)	Area
53.3	6.388	37042
	6.388	36981
79.8	9.581	55465
	9.581	55681
106.5	12.78	73350
	12.78	73374
133.1	15.97	92686
	15.97	92336
160.0	19.16	110588
	19.16	110881
	Correlation coefficient	0.99988
	Slope	5774.1
	y-intercept	70.0
	Analytical y-value[a]	69359
	Bias[b]	0.1%

[a] The analytical y-value is the response at the 100% level

[b] % Bias = $\dfrac{\text{y-intercept}}{\text{analytical y-value}} \times 100$

Recovery Studies

A spiked placebo is made by adding the active ingredient at 3 evenly spaced levels to the excipients over the range of 75-125% of the assay level. The % of active ingredient to placebo is kept constant at each level. These samples are prepared in triplicate, then assayed robotically versus two external standards also prepared by the robot. The mean recovery of active ingredient must be 98.0-102.0% of the theoretical value. The relative standard deviation (RSD) for all recoveries must be less than 2.5%. Table 8 shows the results of a typical recovery study.

TABLE 8. Formulated Product Recovery Study.

Amount Spiked (mg)	% of Label Claim[b]	Amount Found (mg)	% Recovery
22.81	76.0	22.83	100.1
22.36	74.5	22.34	99.9
22.75	75.8	22.81	100.3
30.52	101.7	30.57	100.2
30.33	101.1	30.28	99.8
30.16	100.5	30.14	99.9
37.86	126.2	37.82	99.9
36.86	122.9	36.75	99.7
37.35	124.5	37.37	100.1

Average: 100.0 %
RSD: 0.2 %

[b] Based on 30 mg/tablet

Comparison to the Manual Method

Generally five replicate assays from the same composite and ten content uniformities are done on each lot that is available. A Student's t-test is performed on the results to determine any statistical differences. This is the minimum work that has to be done to compare robotic vs. manually generated results. Table 9 shows some typical results. A more sophisticated statistical comparison protocol is being developed.

TABLE 9. Robotic versus Manual Comparison of Results.

	Robot	Manual
	30.95	30.25
	30.31	29.77
	30.57	30.02
	29.84	30.07
	30.59	29.93
	30.11	30.39
	30.20	30.05
	30.36	30.54
	30.12	30.33
	30.51	30.23
Average	30.36	30.15
s	0.31	0.23
%RSD	1.02	0.76
t-Tabulated	3.92	
t-Calculated	1.61	

No Significant Difference at the 0.1% Level as t-Tabulated is greater than t-Calculated.

CALIBRATION and MAINTENANCE LOGBOOK

This logbook is required by our SOP's (Standard Operations Procedures) and includes both the robotic and HPLC systems. All maintenance performed in-house or by manufacturer service representatives is recorded. Monthly and quarterly preventative maintenance based on the information detailed in the Zymate instruction manual are documented as well as the record of calibration of the balance and a positional check of the robotic arm. Appendix A shows some typical entries into the log book.

COMPUTER INTERFACE SYSTEM

Details for the basic hardware design of the interface are shown in Figure 3. A flow chart that describes how data is exchanged between the systems and what real-time decisions are being made during a robotic analysis is illustrated in Figure 4. A written description of what the interface accomplishes follows.

The HPLC detector signal is processed by the HP-3350A software into a chromatogram. At the end of each chromatographic run a post-analysis program on the HP-3350A obtains all pertinent data such as, named peak areas and heights, time and date of the injection, result file name, etc.

This data is sent to the HP-Vectra where a control and acquisition program reads this information and enters it into a user named data file.

DECISION MAKING

Each product analysis follows the same format with the system-suitability standard being prepared and injected twice. Standard #1 is prepared and injected five times to determine the HPLC system precision. For a system-suitability test injection, a validated program located on the 3350A is called up to calculate peak resolution and tailing. The calculated results are compared to preset limits, the Pass/Fail result is then sent to the Vectra. The mean and relative standard deviation (RSD) of the five standard one injections are then calculated by the Vectra.

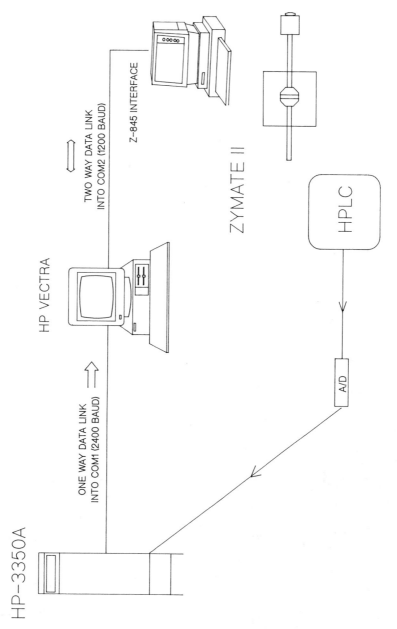

FIGURE 3. Schematic of the Hardware Linkages.

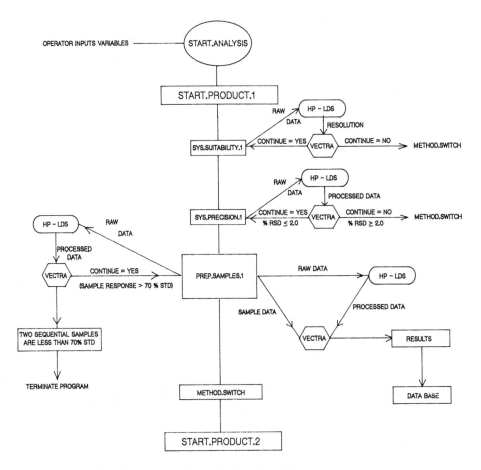

FIGURE 4. Information and Decision Making Flow Chart.

If both system-suitability injections pass, the Vectra allows the robot to continue and the system precision test is performed. If the RSD of the five injections is less than or equal to 2.0%, the Vectra allows the robot to start sample preparation. If either one of these tests fail, the robot will either switch columns or methods depending on what type of run is being performed, - ie., single product or multiple product analysis. The tests are repeated for the new conditions and if a failure condition is recorded again the robot will terminate the program.

In the sample preparation portion of the analysis, if two consecutive sample peak areas are less than 70% of the mean area calculated for standard #1 the robot system will terminate the program. This is considered a fatal error, probably due to HPLC pump or detector failure or a major failure at the capping station.

DATA ANALYSIS and REPORT GENERATION

During sample preparation the Zymate stores all information for each sample in arrays, including all solvent, dilution and tablet or powder weights. Before the next sample is injected, the Zymate's interface is activated and the control and acquisition program on the Vectra takes this information, along with the data from the 3350A and places it in a user named data file.

After the analysis is finished a data reduction and report generation program is called up on the Vectra. The user is prompted for the data file and all product information is entered. The result report is then generated. (See Appendix B for a sample report.)

Work is ongoing to incorporate a Laser Scanner (LASERSCAN[tm], Symbol Technologies Inc., Boehemia, NY) into the Zymate-system. Since our stability data base generates laser bar codes for each sample, the scanner would simplify sample tracking and allow the Vectra to obtain data in a batch mode, permitting direct entry of results into the data base.

SUMMARY

A robotic system used to perform assay and content uniformity tests on solid dosage forms has been described. The system differs from many engaged in these tasks in that only gravimetric data is used to determine final results. Addition of extraction solvent is performed over an analytical balance using a high-volume dispensing system, ensuring accurate and easily validated results. The system has been designed to perform multiple product analysis with a validation scheme developed to rapidly convert manual methods into robotic procedures.

The system has been networked with a laboratory data system and personal computer to perform real time decisions on chromatographic data and to generate reports. Work is ongoing to incorporate a laser scanning device to simplify sample tracking, and to allow direct entry of results into a data base.

ACKNOWLEDGMENTS

The authors would like to thank Boehringer-Ingelheim Pharmaceuticals Inc. for permission to present this paper. The computer interface system was developed in conjunction with MIS department personnel, Mr. Peter Esche, Mr. William Hyuck and Ms. Kathleen McNamara. We also thank Dr. John McCaffrey for providing continuing guidance during the implementation of this project .

REFERENCES

1. G.L. Hawk, and J.R. Strimaitis, eds., Advances in Laboratory Automation - Robotics 1984, Zymark Corp., Hopkington, MA

2. G.L. Hawk, and J.R. Strimaitis, eds., Advances in Laboratory Automation - Robotics 1985, Zymark Corp., Hopkington, MA

3. G.L. Hawk, and J.R. Strimaitis, eds., Advances in Laboratory Automation - Robotics 1986, Zymark Corp., Hopkinton, MA

4. R.B. Anderson and R.F. Quadrel, "Continuous Validation and System Security for Robotics in the Pharmaceutical Laboratory", ibid p.113.

5. W. Haller, E. Halloran, J. Habarta and W. Mason, "Can You Trust Your Robot", ibid, p.557

Zymark, Zymate, and EasyLab are registered trademarks and CONFIRM is a trademark of Zymark Corporation.

Vectra is a registered trademark of Hewlett Packard.

Masterflex is a registered trademark of Cole-Palmer Corporation.

Spectroflow is a trademark of Kratos Analytical.

Appendix A

5. ROBOT MAINTENANCE: ROTARY SERVO CABLE

TURN SYSTEM POWER OFF

The ROTARY SERVO cable is the thinner of the 2 cables wound around the
TURNTABLE. This cable is the most critical to rotary performance.

a. Remove the robot skirts.

b. Grasp either section of the cable between the turntable and the rotary postion feedback
bracket and pull the cable sideways to 0.9 Kgs with the tensionmeter.

c. Record the distance the cable moves.

d. The cable should move 0.4 to 0.5 cm.

e. If the cable moves less than 0.2 cm or greater than 0.7 cm. Use service procedure R4 to
adjust to the proper tension.

Month/year	Result (cm)	Pass	Fail	Date Done	Analyst
Jan/87					
Feb/87					
March/87					
April/87					
May/87					
June/87					
July/87					
Aug/87					
Sep/87					
Oct/87					
Nov/87					
Dec/87					

Appendix A

7. ROBOT MAINTENANCE: WRIST

TURN SYSTEM POWER ON

B. WRIST SELF RESTORING PLAY

1. Manually Attach the SYRINGE hand.

2. Manually rotate the had (gently) in both directions until resistance is felt.

3. Verify that when released from both directions the hand returns to the same position without overshoot.

Failure of this function to perform properly, indicates the need to replace the wrist motor.

Month/year	Date Done	Pass	Analyst
Jan/87	_____	___	_____
Feb/87	_____	___	_____
March/87	_____	___	_____
April/87	_____	___	_____
May/87	_____	___	_____
June/87	_____	___	_____
July/87	_____	___	_____
Aug/87	_____	___	_____
Sept/87	_____	___	_____
Oct/87	_____	___	_____
Nov/87	_____	___	_____
Dec/87	_____	___	_____

APPENDIX B

```
**************************** DATA ANALYSIS REPORT ****************************

              FILENAME :   ROBOT2.DAT

         DATE :   Thu Aug 20, 1987 11:41:45 am


**************************** PRODUCT INFORMATION ****************************

              Name      : PRODUCT 1
              AR No.    : 6613
              Study No. : N/A
              Lot No.   : PD-0700


**************************** STANDARD INFORMATION ****************************

              Name      : PROD1-AI
              AR No.    : 5400
              Lot No.   : BI-00023
              Purity(%) : 0.996

************************** STANDARD RESPONSE FACTOR **************************

                         STANDARD 1

         standard weight   :     28.00
         solvent weight    :     23.56
         concentration     :      1.18
         average area      : 62300.87
         response factor   :    1.9002898891E-05


                         STANDARD 2

         standard weight   :     28.06
         solvent weight    :     23.69
         concentration     :      1.18
         average area      : 60223.84
         response factor   :    1.9585170209E-05

      average response factor :    1.9294034550E-05


**************************** ASSAY RESULTS ****************************

         Sample Name          Area          Potency
         -----------       ----------       -------

         AR 6613-1          62155.00         28.71
         AR 6613-2          71469.75         28.44
         AR 6613-3          60331.88         28.59


********************** CONTENT UNIFORMITY RESULTS **********************

         Sample Name          Area          Potency
         -----------       ----------       -------

         CU-1               62721.50         28.52
         CU-2               63957.75         29.10
         CU-3               62115.00         28.26
         CU-4               63503.75         28.89
         CU-5               61843.75         28.14

******************************* Result Files *******************************

              Sample Id              Result File
              -----------            -----------

              STANDARD 1             ROBO6_022
              STANDARD 1             ROBO6_023
              STANDARD 1             ROBO6_024
              STANDARD 1             ROBO6_025
              STANDARD 1             ROBO6_026
              AR 6613-1              ROBO6_027
              AR 6613-2              ROBO6_028
              AR 6613-2              ROBO6_029
              STANDARD 2             ROBO6_030
              STANDARD 2             ROBO6_031
              STANDARD 1             ROBO6_032
              STANDARD 1             ROBO6_033
              CU-1                   ROBO6_034
              CU-2                   ROBO6_035
              CU-3                   ROBO6_036
              CU-4                   ROBO6_037
              CU-5                   ROBO6_038
              STANDARD 2             ROBO6_039
              STANDARD 2             ROBO6_039
```

AUTOMATION OF THIN LAYER CHROMATOGRAPHY
BY USE OF ROBOTICS

N. Morokoshi, S. Inada, S. Koda and Y. Morimoto
Analytical Research Laboratories
Fujisawa Pharmaceutical Co.,
Kashima 2-1-6, Yodogawa-ku,
Osaka 532 Japan

ABSTRACT

A totally automated thin layer chromatography (TLC) system using robotics was designed and constructed. This system is composed of two processes: the first step is sample preparation, consisting of a series of unit operations such as weighing, extraction, and centrifugation; the second step is the TLC process itself, consisting of spotting and development.

As a result of multiple replications, the precision of each process in this system was confirmed equal or superior to that of the manual method. At present, though, each procedure of the automated system takes longer than when done manually. This problem will be solved by improving the system.

The sample preparation step may be applicable to many other analyses such as HPLC, spectrophotometry and pH measurement.

INTRODUCTION

Recently, various laboratory automation systems are being utilized with the improvement of analytical instruments and development of laboratory robotics.   Thin layer chromatography (TLC) is a widely used analytical method in many pharmaceutical and chemical laboratories because of its simplicity, selectivity, and low cost. But TLC lags behind automation of other analytical techniques such as HPLC because few instruments are available. In the future, however, an automated TLC system will be necessary for routine analyses in most laboratories, so we attempted to construct a totally automated TLC system. In designing the system, our goal was to be able to handle all kinds of medication dosage forms as well as bulk drug substances using the same automated TLC system.

TLC consists of a series of unit operations, divided into two main processes. The first is sample preparation consisting of weighing, extraction and centrifugation. The second is the TLC process itself consisting of spotting, development and detection.   In these processes as shown in Figure 1, we   perform the sample preparation, spotting and development automatically using a Zymate[tm] Laboratory Automation System.

EXPERIMENTAL

System description

A robotic system was designed specifically to perform both the sample preparation and actual TLC process itself based on Zymate System. This system consists of a laboratory robot, a controller with a printer, a master laboratory station (MLS), a power and event controller (PEC), a balance (Mettler AE163), a vortex mixer, a shaker, a capping station, a centrifuge, and three special hands: a vibrating hand, a syringe hand and a plate transfer hand. This system includes automated TLC chambers designed for our system (Taisei

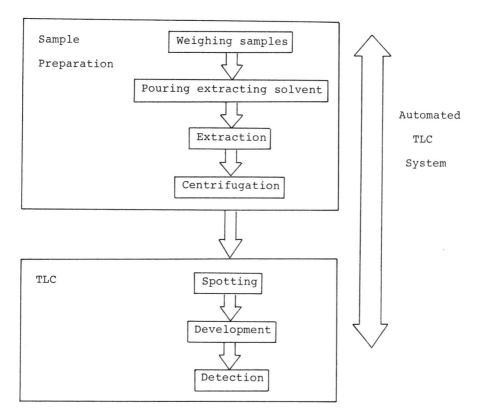

FIGURE 1. Schematic of TLC Procedure.

Kako Co., Ltd., Kanagawa, Japan). An overall view of our system is shown in Figure 2. Figure 3 is a schematic diagram of the system layout.

Procedure

The actual TLC procedure is done in four steps: 1) weighing samples, 2) extracting and centrifuging, 3) spotting the sample solutions, and 4) placing the plate in a TLC chamber to develop. This procedure requires a series of unit operations as explained here in detail.

Weighing:

1.   The robot arm attaches the vibrating hand.

2.   A centrifuge tube is removed from the centrifuge tube rack and uncapped at the capping station.

3.   The centrifuge tube is set on the balance and the balance is electronically tared.

4.   A funnel, used to improve the precision of weighing and to protect against contamination, is set over the centrifuge tube on the balance.

5.   A sample tube containing the solid sample is removed from the sample tube rack and uncapped at the capping station.

6.   Tipping the sample tube over the funnel, the sample substance is gradually poured into the centrifuge tube by vibrating the sample tube (Figure 4).

7.   When the desired sample weight is approximated, vibration of the hand stops.

8.   The controller determines the actual sample weight which is then printed out.

Extracting and Centrifugation:

1.   The centrifugation tube is automatically removed from the balance and set under the nozzle connected to the MLS.

2.   The appropriate solvent for each sample is poured into the centrifuge tube from the MLS.

3.   The centrifuge tube is set in the vortex mixer and the sample is dissolved or extracted.

4.   The centrifuge tube is transferred to the shaker.

5.   If necessary the samples are programmed to be centrifuged.

FIGURE 2. Configuration of the Automated TLC System.

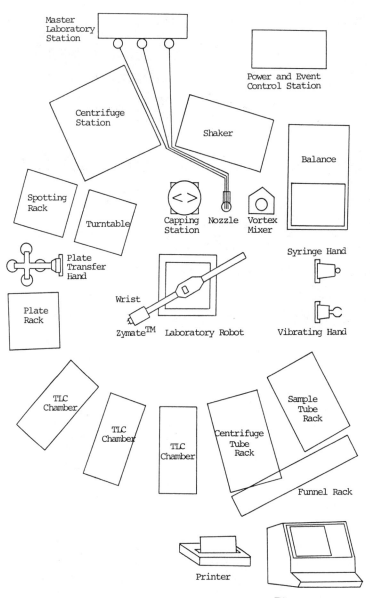

FIGURE 3. Bench Layout for Automated Thin Layer Chromatography.

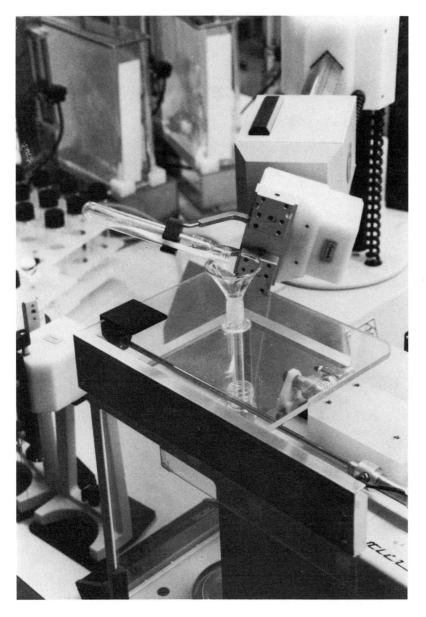

FIGURE 4. Pouring Sample into the Centrifuge Tube.

Spotting:

1. The robot arm attaches the plate transfer hand.

2. A thin-layer plate is picked up from the plate rack by its back side using suction, flipped over and carried to the spotting rack (Figures 5 and 6).

3. After three thin-layer plates are set in the spotting rack, the robot arm exchanges the plate tranfer hand for the syringe hand.

4. The sample solutions are succesively spotted onto the three thin-layer plates (Figure 7).

Developing:

1. The robot arm attaches the plate tranfer hand again.

2. Each thin-layer plate is grasped from the underside using suction, turned over and set on the turntable, rotated 90° clockwise on the turntable and then picked up again (Figure 8).

3. Each thin-layer plate is set into a lifting rack of the automated TLC chamber (Figure 9) and inserted into the glass chamber.

4. When the preset solvent front has been reached (monitored by an optical sensor), development is stopped by removal of the rack from chamber.

RESULTS AND DISCUSSION

Reproducibility

The precision of each unit operation such as weighing samples, pouring extracting solvent, or spotting sample solutions was confirmed to be equal or superior to that of manual methods. The reproducibility of each unit operation is described in detail.

Weighing Samples

Table 1 shows the results of the reproducibility of the weighing procedure. We poured and weighed 0.5g each of lactose powder and granules using the automated process. Since the powder flows poorly and the granules flows easily, they are good examples to test weighing reproducibility. The results were satisfactory.

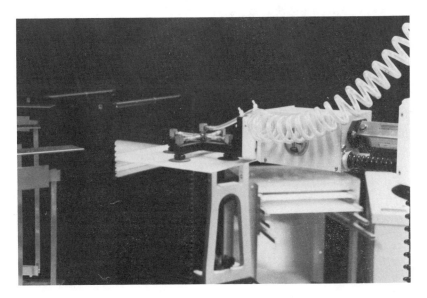

FIGURE 5. Thin-layer Plate Held by the Plate Transfer Hand.

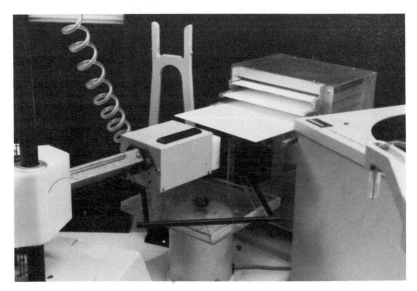

FIGURE 6. Setting Thin-layer Plate into Spotting Rack.

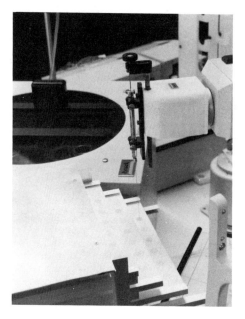

FIGURE 7. Spotting Sample Solutions onto Thin-layer Plate.

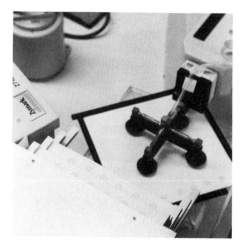

FIGURE 8. Rotating Thin-layer Plate on Turntable.

FIGURE 9. Inserting Thin-layer Plate into the Lifting Rack of the TLC Chamber.

Table 1. Reproducibility of Weighing Process.

Trial No.	Powder (g)	Grannules (g)
1	0.4953	0.4943
2	0.4821	0.5022
3	0.5081	0.5003
4	0.5233	0.5015
5	0.4815	0.5112
6	0.5285	0.4964
7	0.5009	0.4853
8	0.4879	0.5121
9	0.4890	0.4831
10	0.5180	0.5079
Average	0.5015	0.4994
CV(%)	3.4	2.0

Target weight = 0.5g

Pouring Extracting Solvent

Table 2 shows the results of the reproducibility of pouring the extracting solvent from the MLS. We tested water, methanol, and acetone as the extracting solvents. The volume of extracting solvent was estimated by weighing the solvent. The reproducibility of this MLS process was excellent.

Table 2. Reproducibility of the MLS (weight of solvent in g).

Trial No.	Water 10mL	5mL	Methanol 10mL	5mL	Acetone 10mL	5mL
1	9.9983	5.0127	7.8662	3.9546	7.8487	3.9419
2	9.9985	5.0127	7.8648	3.9547	7.8421	3.9400
3	9.9979	5.0120	7.8581	3.9422	7.8395	3.9291
4	9.9988	5.0108	7.8647	3.9537	7.8418	3.9253
5	9.9990	5.0107	7.8657	3.9399	7.8305	3.9243
6	9.9900	5.0059	7.8575	3.9524	7.8363	3.9211
7	10.0069	5.0091	7.8651	3.9410	7.8387	3.9043
8	9.9973	5.0093	7.8549	3.9491	7.8339	3.9304
9	9.9991	5.0074	7.8651	3.9362	7.8397	3.9348
Average	9.9984	5.0101	7.8625	3.9470	7.8390	3.9279
CV(%)	0.04	0.05	0.06	0.18	0.07	0.27

Spotting Sample Solutions

The reproducibility of the spotting procedure was determined by measuring the peak areas of spots using a TLC scanner (Shimadzu CS-910, Shimadzu Seisakusho Ltd., Kyoto, Japan). Table 3 shows the results of comparing reproducibility between the robotic and manul methods.

Table 3. Reproducibility of Spotting (peak area of spots, mm).

	Robotic			Manual		
Trial No.	1	2	3	1	2	3
1	22.15	22.51	21.18	23.64	23.40	24.19
2	22.96	23.14	21.80	23.70	24.25	24.11
3	23.40	24.46	22.74	24.18	23.99	22.53
4	24.03	24.25	22.10	23.77	23.53	24.06
5	23.41	22.93	22.72	23.44	23.18	22.93
6	23.49	23.67	23.48	22.92	23.44	22.36
7	-	-	-	24.05	24.01	23.18
8	-	-	-	22.70	22.97	22.68
Average	23.24	23.49	22.34	23.55	23.60	23.26
CV(%)	2.7	3.3	3.6	2.2	1.9	3.3

Preparation Time

Time required to prepare sample solutions from six powder samples of lactose and to spot these on three thin-layer plates were compared using the robotic and manual methods. The results are shown in Table 4. At present each procedure of the automated system takes longer than when done manually, but the time will be shortened through system improvements.

Table 4. Preparation Time For Six Powdered Lactose Samples.

	Robotic	Manual
Sample Preparation	2 hrs.	45 min.
Spotting	30 min.	15 min.
Total Time	2.5 hrs.	1 hr.

Time to shake   : 10 min.

Time to centrifuge: 10 min.

CONCLUSION

We foresee the feasibility of introducing automation into TLC using the Zymate[tm] Laboratory Automation System, incorporating both sample preparation and the TLC process itself. At this point the reproducibility of each operation, such as sample weighing, pouring extracting solvents or spotting, is very good with the automated system described here. A series of unit operations, from weighing through plate development, is able to be carried out in automated succession for diversely different solid samples without any help. Further implications from these results are that the sample preparation step can be applicable to many other analyses such as HPLC, spectrophotometry and pH measurement. We believe that this system will eventually be developed to the point where it can be of valuable assistance in routine TLC analysis.

ACKNOWLEDGEMENT

The authors wish to Mr. Hideyo Hashimoto of Nissei Sangyo Co., Ltd., Mr. Kinzo Kawata of Hitachi Instruments Service Co., Ltd. and Dr. Takeshi Omori of Tasei Kako Co., Ltd., for their advice and assistance.

REFERENCES

1.   N. Morokoshi, S. Inada, S. Koda and Y. Morimoto : The 36th annual conference of the Kinki Branch of Japan Pharmaceutical Association, Osaka, Japan, 1986, A14-3, p.28.

2.   N. Morokoshi, S. Inada, S. Koda and Y. Morimoto : Laboratory Automation Robotics Symposium 2, Nissei Sangyo (1987).

AUTOMATED SAMPLE ANALYSIS FROM METHOD DEVELOPMENT TO SAMPLE ANALYSIS

E.L. Johnson, K.L. Hoffman and L.A. Pachla
Parke-Davis Pharmaceutical Research Division
Warner-Lambert Company
2800 Plymouth Road
Ann Arbor, Michigan 48105

ABSTRACT

A totally integrated robotic system has been developed to do both method development and sample analysis. An IBM-PC provides the "intelligent" feedback for method development via a liquid/solid extraction procedure using disposable cartridges and a "user friendly" interface for inputting the information for routine sample analysis. Extraction of the samples is done by a generic liquid/solid extraction program that eliminates the need for program modification between assays.

In order to improve the reliability and reproducibility of the system, several miniature pressure transducers are used to monitor the status of the air pressure, nitrogen pressure, and solvent flow through the cartridge. A procedure using the Zymate system to prepare samples in the batch mode using liquid/solid extraction will be described. This procedure is capable of preparing 144 samples in less than 4 hours.

INTRODUCTION

A Zymate Laboratory Automation System, previously described,[1,2] is able to perform automated sample preparation using disposable solid-phase cartridges. This system has been further enhanced to include direct sample injection via a Z310 HPLC Injector and communications with an IBM-PC via the Z845 Interface. Sample preparation using liquid/solid technology has increased dramatically over the past three years. This procedure has become the method of choice in our laboratories over liquid/liquid extraction. A robotic procedure has been developed to automate method development using liquid/solid sample preparation. This allows the robotic system to do both the method development and the sample analysis. An IBM-PC is used to provide the "intelligent" feedback needed for assay development. Composition of the elution solvents and type of packing is controlled by the PC. Information from the chromatographic analysis is obtained by the instrument interface in the Z310 injector and transferred to the PC. This information is analyzed by a basic program on the PC and the results used to determine changes in the solvent composition or cartridge type. The cycle of sample preparation and data analysis continues until user defined conditions are met or until the defined combinations of solvent and cartridge types are exhausted. At this point, if the user defined conditions are met, the robotic system will extract and inject a set of standards to determine the linearity of the assay procedure.

In order to increase sample throughput and provide additional robotic capabilities, the manual procedure using batch sample preparation was analyzed to determine its viability for automation with the Zymate System. The existing manual procedure involves sample preparation in small batches (<13) and would not be applicable to the robotic system. A large vacuum box was designed and custom made that allows sample preparation in batches of up to 144 samples. It is used in conjunction with a Zymate System to allow batch preparation of 100 samples in 3.5 hours.

EQUIPMENT

The two robotic systems consist of the equipment listed in Tables 1 and 2, and the schematic bench layout is illustrated in Figures 1 and 2. All parameters needed for either robotic system are input via a BASIC^{tm} program and a single PC.

Table 1. List of Equipment Used in Method Development System.

Zymark Corporation (Hopkinton, Ma)

   Robot Arm and Controller
   Vortex Station
   Power and Event Controller (PEC)
   Master Laboratory Station (MLS)
   Printer
   Liquid/solid work station
   HPLC Injector Station with 200 ul loop
   Miscellaneous Racks

Pennies Applied Technology (Parkridge, Il)

   Test tube dispenser

Neptune Research (Maplewood, N.J.)

   4-way solvent selection valves

Waters Associates (Milford, Ma)

   Pump (Model 590)
   UV Detector (Model 481)

Hewlett Packard (Avondale, Pa)

   Integrator (Model 3392A)

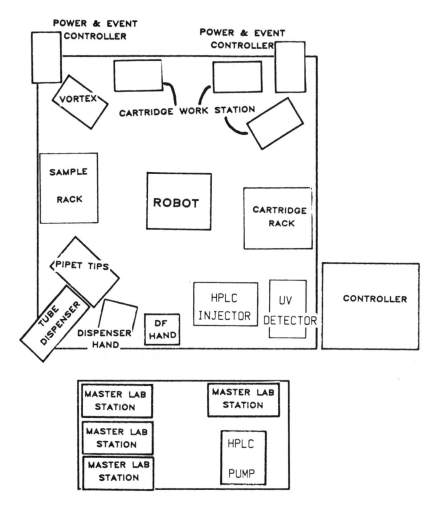

Figure 1. Pharmaceutical Methods Development Bench Layout.

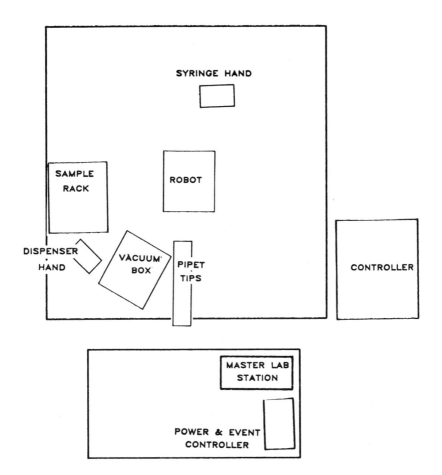

Figure 2. Pharmaceutical Application for Batch Liquid-Solid System Layout.

Table 2. List of Equipment used in Batch Liquid/Solid System.

Zymark Corporation (Hopkinton, Ma)

    Robot Arm and Controller
    Power and Event Controller (PEC)
    Master Laboratory Station (MLS)
    Miscellaneous Racks

Neptune Research (Maplewood, N.J.)

    4-way solvent selection valves

Alltech Associates (Deerfield, Il)

    FMI Solvent Metering Pump

Custom Designed Vacuum Box

EXPERIMENTAL

Automated Method Development System

A maximum of 10 different cartridge types are used for method development. A standard sample is injected into the HPLC to determine the area of the standard peak using the instrument interface. This information is transferred to the PC as the 100% recovery value for the peak of interest. At the present time, the system is designed to optimize the results of a single component. Sample analysis continues as described in the flow diagram in Figure 3.

The procedure is divided into four sections. The first section eliminates all cartridges that do not give adequate retention of the compound. The second section determines the cartridges from which the compound cannot be eluted. By eliminating the cartridges that do not retain the compound and those that retain it too strongly, one obtains a subset of cartridge types that can be used for assay development. The procedure is fine tuned in section three to determine the strongest solvent mixture that will elute less than 10% of the compound and the weakest solvent mixture that will elute at least 90% of the compound.

In section four, sample blanks are run using the appropriate elution solvents and cartridges. If any blank contains less than 1% interference, a standard curve is run to determine the linearity of the assay. After all of the analyses have been completed, a table is printed by the PC containing percent of compound eluted under the various conditions. If there are no acceptable cartridge/solvent mixture combinations, the procedure can be re-run using different cartridge and solvent combinations.

Batch Liquid/Solid Sample Preparation

Solvents are added to the cartridges via a liquid distribution hand using the FMI pump or the MLS station. The FMI pump, controlled by the PEC, adds the various wash solutions and the MLS adds the final elution solvent. Vacuum is controlled and monitored by the PEC. Due to the large size and weight of the vacuum box cover, it must be removed manually. Figure 4 contains a flow diagram of the procedure with manual steps noted. All user inputs for the Zymate System are done via the PC.

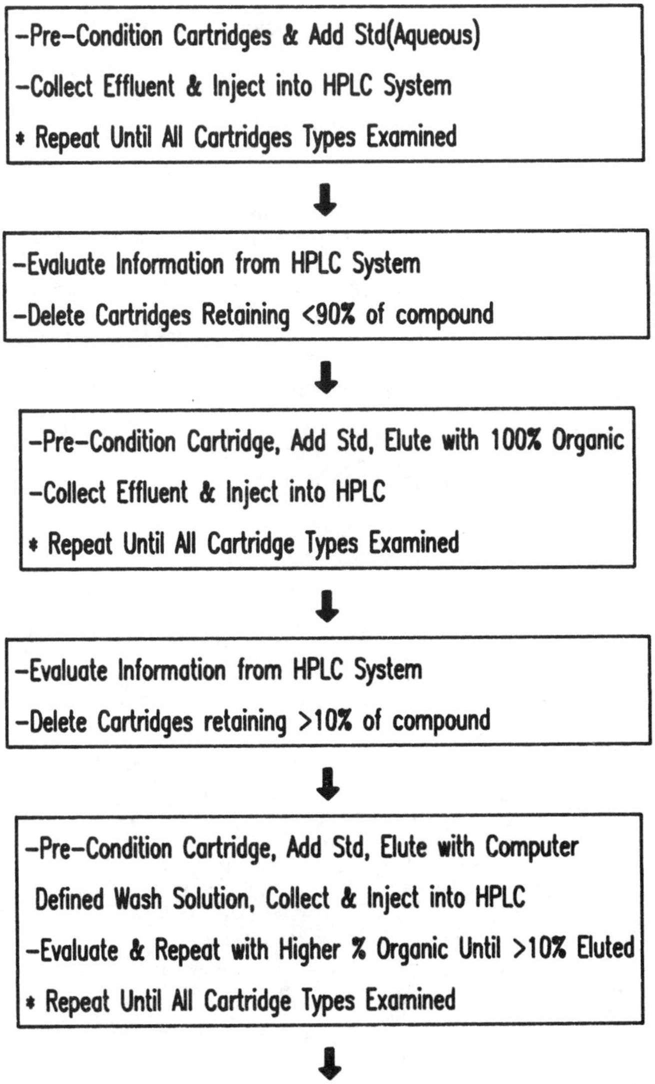

-Pre-Condition Cartridges & Add Std(Aqueous)

-Collect Effluent & Inject into HPLC System

* Repeat Until All Cartridges Types Examined

⬇

-Evaluate Information from HPLC System

-Delete Cartridges Retaining <90% of compound

⬇

-Pre-Condition Cartridge, Add Std, Elute with 100% Organic

-Collect Effluent & Inject into HPLC

* Repeat Until All Cartridge Types Examined

⬇

-Evaluate Information from HPLC System

-Delete Cartridges retaining >10% of compound

⬇

-Pre-Condition Cartridge, Add Std, Elute with Computer

 Defined Wash Solution, Collect & Inject into HPLC

-Evaluate & Repeat with Higher % Organic Until >10% Eluted

* Repeat Until All Cartridge Types Examined

⬇

FIGURE 3. Flow Diagram of Liquid/Solid Extraction Optimization.

-Pre-Condition Cartridge, Add Std, Wash with Solution
Defined Above, Elute with Computer Defined Solution
-Collect Effluent & Inject into HPLC
-Evaluate, Repeat with Higher % Organic Until >90% Eluted
* Repeat Until All Cartridge Types Examined

-Pre-Condition Cartridge, Add Sample Blank, Wash with
Defined Wash Solution, Elute with Defined Elution Solvent
Collect & Inject Into HPLC
* Repeat Until All Cartridge Types Examined

-Evaluate Information from HPLC System
-Delete Cartridges with >1% Impurity Peak

-Extract & Inject Stds Using Computed Defined Conditions
* Repeat Until All Cartridge Types Examined

-Print Information From All Cartridge Types in Table

FIGURE 3. Flow Diagram of Liquid/Solid Extraction Optimization (continued).

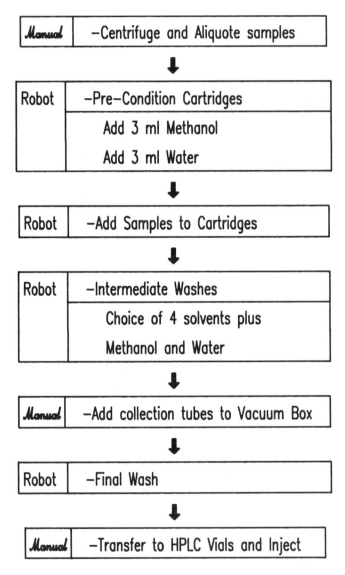

FIGURE 4. Flow Diagram of Batch Liquid/Solid Procedure

RESULTS AND DISCUSSION

During manual method development an individual is often reluctant to examine large numbers of different packings because of the time involved. This is not a problem with the robotic system. The procedure for method development is complete and has been evaluated by comparing the results from manual and automated method development. Both procedures gave similar results, but it has not been tested on unknown compounds at this time. Because the same robotic configuration is used for method development and routine sample analysis, it will allow the system to be used for method development during off-hours. This will greatly increase the usefulness of the robotic system.

The batch liquid/solid procedure is used for routine sample analysis. Two different procedures have been validated and the results were comparable to the manual method. For proprietary reasons this information is not included.

The batch liquid/solid procedure takes approximately two minutes per sample and can prepare 100 samples in 3.5 hours. A maximum of seven different solvents can be used in the sample preparation, and a single solvent can be used more than one time. The pipetting of the sample is the most time consuming aspect of the sample preparation taking from .75 to 1.25 minutes. Therefore, one can use a more involved elution scheme without significantly increasing the sample preparation time.

SUMMARY

A robotic system has been designed to automate the method development for compounds using liquid/solid extraction. After the method is optimized, a standard curve is analyzed to determine the linearity of the procedure. If the procedure provides valid assay results, the robotic system can validate the assay and start routine sample analysis. Method development on the robotic system not only saves times but guarantees the assay is compatible with robotic sample preparation.

The batch mode procedure presents a rapid method of preparing large number of samples in a short time period, thereby allowing the robotic system to do other work in the off-hours. As shown in Figure 2, only one fourth of the robotic work area is needed for this procedure; thereby allowing the robotic system to be used for other procedures. The existing robotic system contains a complete liquid/liquid extraction system in the remainder of the robotic table.

Additional improvements for the robotic system include:

1) Further refinements of the method development software to allow the option of more complicated elution schemes

2) Optimization of a multi-component mixture

3) Elimination of manual step in the batch method

REFERENCES

1. E.L. Johnson and L.A. Pachla, "Generic Robotic Sample Preparation of Drugs From Biological Fluids Using Disposable Cartridges", in Advances in Laboratory Automation - Robotics 1986, J.R. Strimaitis and G.L. Hawk, eds., Zymark Corporation, Hopkinton, MA, 1986, p. 37.

2. E.L. Johnson, L.A. Pachla, and D.L. Reynolds, Robotic Analysis of 3,7-Dimethoxy-4-phenyl-N-1H-tetrazol-5-yl-4H-furo[3,2-b] indole-2-carboxamide in Human Plasma", J. Pharm. Sci, 75, (10), 1003 (1986).

AN AUTOMATED SYSTEM FOR THE SIMULTANEOUS DETERMINATION OF SEVERAL INGREDIENTS IN PHARMACEUTICAL PREPARATIONS USING HPLC AND A LABORATORY ROBOT

Tuguchika Yoshida, Yuji Ito, Mitsuichi Handa,
Osamu Kasai and Hiroshi Yamaguchi
Dept. of Analytical Chemistry Research Center,
Taisho Pharmaceutical Co., Ltd.
403, Yoshino-cho 1-Chome,
Omiya-shi, Saitama, Japan

ABSTRACT

An automation system for the preparation of solutions from solid samples for HPLC analysis has been developed and applied to the simultaneous determination of nine ingredients in cold remedy tablets, capsules and granules. Powdered samples are weighed, added to the extraction solvent containing internal standard substances, extracted by supersonic wave irradiation and vortexing, centrifuged and injected into two HPLCs using a laboratory robot. Two HPLC's and an electronic balance are interfaced with a NEC PC-9801 personal computer. The analytical data are automatically calculated and recorded on floppy discs, and the final reports are generated.

INTRODUCTION

A major effort has been made to automate as many routine analytical procedures as possible in our laboratories. HPLC is mainly used for stability tests and the quality control of pharmaceutical preparations. Analytical chemists carry out a lot of tedious and time-consuming tasks such as weighing, extraction, dilution, adding internal standard solution, etc. Sometimes mistakes are made when performing these processes. Automated analytical systems using robots and HPLC for content uniformity tests have been reported.[1-6] We investigated an automated system for quality control and stability tests of pharmaceutical preparations containing hydrophilic and hydrophobic active ingredients using HPLC, robots and a personal computer.

EXPERIMENTAL

Reagents and Materials

Sodium dodecyl sulfate (SDS) was purchased from Seikagaku Kogyo Co. Tetra-n-butylammonium hydroxide solution (TBA), methanol, acetonitrile, phosphoric acid, phenol and phenanthrene were purchased from Wako Pure Chemical Ind., Ltd. Cold remedy preparations containing 990 mg of bucetin, 7.5 mg of carbinoxamine maleate, 48 mg of dextromethorphan hydrobromide, 48 mg of noscapine, 60 mg of dl-methylephedrine, 180 mg of potassium guaiacolsulfonate, 75 mg of caffeine anhydride, 24 mg of thiamine mononitrate and 12 mg of riboflavin in nine tablets, six capsules or three granules were prepared in our laboratory.

Robotic System

The automation system used for the determination of ingredients in the cold remedies (tablets, capsules and granules) is shown in Figure 1. The robot controller, semimicro-electronic balance and integrator (Chromatocorder 11) were interfaced with an NEC model PC-9801 personal computer by RS-232C.

A list of equipment used is given in Table 1.

High Performance Liquid Chromatographic Conditions

The HPLC analyses were performed with a Hitachi Model 655A-12 liquid chromatograph equipped with a Hitachi Model 655A variable-wavelength UV detector and a stainless-steel column (150mm x 4mm I.D.) packed with chemically bonded ODS silica gel (TSKgel LS-410, 5 um, Toyo Soda, Japan). The mobil phase used was as follows:

Condition A: water-acetonitrile (90:10), containing
2.5 mM tetra-n-butylammonium bromide
and adjusted to pH 6.0 by phospheric acid.

Condition B: water-acetonitrile-phospheric acid
(510:490:1), containing 17 mM SDS.

The column temperature was maintained at 50°C and the flow-rate was 1.0 mL/min. The substances eluted were detected by a UV detector operated at a wavelength of 280 nm for condition A and 210 nm for condition B.

VALIDATION

Validation of the Master Laboratory Station

Delivery of solvents by the MLS was validated in the following manner. A capped 50 mL centrifuge tube was taken from a rack. The tube was tared in the balance. The cap was removed, the liquid was dispensed into the tube by the MLS, and the cap was replaced. The tube was returned to the balance and weighed. The weight was converted to a volumetric measurement considering the density of that liquid. The results of the solvent delivery validation are shown in Table 2.

TABLE 1. Components of an Automated Analytical System.

Robotic System:

1. Zymate II Robot

2. Controller

3. Power and event controller (PEC)

4. Master laboratory station (MLS)

5. Vortex station

6. Vibrator hand

7. Precision microliter syringe hand

8. General purpose hand

9. Capping station

10. Centrifuge station

11. Pipet tip rack

12. Sample tube rack

13. Injection station

14. Nozzle stand

15. Pipet tip remover

16. Optical sensor

17. Ultrasonic actor: Yamato Bransonic 12

18. Personal computer: NEC PC-9801

19. Printer: NEC PC-PR201H

20. RS-232C Multiplexer: Techno Park M-100A

21. Semimicro-electronic balance: Mettler ME-163

22. Integrator: SIC Chromatocorder-11

23. High performance liquid chromatograph: Hitachi 655A

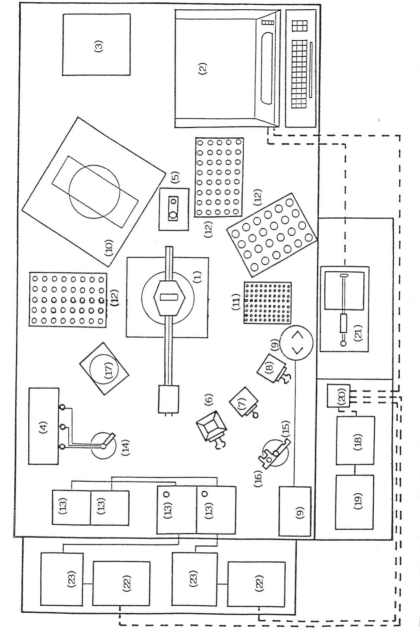

Figure 1. Bench Layout for Robotic System. Dashed lines indicate wiring diagram of data-processing system.

TABLE 2. Validation of the Master Laboratory Station.

Syringe	Volume (mL)	Solvent	Sampling volume(mL)	Average (mL)	C.V. (%)
A	10	Water	5	5.0267	0.01
			10	10.0556	0.03
		Methanol	5	4.9952	0.06
			10	10.0083	0.07
B	5	Water	2.5	2.4901	0.06
			5	5.0031	0.03
		Methanol	2.5	2.4676	0.04
			5	4.9526	0.02
C	2.5	Water	2	1.9961	0.04
			2.5	2.4874	0.03
		Methanol	2	1.9831	0.05
			2.5	2.4635	0.07

TABLE 3. Validation of the Syringe Hand.

Sampling Volume(mL)	Solvent	Average (mL)	C.V. (%)
0.5	Water	0.4969	0.4
0.9		0.8990	0.3
0.5	Water-Methanol	0.4996	0.4
0.9	(1:1)	0.9141	0.4
0.5	Methanol	0.5024	0.3
0.9		0.9122	0.1

Validation of the Syringe Hand

Delivery of the solvents by the syringe hand was validated in the same manner as that of the MLS. A 1 mL disposable pipet tip on the 1 mL of syringe hand was used. The results of this validation are shown in Table 3. These results show that the MLS has superior precision compared to of the syringe hand. So, we decided to use the MLS for dispensing internal standards into the centrifuge tube.

Analytical procedure

A flow diagram of the manual procedure and the automated procedure is shown in Figure 2. The automated procedure was the same as the manual procedure, except for the extraction method. The shaker in the manual procedure was replaced by the ultrasonicator and the vortex station in the automated procedure, and the methanol content in the extraction solvent was increased in the automated procedure.

RESULTS AND DISCUSSION

Chromatograms obtained by the proposed method are shown in Figure 3. Caffeine anhydride, riboflavin, phenol (I.S.), potassium guaiacolsulfonate and bucetin were separated within 30 minutes for HPLC condition A. And also, dl-methylephedrine hydrochloride, noscapine, thiaminemononitrate, dextromethorphane hydrobromide, phenanthrene (I.S.) and carbinoxamine maleate were separated within 20 minutes for HPLC condition B. All peaks were symmetrical.

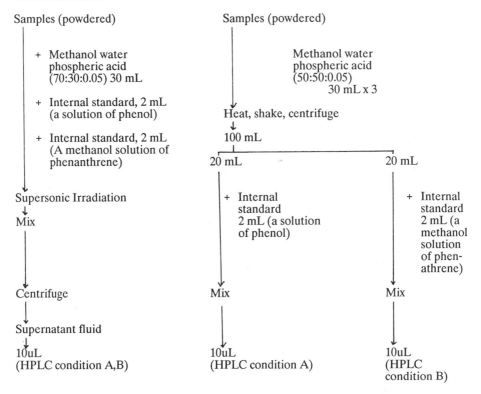

Figure 2. Flow Diagrams of the Manual and Robotic Procedure.

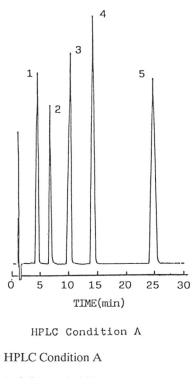

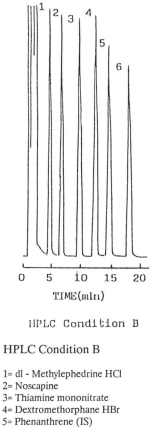

HPLC Condition A

HPLC Condition B

HPLC Condition A

1= Caffeine Anhydride
2= Riboflavin
3= Phenol
4= Potassium Guaiacolsufonate
5= Bucetin

HPLC Condition B

1= dl - Methylephedrine HCl
2= Noscapine
3= Thiamine mononitrate
4= Dextromethorphane HBr
5= Phenanthrene (IS)
6= Carbinoxamine Maleate

FIGURE 3. HPLC Chromatograms Obtained by the Proposed Method.

TABLE 4. Analytical Results for Three Different Types of Samples (n=3, %CV in parentheses).

Samples	Method	B	C	D	N	ME	PG	CA	TN	R
Tablet	Robot	99.8 (0.33)	101.3 (1.10)	99.8 (0.44)	100.0 (1.67)	100.8 (0.29)	100.5 (1.30)	100.5 (0.77)	100.0 (0.63)	100.6 (0.36)
	Manual	98.1 (0.91)	100.0 (1.20)	99.4 (1.24)	99.0 (1.14)	100.0 (1.10)	98.9 (1.17)	100.9 (0.40)	100.8 (0.49)	101.3 (0.99)
Granule	Robot	98.6 (0.64)	99.9 (0.71)	101.4 (0.79)	99.7 (1.49)	100.8 (0.89)	102.0 (0.79)	100.5 (0.29)	99.2 (1.39)	101.9 (1.19)
	Manual	99.0 (0.71)	101.3 (1.21)	98.9 (0.61)	98.7 (0.49)	99.2 (0.19)	101.4 (1.59)	99.7 (0.99)	98.1 (0.91)	100.8 (0.99)
Capsule	Robot	98.8 (0.31)	98.5 (1.32)	100.0 (0.52)	98.9 (0.29)	101.8 (1.00)	100.1 (0.75)	98.3 (0.41)	99.0 (0.86)	——
	Manual	99.0 (1.49)	99.6 (1.44)	100.6 (1.69)	99.6 (0.19)	100.1 (1.30)	100.5 (0.95)	99.6 (1.90)	99.6 (0.89)	——

B=Bucetin; C=Carbinoxamine maleate; D=Dextromethorphane HBr; N=Noscapine; ME=Methyl ephedrine HCl;
PG=Potassium guaiacolsulfonate; CA=Caffeine anhydride; TN=Thiaminemononitrate; R=Riboflavin.

The analytical results for three different types of samples (tablet, granule and capsule) are shown in Table 4. The mean values and the coefficients of variations (C.V.) for the robotic procedure agreed well with those for the manual procedures. The C.V. for three assays ranged from 0.29 to 1.49% for the robotic procedure and 0.19 to 1.90% for the manual procedure, respectively. These analytical data were automatically generated as the final reports. The sample amount, peak areas, the ratio of the peak areas, the percent against the labeled amount, the average, the retention time, and the relative retention time were reported in the final report.

A comparison of the analytical time required for a manual versus a robotic procedure is shown in Table 5. For typical batches of nine samples, the actual working hours related to sample preparation was reduced from 5.0 hours to 1.0 hour. The total assay time was also reduced from 10 hours to 6.5 hours.

TABLE 5. Analysis time for automated and manual procedures.

	Sampling	Extraction	HPLC	Calculation	Total Time
Robot	1.0hr *	← 5.0 →		0.5	6.5
Manual (Auto Sampler was used)	1.0hr *,	4.0 *	4.5	0.5	10.0

* actual working hours

CONCLUSIONS

From the results reported herein, it can be concluded that the Zymate Laboratory Automation System can be effectively used to automate the analytical procedures for making pharmaceutical preparations and should be quite useful for saving time and labor.

ACKNOWLEDGEMENT

We wish to thank Nissei Sangyo Corporation for their help.

REFERENCES

1.   J. Vidgren and J. Taskinen, in Advances in Laboratory Automation Robotics 1986, G.L. Hawk and J.R. Strimaitis, (eds.), P. 99.

2.   G.P. Wheeler, P.A. Litter, G.M. Gustin and M.J. Candon, in Advances in Laboratory Automation Robotics 1986, G.L. Hawk and J.R. Strimaitis, (eds.), P. 125.

3   P. Walsh, H. Abdou, R. Barnes and B. Cohen, in Advances in Laboratory Automation Robotics 1985, G.L. Hawk and J.R. Strimaitis, (eds.), P. 547.

4.   C. Hatfield, E. Halloran, J. Habarta, S. Romano and W. Mason, in Advances in Laboratory Automation Robotic 1985, G.L. Hawk and J.R. Strimaitis, (eds.), P. 599.

5.   E. Siebert, in Advances in Laboratory Automation Robotic 1984, G.L. Hawk and J.R. Strimaitis, (eds.), P. 257.

6.   B. Compton, M. Froome and O.Hinsvark, in Advances in Laboratory Automation Robotics 1984, G.L. Hawk and J.R. Strimaitis, (eds.), P. 287.

AN AUTOMATED STATION FOR THE COLLECTION AND ANALYSIS OF METERED DOSE AEROSOL PRODUCTS

L.L. Lorenz, H.R. Sochon, J.C. Zeiss, and S.L. Buell,
Schering-Plough Corporation
Kenilworth, NJ 07033

ABSTRACT

Schering produces several products which are administered via metered dose aerosols. Unlike most pharmaceutical preparations, the product container is an integral part of the delivery system. Dispensing of the drug from the unit and collection of the airborne aerosol introduce several unique variables into the sample collection technique.

Ordinarily, a sample unit is hand held and the drug is dispensed as a metered dose by manually depressing an actuator attached to the canister. The automated method follows the USP method for collection of metered dose aerosol products. It primes the aerosols, sprays the aerosols into a suitable vessel, and collects the samples in solvent for quantitation.

Automation of the metered dose collection was first proposed to reduce the tedium of this method and to reduce demand on manpower. As development progressed, we discovered that an automated collection and analysis system could lead to a greater understanding and resolution of the effects of agitation time, agitation stroke, and actuation force. In the manual method, these variables were known to exist but could not be easily controlled.

When considering possible automation schemes, we concluded that the best route was to build dedicated equipment specifically for this application. No existing laboratory robotic systems were identified which possessed, as standard equipment, all of the control hardware and software needed for this project. Therefore, we chose to use an IBM Personal System/2 Model 30 with the necessary interface boards as a controller for the station.

Sample weighing, introduction into and collection from the sampling station, analytical dilutions, and reagent additions are directed by a robot. Synchronizing signals between the collection controller and the robotic system are handled either by simple contact closures or through a serial computer communications link.

Independent control of the sampling and collection stations permit them to be interfaced to virtually any robotic system or to be used as stand alone equipment. Since the bulk of the sampling and collection is performed automatically by the equipment, even the latter mode can translate into significant time savings and improved precision.

This paper will discuss details of the technique, essential equipment, and the problems encountered during the development. Special design items such as jigs to hold different varieties of actuators and containers and systems for rinsing the collection vessel with a minimal volume of solvent will also be addressed.

INTRODUCTION

The first metered-dose aerosol appeared on the U.S. pharmaceutical market in the mid-1950's. Today, there are over a half-dozen products on the prescription and OTC markets employing metered-dose technology. Clearly, this unique delivery system is of great importance to many pharmaceutical companies and to the millions of patients that rely upon the products that are administered via metered-dose aerosols.

Prior to a discussion of automated analysis of this device, it will be beneficial to examine the unique components of metered-dose aerosol technology. A complete package of a metered-dose aerosol consists of three major components: 1) a bulk canister for holding the pharmaceutical preparation, 2) a metered-valve assembly for measuring the proper dose, and 3) an actuator assembly for triggering the valve and controlling the proper flow dynamics of the aerosol. Each of these components can contribute to variation of the desired dose delivered to the patient.

Since metered-dose formulations are typically packaged in multi-dose containers, a suitable bulk canister is necessary for holding and storing the pharmaceutical preparation. A typical inhalation preparation would be contained in an extruded metal canister with either a suspension or solution of the active compound along with a suitable propellant. Incorporated into the pressurized canister would be the metered-valve assembly. Once primed, this valve will administer, upon actuation, a precise quantity of a drug substance. The valve is recharged at the end of each actuation cycle, thereby readying it for the next dosing. The actuator assembly is the interface between the patient and the metered-valve. While inhaling, the patient presses the bulk canister and metered-valve assembly into the actuator with a firm, rapid compression motion. This triggers the dose and the airflow through the actuator directs the aerosol toward the desired site in the patient.

A unique aspect of metered-dose aerosol pharmaceuticals is that each component, of what is essentially the package, can affect the amount of active delivered to the patient. Suspensions require agitation to resuspend particulates. Variations in the speed at which the valve is triggered can affect the aerosol pattern and hence the delivery of the active. Finally, the actuator itself affects the aerosol pattern and can retain active from the dosing. All of these variables combine to present a challenge for the assay of the active compounds as the procedure may be dependent upon the rate of agitation prior to dosing, the rate at which the valve is triggered, the orientation of the unit into the collection device, and the interval between doses.

The goal of automating the sample collection and preparation procedure for metered-dose aerosols is to devise a labor saving setup that will either eliminate or control these variables. An automated procedure would provide not only a useful tool for assaying batch results, but also would provide a controlled reference for evaluating new designs of valves and actuators.

EXPERIMENTAL

Schering has several aerosol products, but the mechanics of the sample preparation procedure are essentially the same for all of the products. The actuators, rinse solvent, and internal standards vary, but for the purposes of this presentation we assume that all actuators can be accommodated and that all solvents are methanol. The manual procedure which we wished to automate is outlined in Table 1.

TABLE 1. Outline of Manual Procedure for Assay of Metered-dose Aerosols.

Step	Action
1	Setup collection equipment as shown in Figure 1. Place cotton filter into end of 2 liter separatory funnel with the stopcock in the open position. Connect the stem of the funnel through a flowmeter to a vacuum and adjust flow to draw 10 liters of air per minute through the assembly.
2	Insert a sample canister into an actuator, invert and shake 30 seconds. Prime the sample by alternately shaking and discharging 2 doses into a laboratory hood.
3	Wait for the temperature of the aerosol to reach room temperature and weigh the sample canister and actuator assembly.
4	Shake the assembly for 30 seconds and deliver 2 doses into the separatory funnel approximately 5 seconds apart, shaking the unit between doses.
5	Wait one minute while the aerosol returns to room temperature, shake for 10 seconds, and deliver two additional doses into the same separatory funnel collection setup.
6	Reweigh the sample canister and actuator assembly and record the weight of the delivered doses.
7	Allow the air flow to continue for about 20 seconds after the fourth burst. Disconnect the funnel from the flowmeter and close the stopcock. Set the funnel in a vertical position.
8	Rinse the separatory funnel and cotton filter with 70 mL of methanol divided into 20, 20, 20, and 10-mL portions. Collect in a 100-mL volumetric flask, add internal standard, and dilute to volume.
9	Assay by normal HPLC procedure.

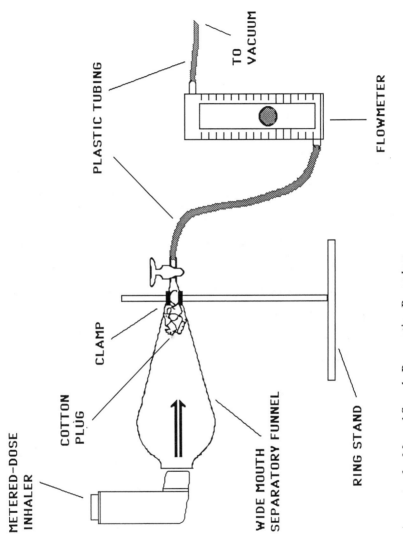

FIGURE 1. Apparatus for Manual Sample Preparation Procedure.

The manual sample preparation requires approximately 20 minutes per sample to prepare a solution ready for HPLC injection. No individual step is particularly difficult or time consuming. However, as each canister is assayed twice and ten canisters per batch are sampled, each batch assayed consumes approximately seven hours of an analyst's time.

The setup for an automated station that primes, doses, and collects the active components of a metered-dose aerosol is shown in Figure 2. The main components are a sample unit which contains the aerosol canister and actuator in an adapter used for holding and positioning the aerosol unit, a shaking and dosing station that agitates the sample unit and doses the aerosol either at a priming position or at the collection station, and a reusable collection station which collects the metered-dose samples and then rinses the trapped material into a suitable flask. Complete automation is achieved by the addition of a computer system for controlling the actions of the dosing and collection stations and coordinating the movements of a robotic arm. The arm is used to feed aerosol sample units to the dosing station, and to remove the sample once it has been collected and rinsed into a flask. Figure 3 shows details of the robotic layout. Table 2 lists components used in the construction of the automated setup.

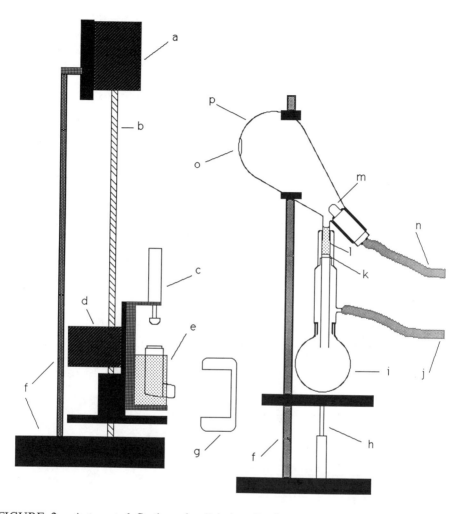

FIGURE 2.   Automated Stations for Priming, Dosing, and Collecting Metered-dose Aerosols, a. stepper motor for height adjustment, b. gear shaft for height adjustment, c. dosing air plunger, d. stepper motor for shaking, e. actuator adapter, f. supports, g. vented priming station, h. adjustable platform for receiving flask, i. receiving flask, j. vent to metered vacuum, k. sintered glass, l. glass beads, m. 60° full cone spray nozzle, n. rinse solvent input line, o. 1 1/2 inch opening for aerosol dosing, p. customized glass collection vessel.

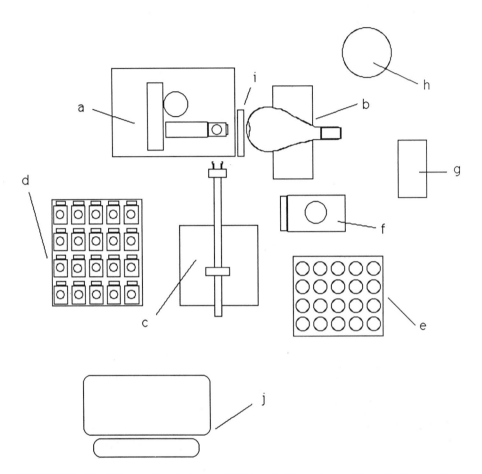

FIGURE 3. Bench Layout for Automated Metered - Dose Aerosal Sample Preparation,
a. shaking and dosing station, b. collection station, c. robot arm, d. rack for actuator
adapters, e. rack for receiving flasks, f. balance, g. master lab station, h. 50 psi pressure
rinse solvent reservoir, i. vented priming station, j. computer and control hardware.

TABLE 2. Automated Metered-Dose Aerosol Sample Preparation Setup.

Shaking and Dosing Station:

- Customized tower for holding and positioning aerosol unit at priming and dosing positions.
- Customized actuator adapters (Prototype Models, Millburn, NJ)
- Stepping motors (CyberResearch, Inc., New Haven, CT)

Collection Station:

- Customized glass collection vessel. (Kontes, Vineland, NJ, and L&K Glass, Lyndhurst, NJ)
- Stainless steel 60° full cone spray nozzle (Spraying Systems Co., Wheaton, IL)
- Stainless steel pressure vessel (Alloy Products Corp., Waukesha, WI)
- Miscellaneous relays, pressure regulators, and air cylinders.

Sampling Unit:

Control hardware
- IBM[tm] Personal System/2[tm] Model 30 (International Business Machines, Armonk, NY)
- Stepper motor controller (CyberResearch)
- 8 channel relay and I/O (CyberResearch)
- Toshiba P351 printer (Toshiba, Tustin, CA)
- Zymate II Laboratory Automation system (Zymark Corp., Hopkinton, MA)

Software:
- Microsoft[tm] Pascal (Microsoft, Inc, Redmond, WA)
- Blaise Pascal Tools, Pascal Asynch Manager (Blaise Computing Inc., Berkeley, CA)
- Solution Systems Brief Editor (Solution Systems, Norwell, MA)
- Zymate EasyLab (Zymark Corp., Hopkinton, MA)

Comparison studies between the manual procedure and the automated collection station were performed using Vanceril[tm] Inhaler, Schering's brand of beclomethasone dipropionate. The automated collection station used a rinse cycle comprised of six washes of approximately 10 mL methanol per wash.

DISCUSSION AND RESULTS

When the manual procedure is divided into the individual units of action, the only difficult step is the rinsing of the separatory funnel used to collect the aerosol after dosing. We had postulated methods of automating this aspect of the assay since the early 1980's. Our R&D Engineering unit had experience with mechanized stations that agitated and dosed different aerosol/actuator configurations, and we did not foresee any great difficulty in devising modifications that would permit samples to be fed in and out of these units. Once the aerosol had been rinsed into a collection flask, final preparation of a sample ready for injection into an HPLC was simply a matter of solution handling. The crucial step in the automation of the aerosol assay centered around the collection vessel. We were faced with three alternatives:

1 - Devise a collection vessel similar to that used in the manual procedure that could be automatically rinsed and reused. The entire procedure could then be automated.

2 - Automate all steps prior to the rinsing of the collection vessel and perform the remaining steps manually. This approach would still provide control over variables like agitation speed, actuation force, etc. Multiple stations would be constructed and time savings could be accomplished.

3 - Create an entirely new sampling procedure that did not duplicate the current manual setup and thus, presumably, did not have the limitations of the manual collection vessel.

Alternative 3 was the least desirable. We had no clear idea for an alternative, reusable collection vessel that possessed the desirable characteristics of our manual setup. Specifically, the setup as shown in Figure 1 is a modification of the USP aerosol apparatus[1] and utilizes a similar rate of airflow through the actuator. Furthermore, the large internal volume of the 2 liter separatory funnel and the long axis into which the aerosol is burst helps in preventing what is termed blowback of the aerosol. Blowback occurs when the escaping aerosol encounters a wall of static air molecules and is reflected back and out of the collection vessel.[2]

Alternative 2 was perceived as feasible and would provide all of the favorable features of the manual setup while controlling variables such as agitation speed and time, actuation force, timing between doses, etc. It would be our alternate position if we were not successful with Alternative 1, our desired automation scheme.

The key to designing a vessel that contained a large interior volume and a long axis and could be automatically rinsed resides with the proper choice and placement of a rinse spray nozzle. An additional requirement is a suitable method of filtering the aerosol particles to prevent them from escaping into the vacuum system. After several attempts of mimicking the manual procedure and rinsing through the same orifice used for dosing, we settled upon the arrangement of a stationary rinse nozzle located at the small end of a custom designed glass flask. The aerosol particulates are entrapped by a bed of small diameter glass beads that prevents any active material from escaping into the vacuum system. This vessel retains the favorable characteristics of our manual setup of a large interior volume and a long axis along the direction of the aerosol spray. Air flow through the collection unit is maintained during dosing. After the proper number of doses, the dosing station retreats and the rinse spray is activated for an appropriate length of time. The conical spray pattern coats the interior walls of the flask with a sheet of solvent within the first two seconds of the rinse spray. The rinse spray is timed to deliver enough solvent to wash the interior walls and to cover the bed of glass beads. After waiting a few seconds for the solvent to drain into the reservoir, the connection to the vacuum is turned on for a brief time to pull the solvent into the drain flask. The rinse cycle can be repeated as often as necessary to completely rinse the flask. The robot arm then removes the drain flask with the recovered active drug, adds internal standard, records necessary weights, and places a new drain flask under the collection station. The unit is now ready for another cycle.

Table 3 compares results from the manual separatory funnel method and results obtained using the automated collection vessel for Vanceril metered-dose aerosol.[3] The results show good agreement between the two procedures.

TABLE 3. Comparison Between Manual and Automated Collection.

Can #	Manual Assay#1 (ug)	Manual Assay#2 (ug)	Automated Assay#1 (ug)	Automated Assay#2 (ug)
1	44.44	43.48	44.61	46.14
2	41.80	41.56	43.64	43.27
3	38.99	39.27	41.10	44.00
4	42.18	42.28	44.72	45.57
5	43.02	44.61	44.83	46.06
6	40.70	43.72	42.23	42.17
7	38.84	42.31	43.75	44.64
8	40.45	41.45	40.36	44.60
9	39.78	41.61	40.61	41.59
10	41.44	41.93	43.06	44.91

Average	Manual	41.64	Automated	43.59
Std. Dev. (+/-)		1.63		1.75

Results for the automated procedure were obtained using only the automated collection vessel. The dosing of the aerosol was performed manually, followed by automatic rinsing and collection of the active component. Results are expressed as ug per dose

SUMMARY

We have demonstrated an automated collection device for the assay preparation of metered-dose aerosol products.   This unit is reusable and provides for airflow characteristics similar to the USP apparatus.   Efforts are continuing on the final construction of the automated shaking and dosing station.   The combined automated stations will permit extensive studies of parameters affecting the assay of metered-dose aerosols to be easily and quickly studied in a controlled manner.   Adaptations should enable this equipment to be utilized for sample preparation for general aerosol products.

ACKNOWLEDGEMENTS

We gratefully acknowledge Walter Ivanoff for his expertise in the design of the shaking and dosing station. We also thank Frank Litterio for many helpful discussions about aerosol technology.

IBM and Personal System/2 are registered trademarks of International Business Machines Corporation.

Microsoft is a registered trademark of Microsoft Corporation.

Vanceril is a registered trademark of Schering-Plough Corporation.

AUTOMATION OF THE QUALITY CONTROL OF VITAMIN A

A. Millier
Rhone-Poulenc/AEC
03600 Commentry,
France

ABSTRACT

Two Zymate Systems have been installed in our Analytical Department for Vitamin A ester quality control.

The first system has been interfaced with a UV-Visible Beckman DU-50 spectrophotometer in order to check the Vitamin A content via UV absorbance measurement, while the other system has been coupled with two HPLC's for residual retinol (Vitamin A alcohol) and isomeric distribution determinations. In both cases, the main difficulty came from the viscous nature of the samples which could not be handled with the classical pipette and syringe technique. This was solved by developing a special device. The device is composed of a small stainless steel spiral attached to a cylindrical aluminum block seized by the robot gripper hand. The size and shape of this spiral has to be carefully designed so that the desired amount (10 to 20 mg) of substance is collected when the spiral is dipped into the sample.

This sampling device is weighed on a Mettler AE 163 balance with the aid of a homebuilt hook system and is then simply dropped into the dissolution flask. The introduction of the sample solution into the spectrophotometer or into the chromatographs has been carried out with standard Zymark procedures. The RSD obtained with ten consecutive determinations is 0.8% for UV analysis and around 1 - 1.2% for chromatography.

INTRODUCTION

The analytical survey along the Vitamin A synthesis route accounts for most of our laboratory workload. The quality control of the end products, namely Vitamin A acetate or palmitate, is of course an important part of the survey. This control consists of three determinations:

A. Vitamin A content in international units per gram.

B. Isomeric distribution of the ester.

C. Residual retinol (Vitamin A alcohol).

The first determination is made via UV absorbance measurement; the other two are performed by HPLC in the normal-phase adsorption mode. The increase in analytical demand and the time consuming nature of these determinations brought us to think about automation.

Near the end of 1985, the first Zymate Laboratory Automation System was installed and dedicated for UV analysis. As this action proved to be quite successful in terms of productivity improvement, we decided to go further the following year and a second robot was bought and interfaced with two liquid chromatographs in order to perform the other two determinations.

EXPERIMENTAL

A. Automation of the UV Spectrophotometric Determination of Vitamin A Content

When looking at the manual procedure used in our laboratory, the following sequence of individual operations must be considered:

Sampling: An amount of about 10 to 15 mg was taken by dipping a small stainless steel loop which has been previously weighed into the warmed sample. The loop was weighed again and the sample amount determined to the nearest 0.01 mg.

Dilution: The stainless steel loop was then introduced into a 100 mL calibrated flask filled to volume with 2-propanol. A 2 ml-aliquot of the resulting solution was pipetted and diluted to 50 mL with 2-propanol in a calibrated flask.

Spectrophotometry: The absorbance was measured at 325 nm (λ max for Vitamin A), 300 nm, and 350 nm and the ratios A_{300}/A_{325} and A_{350}/A_{325} calculated to check the sample purity. As a common practice in Vitamin A analysis, the result was given as the E value referring to the theoretical absorbance of a 1 % solution through 1 cm optical path and from that, in international units per gram with:

$$IU/G = E^{1\%}_{1cm} \quad x \; 1900 \text{ (for Vitamin A esters).}$$

Thinking about automation, we were suspecting that the main problem would arise from the sample itself. At room temperature, Vitamin A acetate is a semi-crystallized substance whereas palmitate is a honeylike material. By moderate heating (40 - 45^{0}C), these compounds turn to viscous liquids that cannot be handled with pipettes or syringes. Higher temperatures lower the viscosity but bring extensive molecular degradation and as a result are quite inappropriate.

The only answer was to reproduce as closely as possible the manual operation. For that purpose, a special device was developed. This device (Figure 1) consists of a small stainless wire twisted into a 4 mm diameter spiral. The wire is attached to an aluminum cylinder of 10 mm diameter x 16 mm length which can be grasped by the standard gripper hand. With one and a half turn, this spiral is able to collect 10 to 20 mg sample with a low percentage of failure.

The system includes the following elements:

   - Robot arm with dual gripper and syringe hand
   - Zymate Controller
   - Master Lab Station (MLS)
   - Power and Event Controller (PEC)
   - Vortex mixer and dilution station
   - Mettler AE 163 balance with pneumatic door opener
   - Heating block for keeping sample tubes at 45^0C (Prolabo, France)
   - Racks for tubes, pipettte tips and spirals.

The analytical instrument (Beckman DU-50 spectrophotometer) is interfaced to the Zymate Controller to send data for subsequent analysis (i.e. absorbances read at 325 nm for Vitamin A titre determination absorbance, at 300 and 350 nm for sample purity checking).

Soon after the first trials and in regard to erratic results, the sample tubes heating block was put under nitrogen atmosphere in a plastic-built box fitted with a pneumatic door opener (Figure 2).

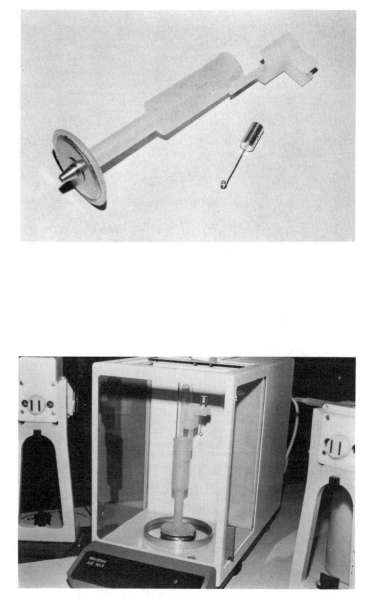

FIGURE 1.   Sampling Device for Handling Viscous Vitamin A Esters with the Corresponding System for Weighing Either the Sampling Device or a Dilution Tube.

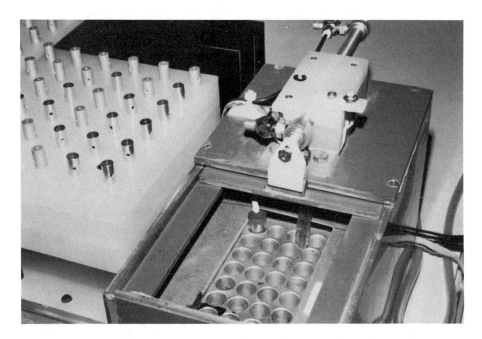

FIGURE 2.   Arrangement for Keeping Samples Warm (45^{0}C) and Under Nitrogen Atmosphere.

The robot takes a spiral to the balance to measure the tare. The spiral is then dipped into the sample tube and brought back to the balance. The sample amount is determined to the nearest 0.01 mg.

The sample-charged spiral is dropped into a dilution tube (160 mm length x 20 mm i.d.) above the mixing station. The first dilution is carried out by adding 20 mL 2-propanol with the MLS and by vortexing for 40 seconds. A 200 uL-aliquot is drawn with the syringe hand into a second dilution tube. The accurate dispensed volume is determined by weighing the tube content and multiplying the result with 2-propanol density.

Again, 20 mL propanol is added, and the mixture is homogenized. The resulting solution is sucked into the circulating cell of the DU-50 spectrophotometer by means of a peristaltic pump. The sample titre in international units per gram is calculated by the Zymate Controller from the sample weight and the absorbance at 325 nm.

Absorbance ratios 300/325 nm and 350/325 nm are also determined and printed on the report. The total cycle time is 15 minutes. Each sample is submitted to two consecutive determinations.

B. Automation of the HPLC Analyses

This task was much easier because the sample problem has already been resolved and because the HPLC analyses use the corrected area normalization calculation method so that there was no need for data exchange between modules. The sample solution concentration is correct. The system consists of the following element:

- Robot arm with dual gripper and syringe hand.
- Zymate Controller
- Power and Event Controller (PEC)
- Solvent delivery unit Dosimate 665 (Metrohm AG, Herisau, Switzerland).
- Magnetic stirrer station.
- Dilution station.
- Mettler AE 163 balance with pneumatic door opener.
- Heating block for sample tubes (Prolabo, Fance).
- Racks for 125 mL Erlenmeyer flasks, pipette tips and spirals.

Two Varian series 2000 chromatographs (Varian Associates, Sunnyvale, California) fitted with Zymark injector stations and Merck D 2000 integrators (Merck, Darmstad, West Germany) complete the arrangement.

The sampling procedure is unchanged but the dilution is performed in one step by using 125 mL Erlenmeyer flasks containing magnetic bars instead of tubes. 100 mL n-hexane are added with two strokes of the Metrohm delivery unit. The mixture is homogenized by gentle magnetic stirring for 2 minutes. Since both HPLC analyses are performed with the same dilute solution, the following sequence of actions is repeated twice.

Using the syringe hand fitted with a 1 mL Hamilton syringe, a volume of 0.05 mL sample solution is drawn, then the piston is moved upwards during transfer to the injector so as to prevent any solution from dripping. When the robot hand is above the injector, a 3-second delay is necessary to exclude air bubbles from the bottom of the pipette tip. The sample solution is then pushed into the Rheodyne valve port so as to rinse and fill the 10 uL injection loop. The pneumatic valve actuator and the integrator start function are simultaneously activated by the PEC. The results, isomeric distribution and retinol content, are printed on the integrators chromatographic charts (Figure 3).

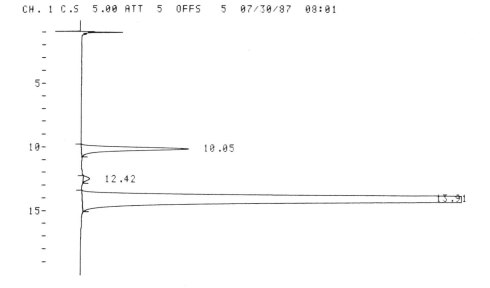

```
CH . 1 C .S   5.00 ATT   5   OFFS   5   07/30/87   08:01
```

```
D-2000                                                    07/30/87   08:01

METHOD: REP.ISOMERIQ   TAG:    211   CH: 1

FILE: 1   CALC-METHOD: NORM%    TABLE:    1   CONC: AREA

     NO .      RT        AREA    TITRE    FACTOR1   BC        NAME
      1    10.05      155347     6.490     0.680    BB     13 AC
      2    12.42        9746     0.493     0.824    BB      9 .AC
      3    13.91     2418156    93.015     0.626    BB     TRANS
   TOTAL
                     2583249   100.000
   PEAK REJ  :      500
   SF        :      100.000
```

- HPLC conditions: column 125 x 4 mm Lichrosorb Si 60 5 um (Merck, Darmstad, West Germany), mobile phase n-hexane-ethyl acetate (995: 5), flow-rate 1.2 ml/min, injection volume 10 uL, detection UV at 325 nm.

FIGURE 3. Chromatogram of the Isomeric Distribution Determination.

RESULTS AND CONCLUSIONS

A. UV Spectrophotometric Determination

To evaluate the robotic technique, a comparison test with the manual procedure was conducted by performing ten replicates on the same sample. The results are listed in Table 1.

The reliability of the robotic system is checked from time to time by duplicating analyses with the manual method. No discrepancy has been observed so far. The robot can perform about 60 to 80 determinations (2 per sample) every 24 hours under the control of one technician during the normal 8-hour workday. The same amount of work required three persons with the manual method.

TABLE 1. Comparison between Robotic and Manual Methods.

SAMPLE 1 (acetate)	Robotic	Manual
Average Concentration (UI/g)	2 668 000	2 673 000
Relative Standard Deviation	0.8 %	1.0 %
SAMPLE 2 (palmitate)		
Average Concentration (UI/g)	1 793 000	1 791 000
Relative Standard Deviation	0.65 %	1.0 %

B. HPLC Analyses

The validation of the robotic procedure was carried out by comparing the results with those obtained with the manual method over a one month period. The Zymate System provided the desired level of accuracy and precision with all results well within our prescribed limits for the test. The RSD was 1 % on ten consecutive determinations of the all-trans isomer and about 1.2 % for the retinol content. The manual methods gave 0.8 and 1.2 % respectively. These results confirm what is found in the literature for comparible analyses.[1]

In terms of productivity, the gain was difficult to quantify because the former so-called manual methods were already partly automated with autosamplers allowing unattended overnight work. However the robotization avoids some tedious manipulations like weighing and diluting samples so the operator's contribution is alleviated to a certain extent, making him available for other tasks. Another point is that, due to the rather long HPLC analysis cycle time (15 minutes), the robot is left idle for 9 minutes after each sample preparation. One of our future projects will be to use this free time to the best advantage.

The reliability of the robotic system is checked from time to time by duplicating analyses with the manual method. No discrepancy has been observed so far. The robot can perform about 60 to 80 determinations (2 per sample) every 24 hours under the control of one technician during the normal 8-hour workday. The same amount of work required three persons with the manual method.

ACKNOWLEDGEMENTS

I would like to thank Mr. Yann Filadeau and Mr. Xavier Delamare from Zymark S.A., Pantin, France, for their technical assistance in programming the robot systems and in developing special modules to fit our requirements.

REFERENCES

1. J.N. Little, J. Liquid Chromatog. 9 (14), 3033-62 (1986).

THE APPLICATION OF A ROBOTIC WORK STATION TO THE HANDLING OF MICROBIAL COLONIES

Otis Godfrey[1], Alex Raas[2] and Paul Landis[2]
Fermentation Products Research[1] and Physical Chemistry Research[2]
Lilly Research Laboratories
Eli Lilly and Company
Indianapolis, Indiana 46285

ABSTRACT

A robotic work station was installed to inoculate microbial colonies into vials of fermentation medium. Colonies derived from single cells are inoculated individually into a modular array of fermentation vials using a PUMA 560 (Westinghouse, Pittsburgh, PA). The robot is equipped with an optical system that scans an agar plate containing microbial colonies and fixes the colony location in the computer memory. The robot then moves to the colony position, plugs the colony, moves to a blank plate where the plug is touched on the agar surface to provide a replicate colony. The robotic arm then moves to the fermentation module where the remaining colony material is blown into a fermentation module position. The robot returns to the carrousel and replaces the tip for heat sterilization. The entire cycle is then repeated until 120 colonies have been picked, copied and inoculated into a module containing 120 vials.

INTRODUCTION

New compounds continue to be discovered from the fermentation of soil micro-organisms. Recent advances in biotechnology have aided both the discovery and follow-up studies of fermentation products. Radioimmunoassays have increased the sensitivity of detection systems, while high pressure liquid chromatography (HPLC) and overpressured thin-layer chromatography[1] (TLC) have provided better quantitation and characterization of these compounds.

Once a compound is discovered, it's titer must be increased to facilitate both "in vivo" testing and structure activity studies. Such increases are often obtained by strain selection programs. Strain selection, which includes mutation, inoculation, fermentation, sample preparation and assay, is a very labor intensive operation - the most laborious aspect being the inoculation of mutated colonies into fermentation modules.

The requirements for the automated inoculation of colonies are: intelligent automation, machine vision and excellent software. The vision system must locate colonies and transfer their XY coordinates to a machine, which in turn does the inoculation. Vision systems have already been integrated with robots in the automobile industry and have proved their reliability. These industrial robots possess the speed, reach, dexterity, fault detection, computer and software requirements necessary for the inoculation process.

SYSTEM DESIGN

Design Consideration

The robotic work cell was designed in such a manner as to reduce secondary aerosol formation. By the combination of a controlled path for the inoculation tool, an indexing lid, a horizontal flow laminar hood and the elimination of palsy, it was possible to reduce accidental inoculation of vials resulting from secondary aerosol formation. A further consideration was that the robotic work cell must be highly reliable and still possess the flexibility for handling a number of different bacterial and fungal colonies under a number of different inoculation protocols. The goals were to

i) increase sample throughput,

ii) increase the precision of the inoculation process, and

iii) provide a system with sufficient flexibility to enable further expansion of operations.

Overall System Configuration

The overall system configuration is illustrated in Figure 1. There are six major pieces of equipment that make up the system - robot, carrousel, plate hold downs, camera, lid remover and laminar flow hood.

PUMA Robot

A PUMA 560 Robot (Figure 2) and the Vial II^{tm} Software Package was purchased from Westinghouse. The robot is electric and is controlled by a DEC LSI-11 Computer (Digital Equipment, Maynard, MA).The articulated arm has six axes of rotation, a reach of 36 inches, a payload of 5 pounds, repeatability of 0.004 inches, and a linear speed of 0.5 M per second. In addition to the robot, there is an ADDS Regent 20 Monitor and a Hewlett Packard Think Jet Printer.

Carrousel

The carrousel is illustrated in Figure 3. It is used to sterilize and clean the ceramic inoculation tools. Thirty-six tools are mounted on the carrousel which rotates them past four burners. The tools are cooled to room temperature prior to use. Fumes and hot air are passed through a heat exchanger and then vented to the outside. A force sensor is mounted between the flange and the end tool effector, and is used to verify tool pick up.

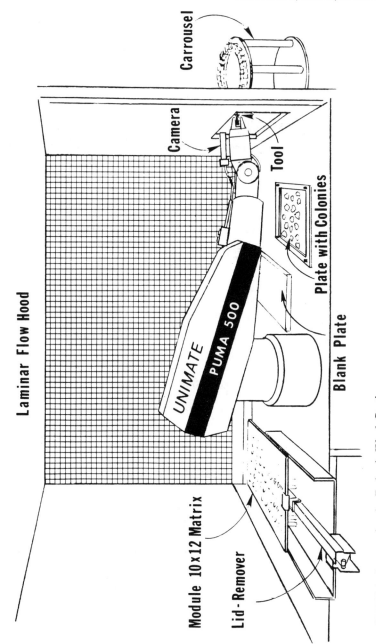

FIGURE 1. Layout for the Robotic Work Station.

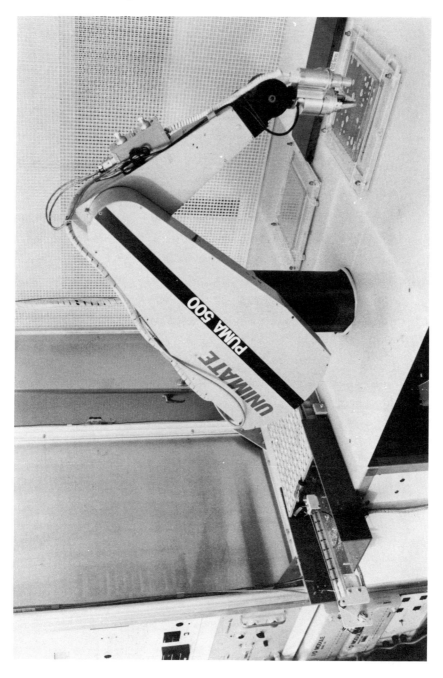

FIGURE 2. PUMA 560 Robot.

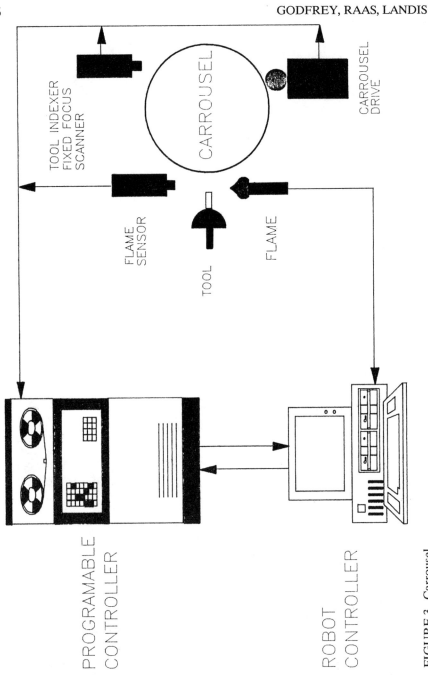

FIGURE 3. Carrousel.

Plate Fixtures

An agar plate containing colonies and an agar plate for archiving the colonies are held in place by vacuum chucks.

Camera

The robot moves an optical edge detector over the rows of colonies (Figure 4) and records the location of each colony in computer memory. The edge detector consists of two linear photo arrays that are focused on the agar surface which is uniformly back illuminated. A differential response in light intensity of the two photodetectors indicates the edge of a colony. Colonies that are 2mm or larger in diameter can be detected with an accuracy greater than 95%. Plates containing up to 120 colonies can be scanned in 60 seconds.

Lid Remover and Laminar Flow Hood

A lid is placed on a fermentation module and attached to the lid remover (Figure 5). After each row of vials is inoculated, the lid is indexed to expose the next row of vials. A laminar flow hood (horizontal) is used to maintain sterility in the robotic work station.

MODULE INOCULATION

The module inoculation process is illustrated in Figure 6. The robot scans an agar plate containing microbial colonies and fixes the colony location in the computer memory. The robot then moves to the colony position, plugs the colony, moves to a blank plate where the plug is touched on the agar surface to provide a replicate colony. The robotic arm then moves to the fermentation module where the remaining colony material is blown into a fermentation module position. The robot returns to the carousel and replaces the tip for heat sterilization. The entire cycle is then repeated until 120 colonies have been picked, copied, and inoculated into a module containing 120 vials.

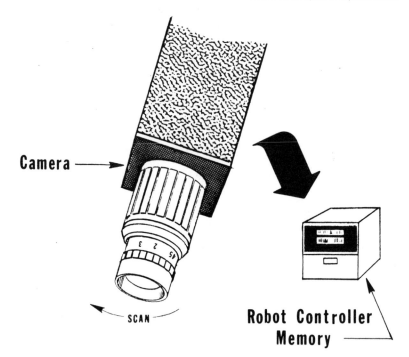

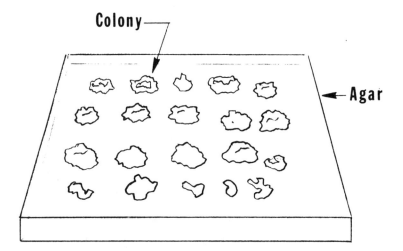

Figure 4. Colony Detector.

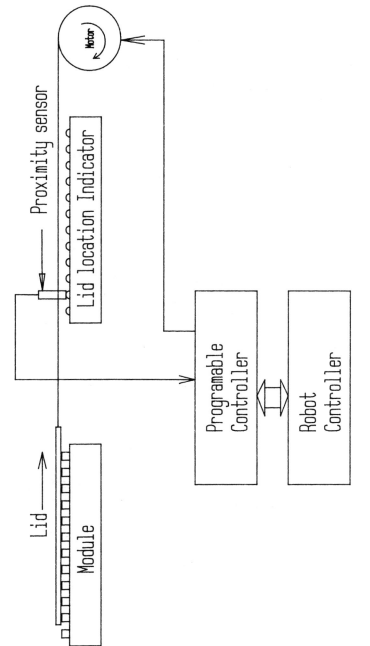

FIGURE 5. Lid Remover.

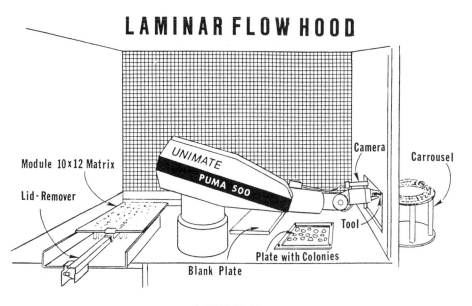

LAMINAR FLOW HOOD

STEPS

1. Colonies Located on Agar Plate
2. Tool Picked up from Carrousel
3. Colony Cored from Plate
4. Copy Made on Blank Plate
5. Colony Blown into Module
6. Tool Returned to Carrousel

Figure 6. Module Inoculation.

EXPERIMENTAL

Aspergillus nidulans A42355, is a soil isolate that produces a cyclic peptide antibiotic. Streptomyces gardneri A10255 is a soil isolate that produces a sulfur-containing, modified, peptide antibiotic.

Germlings of A. nidulans were treated with N-methyl-N'-nitro-N-nitrosoguanidine and then stored in the vapor phase of liquid nitrogen. A tube containing the mutated cells was thawed and appropriate dilutions made. A Microbot Alpha II Robot (Alpha Robotics, St. Louis, MO) interfaced with a peristaltic pump was used to deliver the cells onto agar plates. Extreme care was taken to keep the cells in suspension during delivery. Mycelial fragments of S. gardneri were treated in an analogous manner.

Sterile fermentation medium was delivered into sterile modules by a modified Tektronix Digital Plotter (Beaverton, OR). Insolubles were kept in suspension by an EI Vibramixer (Cempac, Mannedorf, Switzerland). After inoculation, the modules were incubated with shaking until the maximum amount of antibiotic was produced. The broths were then prepared and assayed by standard protocols.

RESULTS

Cross Contamination Studies

Studies were initiated with S. gardneri and A. nidulans to determine the extent of accidental inoculation with the robotic work station. In the first experiment, every other row of each module was inoculated with S. gardneri colonies. The modules were incubated for 7 days and then the uninoculated vials scored for growth. Of the 1200 uninoculated vials, only 0.25% had growth. This experiment was repeated with A. nidulans colonies. Of the 1200 uninoculated vials only 0.17% had growth.

Strain Selection

Strain selection programs were initiated with A. nidulans and S. gardneri. Germlings of A. nidulans were mutated and colonies subsequently screened for increases in titer. Approximately 18,000 colonies were inoculated by the robotic work station. Several superior strains were obtained. One strain produced twice as much compound as the parent (870 vs 428 ng/mL). Young log phase cells of S. gardneri were mutated and colonies subsequently screened for increases in titer. Approximately 28,000 colonies were inoculated by the robotic work station. Several superior strains were obtained. One strain produced sixteen-fold more compound than the parent (290 vs 18 ng/mL).

DISCUSSION

The robotic work cell was designed in such a manner as to reduce secondary aerosol formation. We sought to reduce cross contamination by controlling the path of the inoculation tool and eliminating palsy. The data from the two cross contamination studies demonstrate that secondary aerosol formation and the resultant accidental inoculation of vials are very rare events (0.24 and 0.17%) with the robotic work station. The colonies of S. gardneri and A. nidulaus produced massive amounts of spores. Spores are very hydrophobic and thus tend to aerosolize more readily than cells. It is our experience that a technician can also inoculate a small number of vials with low levels of cross contamination. However, inoculation of 20,000 colonies is another matter.

The strain selection programs with A. nidulans and S. gardneri were very successful. Superior strains were isolated from each culture. Mutation conditions were optimized to produce high mutation frequencies and minimal genetic damage. The mutation frequencies are such that an average of 10,000 colonies must be screened to obtain a superior strain. The magnitude of the yield increase is highly dependent on the initial titer of the producing culture. It is not surprising to expect a larger increase (sixteen-fold) with a poor producing culture such as S. gardneri (16 ng/mL) . Whereas smaller yield increases are expected (two-fold) with a good producing culture, such as A.nidulans (428 ng/mL).

The robotic work station can be operated completely unattended thus saving human resources. On a sustained basis it is 30% faster than a technician performing an equivalent task. One module can be inoculated in 50 min. The workstation possesses the flexibility for inoculating different colonies, i.e. Aspergillus and Streptomyces. In addition, it can inoculate modules of different design. Although the workstation was designed for strain selection, it has also been used to inoculate colonies isolated from soil suspensions and colonies generated by recombinant experiments. An automatic feed system is being constructed that should allow continuous operation (24 hrs per day).

During the past several years, there have been considerable technological advances in image aquisition, processing and analysis. Vision systems are now available that can rapidly screen a large number of colonies at multiple wave lengths. We are in the process of interfacing the robotic work station with such a vision system. This would enable us to prescreen a large number of colonies for the production of a fermentation product [2,3] prior to inoculation.

SUMMARY

A robotic work station was installed to inoculate colonies into vials of fermentation medium. With this unit we were able to increase sample throughput, increase precision, and provide a system with sufficient flexibility to enable further expansion of operations.

ACKNOWLEDGEMENTS

We wish to thank technical associates, Mrs. Lynda Ford and Mr. Thomas Eaton, for their invaluable assistance in this effort. Dr. Lawrence Day and Dr. Kay Koch have provided management support and considerable encouragement.

REFERENCES

1. Z. Witkiewcz and J. Bladek, "Overpressured Thin layer Chromatography", J. of Chromatography 373, 111 (1986).

2. K. Yabe, Y. Ando, M. Ito, and N. Terakado, "Simple Method for Screening Aflotoxin-Producing Molds by UV Photography", Appl. Environ. Microbiol. 53, 230 (1987).

3. R. Legocki, M. Legocki, T. Baldwin, and S. Szalay, "Bioluminescence in soybean root nodules: Demonstration of a general approach to assay gene expression in vivo by using bacterial luciferase," Proc. Nat'l. Acad. Sci. 83, 9080 (1986).

Val II is a registered trademark of Westinghouse Corp.

THE APPLICATION OF ROBOTICS IN FOOD MICROBIOLOGY

Dr. Fritz-Peter Gork
Lufthansa Service GmbH
Quality Assurance
Airport East
D-6000 Frankfurt 75
Federal Republic of Germany

ABSTRACT

Microbiological test procedures are regarded as one of the most important elements of quality assurance in the food industry. Due to their complexity, these tests are carried out mainly by manual steps with only a few automatic equipment components. The first application of a modular and flexible robotic system in the field of food microbiology which meets all complex requirements has been developed by the Food Laboratory of Lufthansa Service GmbH in Frankfurt.

The following equipment components have been used: Zymate II Robot, Zymate Controller, special robot hands, microliter syringe, master laboratory station, electronic balance, various racks for samples, Petri dishes and pipet-tips, incubator, ultrasonic waterbath, various small auxiliary equipment, tubes and valves for liquids, pressured air and vacuum.

This system allows quick and reliable standardized microbiological analysis of food items and surface contamination considering different microorganisms. The robot system weighs, homogenizes, and dilutes the sample in order to inoculate it onto different solid nutrient media in Petri dishes by spiral-and drop-plating. Afterwards the Petri dishes are placed into an incubator for incubation.

After every analysis cycle all tubes, valves and equipment, which are contaminated by the last sample material, are cleaned with sterile water and sterilized with a highly effective disinfectant solution. The automatic disposal of all used materials, liquids and sample leftovers runs continuously during the whole operation.

The average time per analysis cycle is only 6 minutes, so that a throughput up to 70 samples per day-shift can be achieved by the described system. Higher throughputs are possible by expansion, e.g. additional robot arm or operating during the second and third working shift. However, effective monitoring systems have to be installed in the case of unattended operation.

In contrast to the food analysis, the procedure for the microbiological test of surface contamination needs only 1.5 minutes per sample before the incubation period starts.

INTRODUCTION

Quality assurance units in the food industry are using more and more microbiological test procedures, because the risk of hygienic hazards and consequently the number of outbreaks of foodborne infections and intoxications have increased steadily in the past. Especially in the field of mass feeding and catering, microbiological tests of food, water, surfaces, air and personnel have become important instruments of quality control to secure safe food for human consumption.

Contrary to chemical analysis, microbiological examinations need a relatively long time until reliable test results are available due to the specific growth characteristics of microorganisms. Also, the technique of sample preparation, which requires absolute sterility after each test item, has limited the implementation of automatic procedures. Only some steps of the test procedure were able to be automated through laboratory equipment, e.g. the Stomacher[tm] (Colworth Laboratory Equipment, A.J. Seward, London, U.K.) or the Spiral Plater[tm] (Spiral Systems Marketing, Bethesda Maryland).

OBJECTIVES OF AUTOMATION

The necessity also to rationalize the laboratory operation led finally to the consideration to integrate a laboratory robot within the highly complex microbiological test procedure for food items. The basic idea was to use existing equipment and to reproduce manual working steps as far as possible.

The microbiological test procedure for food items can normally be divided into the following sections:

A. Sampling

B. Sample preparation

C. Inoculation

D. Incubation

E. Evaluation

Out of these sections only the "sample preparation", "inoculation" and "incubation" are suitable for automation handling by a robot, provided that standardized procedures are applied. In detail it refers to the following laboratory unit operations:

B. Sample Preparation

- filling the food sample into a plastic pouch

- weighing the food sample

- diluting with a physiological nutrient solution, e.g.peptone water

- mixing and homogenization

A 1:10 dilution of the food sample is the result of the operation.

C. Inoculation

    - of several solid nutrient agars, using the spiral-plating method

    - of several solid nutrient agars, using the drop-plating method

D. Incubation of the inoculated agars in the incubator

The incubated nutrient media are used for the final counting of the grown bacterial colonies or to further identification procedures.

In summary, a laboratory robot system must be able to perform the following operations fully automatically and in any programmable sequence:

    - mechanical gripping and motion steps

    - dosage of several liquids

    - electric switching

    - electronic data processing

    - time control

TECHNICAL SOLUTION

Based on these requirements it was necessary to slightly modify the conventional test procedure to guarantee a safe and fully automatic sequence of all laboratory unit operations.   Therefore, the complete structure of the test system is divided into several sub groups which are described as follows and illustrated in Figure 1.

Robot System

The technical specifications of the Zymate II Robot meet in an excellent way the requirements to perform the various laboratory unit operations for this procedure. Additionally, the interchangeable robot hands permit complicated gripping-, motion- and dosage-operations.

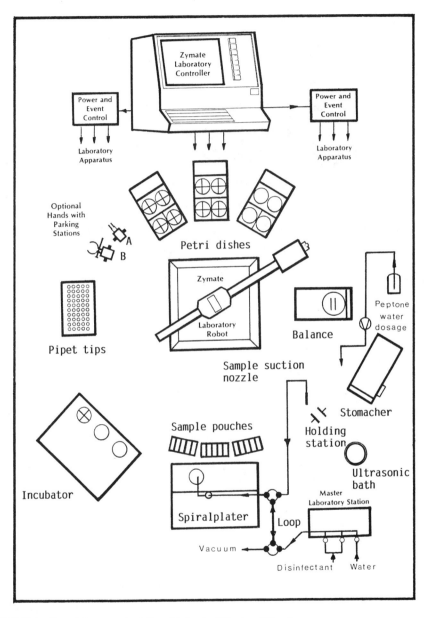

FIGURE 1. Bench Layout for Microbiological Tests of Food.

The Zymate II System consists of following basic components for the intended application:

- Zymate Laboratory Controller including a variety of software

- Zymate Laboratory Robot

- robot hand A with two pairs of gripping fingers

- robot hand B with a microliter syringe and one pair of gripping fingers

- two power and event control stations (PEC)

- master laboratory station (MLS) for dispensing disinfectant and water

The Zymate Robot performs all mechanical operations using the two robot hands. The robot hand A is specialized for gripping, opening, closing, and transporting the plastic sample pouches and for moving the so-called "sample-suction-nozzle". The two gripping jaws are equipped with vacuum-connected suction openings so that they can carry the open plastic pouch with a total weight up to 150 g.

The robot hand B performs the mechanical handling of the Petri dishes and carries a microliter syringe. Using disposable pipet tips, a certain amount of the 1:10 sample dilution can be transferred to inoculate it later on different nutrient media.

The entire robot system is controlled by the Zymate Controller. The installed EasyLab software enables relatively simple programming of the entire procedure, by using the "teach-and-name" method for fixing of all positioning operations. The software supplement, Concurrent EasyLab, allows two different program sections to run in parallel to considerably accelerate the test procedure.

The MLS provides automated liquid handling for sterile water and a disinfectant solution. All electrical laboratory equipment and magnetic valves are connected to two PEC's which are directed by the Zymate Controller according to the test program.

Laboratory Equipment

The following existing laboratory equipment could be integrated into the Zymate Laboratory Automation System:

1. The Stomacher with the following modifications:

> - automated opening and closing of the front shutter by a servomotor
>
> - installation of electronic solid state relays to be connected with the PEC

2. The Spiral Plater with the following modifications:

> - modification of the turntable with a drip pan for liquids (water, disinfectant, sample dilution)
>
> - modified supply of the sample dilution
>
> - installation of electronic solid state relays to be connected with the PEC

3. The electronic balance Mettler PE 600 with:

> - an interface to be connected to the Laboratory Controller
>
> - an attachment for holding the sample pouches during weighing

4. The incubator with racks for positioning the inoculated Petri dishes

Racks

The Zymate System needs racks:

> - for the plastic sample pouches, which are filled with about 10g food sample
>
> - for the Petri dishes before inoculation. Each different nutrient agar needs its own rack. The racks are filled and emptied according the "first-in/first-out" principle, so that a continuous filling during operation with identified Petri dishes is possible.
>
> - for sterile pipet tips, which also can contain 2 mL culture tubes if a direct pipetting out of the tubes onto the nutrient media is necessary.

All racks have capacity so that about forty food samples can be tested without refilling.

Dosage of Nutrient Solution

The dosage of the physiological nutrient solution, e.g. Peptone water, is performed by a time-controlled pump in accordance to the actual net weight of the sample material. A specific formula in the computer program always calculates the correct amount of added solution to prepare a 1:10 sample dilution. A 5 liter bottle serves as a reservoir for the Peptone water, which finally flows out of a glass nozzle into the open sample pouch.

Sample Transfer System

After homogenization of the food sample with the Peptone water in the Stomacher, this dilution has to be transferred to the Spiral Plater. A "sample-suction-nozzle", which is connected by tubes to the Spiral Plater and a vacuum bottle, sucks the 1:10 dilution directly out of the sample pouch into a tube loop, which is shut off by two 3-way-valves. Then, sterile water dispensed by the MLS pushes the sample dilution into the syringe of the Spiral Plater for final inoculation.

Auxiliary Equipment

Some additional equipment is necessary for the handling of the pouches and Petri dishes:

1. Holding station for the sample pouches containing the 1:10 dilution. This station is equipped with two pneumatically driven cylinders which carry gripping jaws with vacuum connected suction openings, similar to those of the robot hand type A. This configuration allows opening and shutting the pouch for transferring the sample dilution.

2. Holding station for the lids of the Petri dishes during inoculation

   - in combination with the Petri dish racks, where the direct drop-plating is performed

   - in combination with the Spiral Plater, where the lids have to be taken off before the Petri dishes are placed onto the turntable

In both cases the lids are held by vacuum suction cups.

Disposable Materials

The following disposable materials are necessary to guarantee a safe automatic robot operation :

1. Undivided Petri dishes

2. Divided Petri dishes which permit up to four different drop-platings to be executed on one dish.

3. Plastic pouches for carrying the food sample. These pouches have to be of a high mechanical resistance because of its strong treatment in the Stomacher.

4. Pipet tips for the drop-plating procedure

Cleaning and Disinfecting

After each analysis cycle, the sample transfer system and the Spiral Plater, which are contaminated by the last sample material, must be cleaned and disinfected. This operation is activated by the MLS and proceeds in the following three steps:

1. Sucking off the remaining sample dilution into the suction bottle

2. Combined cleaning and disinfecting by the highly effective disinfectant Gigasept^{tm} (Schulke & Mayr, Hamburg, Germany)

3. Final rinsing with distilled and sterilized water

Due to its heavy contamination the "sample-suction-nozzle" is treated by ultrasonic in combination with a disinfectant solution.

Waste Disposal

All sample leftovers and disposable plastic material, which are used during the test procedure, will be disposed automatically into two containers:

1. One plastic sack in a holding device for the disposal of

    - all liquids, which are used during all cleaning and disinfection procedures

    - all used sample pouches

    - all pipet tips, which are slipped off at a special device directly above the opening of the sack

2. One vacuum suction bottle for the disposal of liquids, which are sucked out of the sample transfer system and the Spiral Plater.

After each test series the waste sack and the contents of the suction bottle will be disposed for neutralization.

Energy Supply

The Zymate Laboratory Automation System has the following energy requirements:

    - Electricity (220 V) which should be protected through a filter against voltage peaks

    - Compressed air to operate the various air cylinders

    - Vacuum for the suction cups and gripping jaws as well as for transferring liquids. Independent vacuum systems are recommended to avoid an undesirable pressure increase.

IMPLEMENTATION

The system as described is the first application of robotics in food microbiology. Thus, a highly time-consuming development of the whole test procedure, the custom system components and the equipment modifications was necessary. After more than two years work, the Zymate Laboratory Automation System was implemented in the food laboratory of the Quality Assurance Department.

This system is now destined to perform approximately 6,500 food analysis and 8,000 microbiological tests on surface contamination per year. It still needs limited supervision, although a self-control system is under development, to permit unattended operation over night. The average time per analysis cycle is only 6 minutes, so that an output up to 70 samples per day shift can be achieved. Higher outputs are possible by expansion, e.g. an additional robot arm or operating during the second and third working shift. The procedure for the surface contamination test needs only 1.5 minutes per sample before the incubation period starts.

Before final implementation into routine quality control, the system was checked and adjusted for its reliability according to the following criteria:

1. Calibration of the plastic pouches to get the average tare weight.
2. Calibration of the Peptone water dosage in relation to the net sample weight.
3. Calibration of the pipetted amount during drop-plating.
4. Demonstration of absolute sterility after each sample preparation.
5. Demonstration of conformity between automatic and manual sample preparation.

SUMMARY

The first application of a modular and flexible Zymate System in the field of food microbiology which meets all complex requirements has been developed by the Food Laboratory of Lufthansa Service GmbH in Frankfurt. The robot emulates a person's action by automatically performing existing manual procedures. All necessary laboratory equipment, which is electronically controlled by a computer program, is placed within the reach of the robot to perform the sample preparation of food items and surface contamination specimen.   A high grade of precision and reliability to do routine checks on several hygiene indicators has been proven.

Stomacher is a registered trademark of Colworth Laboratory Equipment, A.J. Seward, London, U.K.

Spiral Plater is a registered trademark of Spiral Systems Marketing, Bethesda, Maryland.

Gigasept is a registered trademark of Schulke & Mayr, Hamburg, Germany.

AUTOMATIC MICROBIOLOGICAL TESTING OF COSMETICS USING ROBOTICS

A. Lebec
Bourjois
93401 Pantine
FRANCE

ABSTRACT

In a cosmetic company's control laboratory, the same micro-biological tests are made on a large number of samples of raw materials, bulk chemicals, and finished products every day. New methods in the microbiology laboratory (bioluminescence, bactometer, bioscreen, etc.) are not applicable for analyses of the various classes of cosmetic products. In addition, the equivalent realibility of results are not demonstrated. So we chose to automate the expert French method.[1] This method is similar to the USP[2] and CTFA[3] plate method.

A Zymate Laboratory Automation System was developed for this method. The robot's arm is located in a laminar flow work station. A single hand picks up and sets the test tubes, picks up and sets the sterile Petri dishes, pipets 1 mL of the final dilution and introduces it in a sterile Petri dish. The Easylab Software controls other modules which mix the sample solutions, extract the melted agar medium, and mix the inoculated Petri dishes.

After inoculation, the Petri dishes are stored on a heated tray for incubation. This Zymate System allows preparation of 400 Petri dishes a day. Now, the microbiologist is free from routine and boring tasks.

INTRODUCTION

The different legislation concerning cosmetic products (French, E.E.C., C.T.F.A. , etc.) recommends microbiological control of all finished products before commercialization. The official recommended limit values and the identity of the micro-organisms contained in the finished cosmetic products are based on the plate method.

This method requires a long incubation period as well as tedious and repetitive operations for the preparation of the samples under a laminar flow hood. In order to detect the micro-organisms more quickly (i.e, reduce the time of incubation), new methods using either bioluminescence or the change in the impedance of the medium are currently being developped in microbiology laboratories. Until now these methods :

- only generally enable sterility control, without the possibility of examination for specific micro-organisms

- are not applicable to all classes of cosmetic products

- use expensive reagents

- don't significantly reduce the period required for a response.

We decided to retain the official method of microbiological analysis for our laboratory. In face of the development of our activity and in view of the repetitive nature of the operations and the large number of samples treated each day, we decided to automate the phase preparing for the incubation step.

EXPERIMENTAL

The plate method consists of :

- pipetting 1 mL of final solution

- introducing it in the Petri dish adding melted nutrient agar cooled to and kept at about 45°C

- closing the Petri dish

- shaking the Petri dish with an orbital movement

Aseptic precautions must be observed in handling the samples.

The automation of these operations was developed by using a Zymate[tm] System with the following modules: Zymate Controller with EasyLab[tm] Software, Zymate Robot, power and event controller (PEC), and a master laboratory station (MLS). The work bench with the robotic arm in the center is placed in a horizontal laminar flow hood. The arm is equipped with only one multi-function hand. Figure 1 shows the multi-function hand gripping a test tube. The Petri Dish fingers extend out from the front of the hand. The syringe for pipetting is above the hand in this photo.

Other modules - vortex station, shaking table, tube racks, tip racks, Petri dish columns, and oven trays - are placed at the edge of the bench. The Agarsterilizer and the perilstatic pump used to prepare and deliver the gelose are placed on a bench near the robot area. Figure 2 illustrates the bench layout for this application.

All of the operations putting the solutions for analysis in contact with the outside take place in the laminar flow hood. The test tubes containing the final dilutions are placed in the tube racks in accordance with a specific plan. The tube racks comprise 112 places - 48 in the upper position and 64 in the lower position.

FIGURE 1. Multi-function Hand for Microbiological Testing of Cosmetics.

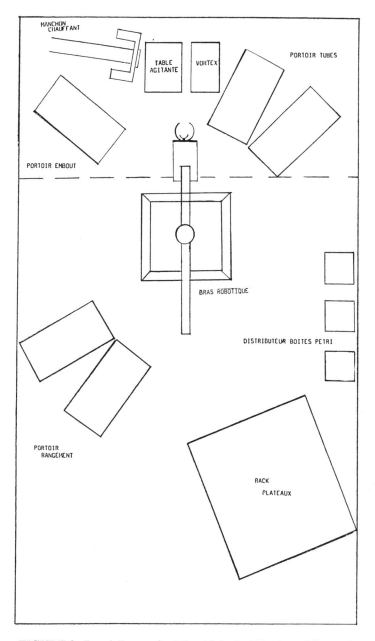

FIGURE 2. Bench Layout for Microbiological Testing of Cosmetics.

The robotic arm, equipped with its tube hand, takes the test tube from the rack and brings it to the vortex where the dilution is homogenized. The robotic arm equipped with its Petri dish hand (turning of the wrist) looks for a sterile Petri dish stored in one of the three distributing columns. The hand carries the Petri dish to the shaking table where the different seeding operations are carried out.

By means of the MLS and the syringe hand equipped with a disposable sterile tip, 1 mL of the homogenized dilution is pipetted and then introduced in the open Petri dish. At the same time, 15 mL of sterile nutrient agar kept at 45^0C is introduced in the Petri dish by the MLS. After closing, the Petri dish is gently shaken with an orbital movement. The Petri dish hand then places the Petri dish on a tray in a well specified area. The microbiologist manually places the trays with the Petri dishes in the incubator.

DISCUSSION

Implementation

Several aspects of the system were a challenge to develop. In increasing order of difficulty, these were:

- the distribution of the Petri dishes
- the agar addition work station
- the distribution of the liquid gelose kept at 45^oC, at 3 minute time intervals.

The first point was solved by Zymark by designing three columns that could each store 70 sterile Petri dishes and remove them one at a time so that they could be picked up by the Petri dish hand and carried to the work station.

The agar addition work station is a shaking table. Nearby, several actuators commanded by the PEC enable the Petri dish to be opened and closed and the agar pouring tip to drop down to the Petri dish. These operations as well as pipetting of the dilution were made reliable by the introduction of safety arrangements throughout the entire program.

The distribution of the melted agar was resolved through the use of a peristaltic pump as close as possible to the outlet from the agar sterilizer. A thermostat cover maintains the heat of the agar until it reaches the pouring tip.

Validation

Once the complete automatic plate method was developed, five sets of 100 sterile and contaminated samples were inoculated in parallel, automatically and manually. Two tubes containing sterile water were added to each set. The reading of the incubated Petri dishes showed a perfect correlation between the results and no associated contamination was noted.

Results

The cycle requires three minutes. The perfectly autonomous robot can operate without stopping for 22 hours. The limiting factor is the volume of the Agarsterilizer (8 litres).

On the average, we inoculate 200 Petri dishes per day and 360 Petri dishes on "heavy" days. We have kept the same disposable equipment and reagents. So, the cost of one analysis has remained the same and is about four times less than that of the new methods of microbiological analysis.

CONCLUSION

The preparation stage of the dilutions of cosmetic finished products can not be automated due to the diversity of the contents. In fact, what robot could sample and weigh in sterile conditions one gram of cream contained in a jar or tube, one gram of mascara contained in a bottle, and one gram of compact powder contained in a box?

The automation of the seeding sequence enables the microbiologist to prepare dilutions, take readings and examination for specific microorganisms and analyse the results. Without the robotics system, a second microbiologist would be needed in the microbiology control laboratory in order to carry out these repetitive tasks. This robotics system has already been in operation for two years and has already seeded 70,000 Petri dishes. It will have paid for itself in 1988.

REFERENCES

1. "J.0.", France, August 8, 1972, pages 8551-8553.

2. US Pharmacopeia XIX, U.S.A. , pages 588-592.

3. C.T.F.A. Microbiological Limit Guidelines for Cosmetics and Toiletries.

AN INTEGRATED ROBOTIC SAMPLE PREPARATION AND HPLC ANALYSIS OF BIOSYNTHETIC HUMAN INSULIN

Steven D.Hamilton
Eli Lilly and Company
Lilly Corporate Center
Indianapolis, IN 46285

ABSTRACT

The sample preparation and HPLC analysis of our biosynthetic human insulin product has long been one of the most labor intensive and technique dependent analyses done in our analytical area. The process involves 27 discrete manual steps, with 8 different incubation stages totaling 11 hours. A major portion of the sample preparation utilizes CNBr, requiring containment of hazardous vapors. The HPLC run time is 45 minutes, with the restriction that any given lot of samples must be run on the same instrument. Sample loads may be as high as 80 samples per day. The robotic system that performs this procedure resides on a 6x7 foot table, interacting with a variety of custom peripherals such as an automatic HPLC vial filling/capping/crimping station, a pipet tip dispenser, stir bar dispenser and an autosampler interface to two HPLC's. All devices are operated by a programmable controller interfaced to the Zymate[tm] Power and Event Controller. Samples are identified by bar code labels and sample preparation decisions are made via communications to our HP1000 mainframe through an IBM-PC.

INTRODUCTION

The automation of the manual sample preparation and HPLC analysis for biosynthetic human insulin has been one of our goals since we began developing robotic methods three years ago. This multistep procedure is very labor intensive, requiring 12 manhours during the day and evening shift. Although samples are submitted throughout the day, the length of the manual procedure allows the process to be started only at the beginning of the day shift, causing some samples to be held an additional day. The method is also very technique dependent and has been performed almost exclusively by one person during the last four years. Problems arise of course when this person is absent. Several of the reagents used, such as cyanogen bromide and methyl sulfide, are toxic and human contact must be minimized.

Despite the strong motivations for automating this task, we chose to wait until both our expertise and robotic technology had several years to advance.[1] The number of discrete steps and devices used in the 12 hour manual procedure make the design and programming of a robotic approach very challenging. Because the robotic sample throughput is slower than the manual method, interface with two HPLC instruments is necessary to maintain timely delivery of results. Containment and verification of containment of toxic gases with an automated system poses additional constraints. To meet these challenges, we have designed a robotic system on a large work table, utilized a number of custom peripherals and interfaced the robot with several computer systems.

EXPERIMENTAL

Procedure

The manual cleavage and sulfitolysis of the polypeptide chain prior to HPLC analysis involves 27 discrete steps. Adaptation of this methodology has resulted in a robotic procedure with 11 stages or preps (Table 1), each separated by a non-robotic incubation

TABLE 1. Robotic Procedure for Biosynthetic Human Insulin.

Step	Action
PREP1	Transfer aliquot of fermentation broth from bar coded submission tube (reading bar code) to assay tube. Centrifuge tube for 2 robotic cycles (36 minutes).
PREP2	Decant supernatent, add stir bar, place on magnetic stir plate in hood and add first two cleavage reagents. Stir for 18 minutes.
PREP3	Add CNBr. Stir for 4 hours.
PREP5	Add two inactivating reagents. Stir for 18 minutes.
PREP6	Add acetone. Centrifuge tube for 36 minutes.
PREP7	Aspirate acetone, add second aliquot of acetone while stirring. Centrifuge tube for 36 minutes.
PREP8	Aspirate acetone. Place tube in drying rack for 1 hour.
PREP9	Add sulfitolysis reagent, remove from hood and place on magnetic stir plate outside hood for 4 hours.
PREP10	Remove tube from stir plate. Centrifuge for 18 minutes.
PREP11	Pipette aliquot of supernatent, standard or control sample into HPLC vial(s) for appropriate instrument, based on communications with HP1000. Pipette additional sample into chilled vial for long term storage. Remove stir bar from tube, decant excess sample and discard tube.

stage. The total non-robotic time is approximately 11 hours. The robot cycle time is about 18 minutes, and the dwell time for any one sample in the process is 12 hours.

During the development portion of this project, several troublesome manual steps were systematically eliminated or modified. These included such operations as chopping the dried centrifuge pellet, scraping the sides of the test tube during stirring steps to remove particulate, multiple removing and adding of stir bars, decanting into beakers to catch lose precipitate and high speed homogenization of the wet centrifuge pellet before adding reagents or washing. These changes were essential to make automation possible and all modifications were tested and implemented before the robotic equipment was purchased.

Robotic System Components

As we began planning this project, it became obvious that in addition to standard components of the Zymate Laboratory Automation System we would require numerous custom work stations to maximize space utilization and improve system throughput. The number and complexity of these devices grew until we also had to use a programmable controller to operate them. Table 2 lists the various components of this robotic system.

The robotic table is 6'x 7', placed on a castered cart (Figure 1). A large portion of the work space is occupied by a fume hood which contains a sunken centrifuge, 30 position magnetic stir plate, 6 position evaporating station and one MLS (Figure 2). The rest of the components are arranged around the table as shown in Figure 3. Attached to the sides of the cart are air control devices, the programmable controller, the CNBr gas detector, and waste containers for liquids, tubes and pipette tips. Below the cart are two HP-1084 HPLC's, the Zymate II controller, and circuitry for the barcode reader, watchdog timer and HPLC-HP1000 interface (Figure 4 a,b).

Table 2. Robotic System Components for Biosynthetic Human Insulin Procedure.

Zymate Components

Zymate II Robot and Controller III
Power and Event Controller (PEC)
Vortex Station
Printer
2 - Centrifuges
3 - Master Lab Stations (MLS)
Remote Control Interface Module
Concurrent EasyLab[tm] Module

Non-Zymate Components

IBM PC/XT[tm]
Omron[tm] C120 Programmable Controller (Distributed by Tapco Products Inc., Cincinnati, OH)
Symbol LaserScan 6500[tm] (Symbol Technologies Inc., Bohemia, NY)
2-Hewlett Packard 1084 HPLC's
Haake A81 Chilled Water Bath (Haake Buchler Instruments Inc., Saddle Brook, NJ)
TGM 555 Air Monitor (CEA Instruments Inc., Emerson, NJ)
2-Variomag[tm] solid state multiposition magnetic stir plates (Distributed by Cole Parmer Instrument Co., Chicago, IL)

Custom Components

2-Stacked, chill racks for tubes
2-Stacked, chill racks for vials
2-HPLC vial crimper/capper stations
2-HPLC autosampler/injector mechanisms
2-HPLC lifting carts
2-Pipet tip dispensers
Stir tube sealer
Evaporating station
Tube dispenser
Stir bar dispenser
Waste conveyor
Fume containment hood

FIGURE 1. Robot "LITTLE JOHN" Side View.

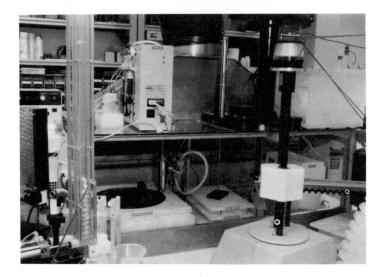

FIGURE 2. View of Robotic Fume Hood. Left to Right, Sunken Centrifuge, Aspirator/Dispenser, Stir Rack with Retractable Tube Cover, Drying Station with Retractable Air Manifold, Master Lab Station.

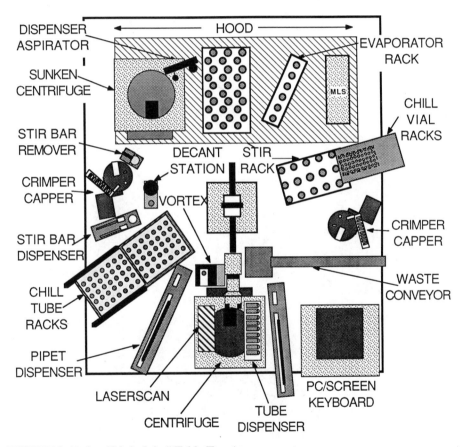

FIGURE 3. Robot "Little John" Table Top Arrangement.

FIGURE 4a. Side View of Robot Table with HPLC Underneath.

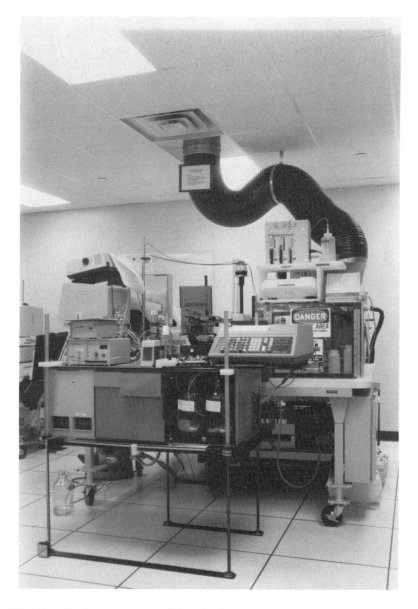

FIGURE 4b. HPLC Extended on Lifting Cart for Maintenance Access.

All custom peripheral devices are controlled via an Omron programmable controller (PLC) interfaced to the Zymate PEC. The Zymate uses the five contact closures to send a BCD signal to the PLC for selection of the desired operation. A sixth closure is used to execute the command. A PEC input is used to monitor an error line from the PLC. This arrangement allows up to 32 different events to be executed by the Zymate.

Some of the more complex peripherals execute multiple steps under control of the PLC after the Zymate has initiated the sequence. The best example is the HPLC crimper/capper station (Figure 5a,b). The first command from the Zymate System initiates the feeding of a HPLC vial from a storage bin into a stepping rotor, followed by rotation ending under a pipette tip guide. The robot fills the vial and then orders the next sequence to begin. The rotor again moves, and at discrete positions a cap drops on the vial, the cap is crimped and the crimped vial is dropped down a chute to a custom HPLC autoinjector (Figure 6). The chute acts as autosampler storage for the vials, allowing the robot complete samples faster than the HPLC. Using this peripheral, the robot does not handle the HPLC vials or caps, and no robotic time is needed other than to fill the vial.

We were compelled to go to such lengths to meet the constraints placed by our HPLC and sample prep group. The manual method allows a full set of samples to be finished and loaded on an HPLC by the end of the second (and last) shift. The automated method cannot prepare samples as quickly. Robotic injection of finished samples during the night is necessary to avoid delaying final results. The robotic cycle time is 18 minutes, compared to the HPLC run time of 45 minutes. Samples cannot be easily multiplexed between several instruments to overcome this mismatch, because any one lot or group of samples must be run on the same HPLC for optimum results. Therefore some type of buffering autosampler is necessary to allow efficient use of the robot. We were also restricted to

FIGURE 5a. HPLC Crimper/Capper Station, from the Vial Feeding Side.

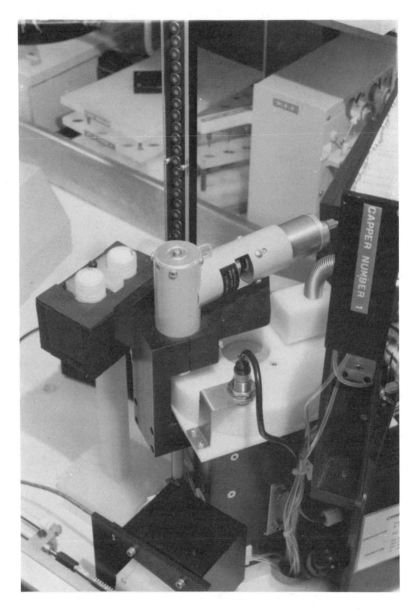

FIGURE 5b. HPLC Crimper/Capper Station, from the Crimping Cap Detection Side.

FIGURE 6. HPLC Injector. Chute Connection for Dropping Vials is Center Left.

using existing HP1084 HPLC's for reasons beyond the scope of this paper. Our solution to this situation is the set of crimper/capper and injector devices mentioned earlier.

Other peripherals were necessary to overcome space restrictions. The pipet tip (Figure 7 a,b) stir bar and test tube dispensers (Figure 8 a,b) were designed to store these items outside of the robot's working reach and to present the stored item to a location inside the working envelope for pickup by the robot. Racks for storage of sample tubes (Figure 9 a,b) and backup final sample vials (Figure 10) are stacked vertically and pneumatically extended for robotic access. Getting rid of disposable items was not straightforward, because the robot cannot reach the edge of this table, space under the table is occupied, and no space is available on the table for waste storage. The solution was a conveyor to shuttle spent items to bins at the edge of the table (Figure 11). The conveyor automatically moves to drop items into one of two bins, one for reusable assay tubes and the other for disposable pipette tips.

The Zymate Controller is interfaced to an IBM PC/XT through the Z845 Remote Control Interface. As bar-coded ID's are read, they are stored in the PC. When that sample reaches the HPLC injection stage 12 hours later, the PC communicates with the HP1000 Lab Chromatography System to determine if that sample has been designated for injection into one of the HPLC's. If so, the PC will inquire if the sample should be preceded or followed by a standard or control injection, and then vials are filled at the appropriate crimper/capper station. If the sample has not been logged for either HPLC, only a backup vial will be filled. The action taken for each sample is logged on the PC for later printout. The robot concurrently enters the remote mode briefly several times during each cycle to receive sample preparation instructions from the PC.

FIGURE 7a. Pipette Tip Dispenser, Retracted.

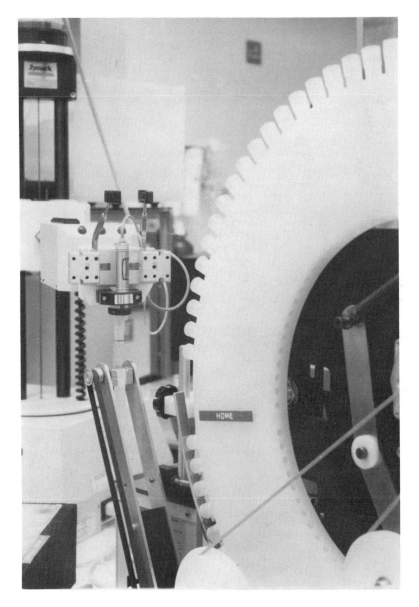

FIGURE 7b. Pipette Tip Dispenser, Extended with Tip Ready for Pickup.

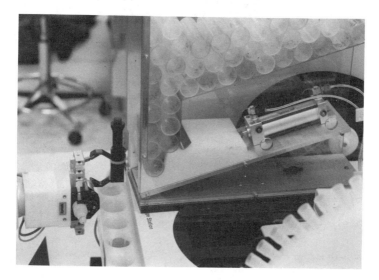

FIGURE 8a. Tube Dispenser, Retracted.

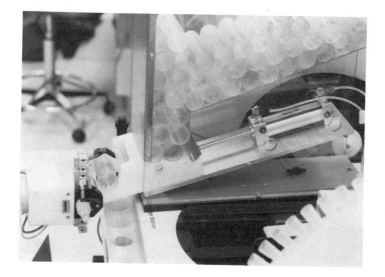

FIGURE 8b. Tube Dispenser, Extended for Tube Pickup.

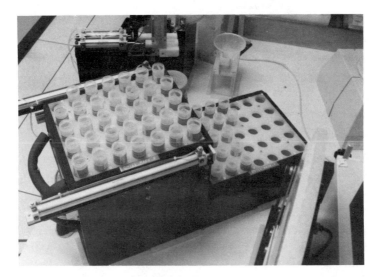

FIGURE 9a. Chilled Sample Storage Positioned for Access to Lower Rack.

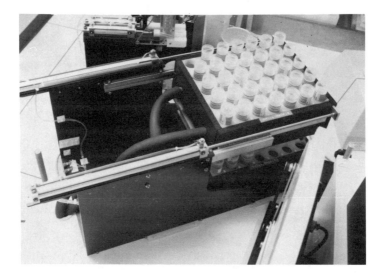

FIGURE 9b. Chilled Sample Storage, Positioned for Access to Upper Rack.

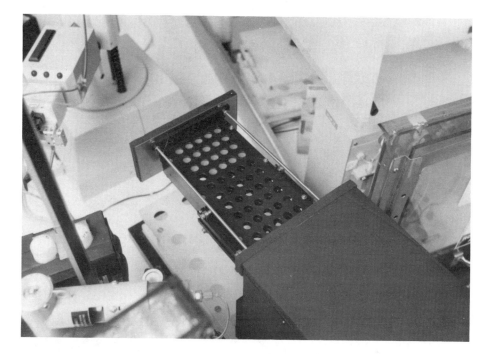

FIGURE 10. Chilled Vial Storage, Positioned for Access to Upper Rack.

Error detection is especially important in this application because of the use of CNBr. In addition to the usual use of robotic tactile feedback, optical and microswitch devices, the PLC provides a constant status check on all devices it controls, and displays error messages on an alphanumeric display above the robot. A wet chemical segmented flow instrument is used to monitor for stray CNBr gas. A positive response will cause the robot to stop operation and signal plant security. All error situations sound both audible and visual alarm and begin a phone dialer sequence to alert appropriate people.

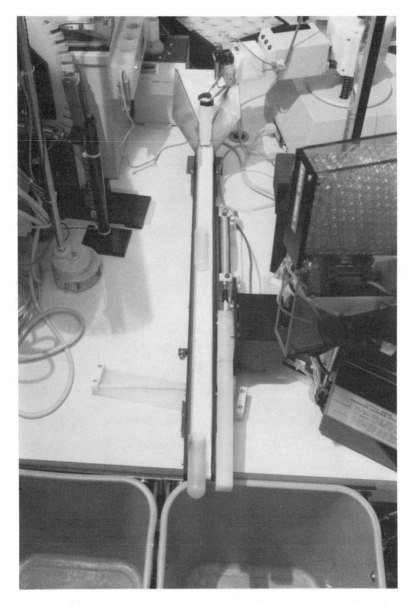

FIGURE 11. Waste Conveyor, with Tubes Moving to One of Two Waste Containers.

CONCLUSIONS

After a long period of system construction, programming and detailed validation of the many sample preparation steps, this robotic system became operational in September of this year. As has been our experience in the past, daily precision and accuracy of the robotic method is about the same as that produced by a very conscientious and methodical technician. The automated system will free significant manpower for other use and give much greater flexibility in the processing of these type of samples.

ACKNOWLEDGEMENTS

A large number of people have played a part in the successful completion of this project. I wish to thank my technical associate, Mr. Jeff Gygi for his valuable work. The custom devices and PLC control are the work of Mr. John Huzenga, Mr. Gregg Basset and Mr. Don Hennert. Modification and validation of the methodology have involved Dr. Avinash Lagu, Dr. Hamilton Niss, Mr. Norm Taylor and Mr. Jim Powell. Management support is provided by Dr. Frank Gainer.

REFERENCES

1. Hamilton, S.D. "Robotic Assays for Fermentation Products", in Advances in Laboratory Automation Robotics 1986. J.R. Strimaitis and G.L. Hawk (Zymark Corporation, 1986) p.1.

Symbol is a registered trademark and Laserscan is a trademark of Symbol Technologies.

IBM and IBM PC/XT are registered trademarks of International Business Machines Corporation.

Variomag is a registered trademark of Dr. Hoiss and Partner GmbH, Munich, West Germany.

Omron is a trademark of Omron Electronics Inc.

AUTOMATED PREPARATION OF PROTEIN CRYSTALS: INTEGRATION OF AN AUTOMATED VISUAL INSPECTION STATION

William M. Zuk, Mary Ann Perozzo, and Keith B. Ward
Laboratory for the Structure of Matter
Naval Research Laboratory
Washington, DC 20375-5000

ABSTRACT

The routine preparation of single crystals suitable for x-ray diffraction studies is of primary importance to the field of protein crystallography. Several crystallization techniques developed within the past three decades require accurate manual manipulation of microliter quantities of protein, buffer, and precipitating solutions, processes which can be tedious at best. Two of these techniques, the so-called "hanging drop" and the related "sandwiched drop" methods, involve procedures which are particularly appropriate for automation.

Droplets of admixtures of protein solutions, buffers, and precipitating agents are suspended from a glass coverslip placed above a reservoir solution in a single well of a crystallization plate, attaining vapor equilibrium with the reservoir solution. The droplets are then periodically inspected for the presence of crystals. Under suitable conditions, large (0.1-1.0 mm) single crystals will grow within 1-30 days. We have developed a system to automate the "hanging drop" technique using a Zymate II laboratory robot with customized accessories. Recently, we have incorporated an automated visual inspection station into our system which will ultimately allow complete automation of protein crystallization experiments. In collaboration with Dr. Noel Jones of Eli Lilly Co., we have also developed a new crystallization plate which is more "robot friendly" than previously used plates, and which will greatly facilitate automated inspection of droplets.

Analog video images of crystallization droplets are obtained with a monochrome RCA closed-circuit TV camera and are stored individually on an optical disc with a Panasonic TQ-2025F Optical Memory Disc Recorder, which is capable of storing 15,000 frames on a single optical disc. Images recorded on the video disc are then digitized with a PCVISION[tm] frame grabber installed in a Zenith Z-248 AT-compatible personal computer. Both analog and digitized images are displayed on a standard NTSC video monitor. Digitized images are subsequently analyzed using IMAGETOOL[tm] image processing software. Edge detection methods are used to determine if protein crystals, precipitate, or other objects are present in the droplets. The information obtained from the automated video inspection and image analysis of droplets under various conditions will allow the host computer to ascertain the optimum conditions for growing a given set of protein crystals. Software to be implemented will permit automated redesign of experiments based upon results from previous experiments.

Complete automation of protein crystallization experiments will not only lead to greater control and reproducibility of the crystallization procedures but will also allow experiments to be conducted in hostile environments, such as a cold room or a microgravity environment, or with hazardous materials. Progress of these experiments will be discussed and image acquisition and analysis methods will be described in further detail.

INTRODUCTION

The most prevalent technique currently in use for the determination of macromolecular structure is x-ray crystallography. At present, x-ray diffraction studies provide the best means of obtaining detailed information regarding the conformation of large biological molecules, including proteins. A primary concern of protein crystallography analyses, however, is the routine preparation of large single crystals suitable for diffraction studies. Several procedures have been developed for growing protein crystals,[1-3] including the technique most commonly used, the vapor diffusion method.[1] All procedures designed to grow crystals fundamentally involve trial and error and entail accurately and reproducibly mixing small volumes of highly purified protein solutions and solutions of precipitating agents, buffers, and other additives. In order to find optimum conditions for crystal growth, it is necessary to conduct numerous individual crystallization experiments. Procedures required to grow protein crystals by the vapor diffusion method are, however, well suited for automation. Recent efforts in our laboratory have focused on emulating manual methods with laboratory robotics.[4]

Automation of protein crystallization experiments provides several immediate advantages. An automated system permits a routine and reproducible survey of crystallization conditions, providing information which may be used to determine the optimum conditions for crystal growth, and allows very accurate duplication of those conditions. Furthermore, automated procedures are ideal for conducting experiments in controlled environments, with toxic substances, or given proper adaptation, in microgravity conditions.

In order to fully automate protein crystallization methods, we are currently integrating an automated visual inspection station into our laboratory robotics system. The visualization system provides digitized images of individual crystallization droplets which may be analyzed by a host computer to determine whether the protein has remained in solution or if a precipitate has formed, whether it is amorphous or crystalline. Based upon these analyses, parameters for new crystallization experiments can be determined with software on the host computer, and the host may then instruct the robot to conduct new experiments using these parameters. This report details modifications in equipment and experimental procedures we have made in order to facilitate automation and describes our efforts to incorporate an image acquisition and analysis system.

AUTOMATION OF PROTEIN CRYSTALLIZATION EXPERIMENTS

Methods

The manual methods used to prepare protein crystals by the "hanging drop" vapor diffusion method have been previously described.[4] Individual crystallization experiments are conducted in single wells of a tissue culture plate, such as the Linbro model 76-033-05. Approximately 1 mL of buffered solutions of precipitating agent are placed in each of the wells of the tissue culture plate, and a drop (about 5-20 uL) containing protein solution, precipitating agents and buffer is suspended from a glass coverslip positioned above each reservoir. The volatile component (usually water) diffuses from the drop into the reservoir until equilibrium is attained, during which the droplet slowly becomes more concentrated in both precipitating agent and protein. Under suitable conditions, protein crystals develop within the droplet. Under other conditions, however, protein may precipitate from solution as an amorphous solid, a state which is not desirable. In order to find the optimal conditions of crystal growth, hundreds or thousands of such experiments, each involving the manipulations of very small volumes, need to be arranged, making the technique ideal for automation.

Changes in Equipment and Procedure

The system designed to automate protein crystallization experiments originally reported by our laboratory[4] utilized a Zymate Laboratory Automation System with customized accessories to emulate the methods described above. Several changes have since been made to that system. The new configuration is shown in Figure 1. Principal among the changes is a new crystallization plate, the CRYSTAL PLATE[tm], developed by Dr. Noel Jones of Eli Lilly Co. and Keith Ward and Mary Ann Perozzo of our laboratory.[5] The new plate was specifically designed for protein crystallizations using laboratory robotics. Previously, the Linbro tissue culture plate described above was used to contain hanging drops suspended from a glass coverslip above a reservoir solution. Visual inspection of droplets in the Linbro plates was difficult due to the "lens effect" of the droplet itself and the poor optical quality of the reservoir and the plastic bottom of the tray, which of necessity were in the optical path. These problems are eliminated with the CRYSTAL PLATE since the reservoir is located to the side of the droplet, and the drop is sandwiched between two glass coverslips, providing a clear, non-polarizing, optical path. Other features of the new tray include robot-friendly stacking capabilities, troughs for sealing oil which allow automated dispensing to accomodate sealing coverslips automatically, and channels in the tray sides for moving them with a fork-lift hand.

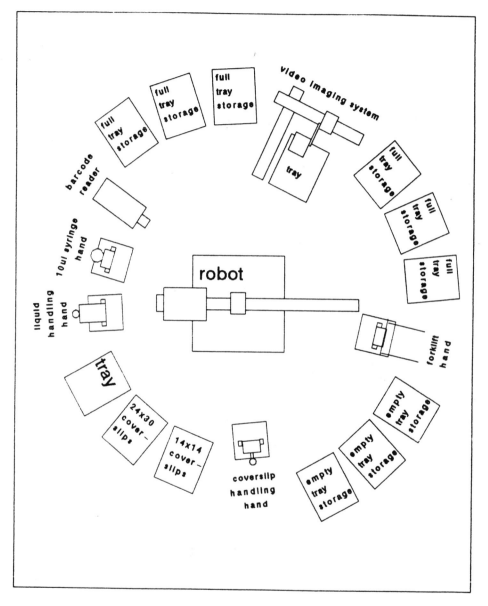

FIGURE 1. Configuration of Zymate Laboratory Robotics System Components and Video Image Acquisition Station.

We have also made several changes in the methods of delivering solutions to the reservoirs of the CRYSTAL PLATE. The liquid delivery system under development allows measuring, mixing, and delivery of up to five solutions in one step. Five Pharmacia MV-8 valves are interfaced to a Zenith Z-248 microcomputer via a Keithley System 501 Scientific Workstation. Each of these valves selects one of eight solutions that are subsequently pumped by the master laboratory station (MLS) syringes in differing proportions into a mixing device. In this device, each of the five solutions are passed through tubes which converge radially to a common mixing chamber. The mixed solution then leaves this small chamber through a single outlet tube and is delivered to the crystal plate reservoir. Thus the predetermined volumes of the five solutions are mixed and delivered in one operation.

The host computer for the entire automated system will be a Zenith Z-248 AT-compatible microcomputer. The Z-248 not only will be used for all video image acquisition and analysis, but it will also control the Zymate robotics system and, as noted above, will control liquid delivery through the Keithley workstation. It will also make all necessary experimental calculations, and create data storage files for all experiments generated.

Image Processing Equipment

The primary goal of this research is to design an expert system which is capable of designing and conducting new crystallization experiments based upon results obtained from previous experiments. We are therefore developing an automated video inspection system and image analysis routines which may be used to examine and interpret individual crystallization droplets.

The video acquisition system under development in our laboratory currently consists of an RCA TC 1005/01 high-resolution monochrome monitor, a Panasonic TQ-2025F Optical Memory Disk Recorder, a PCVISION^{tm} frame grabber installed in the Zenith Z-248 microcomputer, and an NTSC monochrome monitor. Images shown in the figures included in this paper were obtained by mounting the RCA camera onto a Bausch & Lomb Stereozoom microscope equipped with polarizing and analyzing filters. In order to afford the greatest flexibility in our system, we now use a Titan Tool Supply Co. zoom objective and the RCA video camera attached to a motorized X-Y-Z stage (Figure 2). The stage consists of two Unislide B2509W1J assemblies as the x and y-axes, and a Unislide B2506J assembly as the z-axis. Movement of the camera is effected through three Bodine Model 2001 stepper motors and Velmex motor controllers which are interfaced to the Keithley Workstation for computer control. This configuration gives the added advantage of minimizing movement of the crystallization plate and lessening vibrations within the droplets.

The images of droplets obtained with the RCA video camera are stored on a Panasonic TQ-2025F Optical Memory Disc Recorder. The OMDR is capable of recording 15,000 monochrome images on a single write-once optical disc, and individual images may be accessed randomly and quickly. In addition, the recorder may display single images for extended periods of time with no synchronization problems, permitting easy digitization, and it allows relatively efficient storage of images. If the digitized images we use were stored on computer media, for instance, each image would take up to 256 Kbytes of memory. We therefore chose to use the OMDR for primary data storage, and digitize the droplet images as needed.

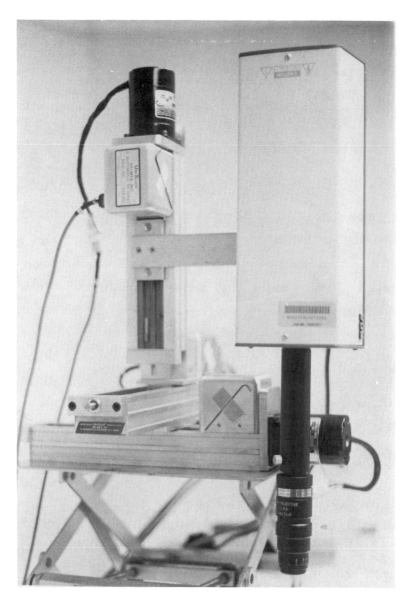

FIGURE 2. X-Y-Z Stage for Automated Video Inspection of Crystallization Droplets.

The analog images are subsequently retrieved from the TQ-2025F and digitized by an Imaging Technology Inc. PCVISION^{tm} frame grabber which is installed in a Zenith Z-248 personal computer. The digitizer produces images with 512 x 512 x 8 bits of resolution, allowing 256 levels of gray shading. Images are acquired and manipulated using IMAGETOOL^{tm} software from Werner Frei Associates. Digital images are displayed on a standard NTSC monitor, in our case, a Sony PVM-122 black and white video monitor. The PCVISION frame grabber also contains a pseudocolor module which assigns red, green, and blue colors to appropriate gray levels. Although we do not utilize the pseudocolor facility at present, we plan on displaying the colorized images on a Sony KV-1311CR color monitor.

System Components

In summary, the complete system comprises the following components:

A. Zymark Components

1. Robot hands

    a. Coverslip handling hand (custom design on blank hand)
    b. Forklift hand (custom design on blank hand)
    c. Liquid/oil delivery hand (custom design on blank hand)
    d. 10 uL syringe hand

2. Master laboratory station (2)
3. Power and event controller
4. Robot and controller

B. Other Robotic Components

1. Pharmacia MV-8 valves (5)
2. Automated "remote" syringe washer

C. Racks and Work Station

1. Empty plate rack
2. Plate holder work station
3. Rack for 14 x 14 mm. coverslips
4. Rack for 24 x 30 mm. coverslips
5. Protein vial rack
6. Plate storage rack

D. Expendable items

1. Protein crystallization plate
2. 14 x 14 mm. glass coverslips
3. 24 x 30 mm. glass coverslips
4. Buffers, salt solutions, detergents, protein solutions

E. Computer components

1. Zenith Z-248 microcomputer
2. Keithley System 501 Scientific Workstation

F. Image processing equipment

1. RCA TC 1005/01 video camera
2. Panasonic TQ-2025F Optical Memory Disk Recorder
3. PCVISION[tm] frame grabber
4. Sony PVM-122 NTSC monitor

IMAGE ANALYSIS

Analysis of Crystallization Droplets

Once the images of crystallization droplets have been acquired and digitized, they must be analyzed to determine if crystals are present. The first step in an analysis of an image is to ascertain if any objects, of whatever origin, may be seen in the droplet. These objects may not necessarily be crystals. They could be solid impurities in the droplet, such as laboratory tissue fibers or other particulates, or they may be amorphous precipitate. Therefore, it is also necessary to identify distinguishing features of the crystals in order to differentiate them from impurities.

Most protein crystals, regardless of size, have straight edges as boundaries. This feature may be used to effectively distinguish the crystals from impurities, since precipitate and particulate materials usually do not exhibit this property. Because the edges are simply short line segments, we are currently developing a series of routines to accentuate edges of objects in an image and then search for line segments in the processed image.

Image Analysis Routines

In order to locate edges in a digitized droplet image, it is necessary to employ both fundamental digital image processing methods and pattern recognition techniques. For our purposes, we utilize digital filtering routines accessed with IMAGETOOL[tm] software to enhance the crystal edges and smooth the image to remove high frequency noise. Both routines are examples of image or spatial convolution operations.[6] A digitized image consists of a large array of pixel intensities. An image convolution (Figure 3) involves operations on individual pixels of the digital image by a matrix of numbers known as a convolution mask or kernel. Convolution masks are usually square and contain an odd number of rows and columns.

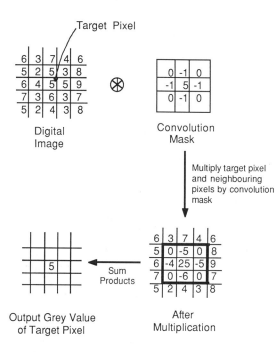

FIGURE 3. Convolution Operation.

The convolution operation on a pixel involves two steps. As shown in Figure 3, the elements of the kernel are first multiplied by the intensities of the pixel of interest, sometimes called a target pixel, and its nearest neighbors. The center element of the convolution mask is multiplied by the target pixel. Secondly, the results of the multiplications are summed, giving the final value of the processed target pixel. Therefore, the final intensity of the convolved pixel depends not only on the original intensity of the pixel, but on the intensities of its neighbors. The operation may be written as

$$P = I \circledast M$$

where **P** is the processed image, **I** is the original image, **M** is the convolution kernel, and $\circledast$ denotes the convolution operation. Depending on the elements of the convolution mask, the convolution operation may be used to smooth and sharpen images, or accentuate edges or other features of an image.

To process a digitized droplet image, we use three convolution masks: a smoothing filter, and a two simple edge detection kernels. Two edge detection filters are used independently to accentuate vertical and horizontal edges of objects, respectively. The three masks are depicted in Figure 4. When an image is retrieved from the Panasonic TQ-2025F and digitized, it is first processed with the vertical edge detection mask and the resulting image is saved as an array. The original digital image is then subjected to the horizontal filter. The two resulting images are then smoothed to decrease extraneous noise and each is processed to locate edges and display them as one pixel-wide white lines on a black background. The two processed images are subsequently superimposed to combine all enhanced edges. Combining the two "line drawings" tends to provide a fairly complete two dimensional projection of objects in the image. Although we use this rather simple approach, other more complicated techniques have been developed for edge

Smoothing
Mask

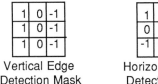

Vertical Edge   Horizontal Edge
Detection Mask   Detection Mask

FIGURE 4. Convolution Masks Used in Processing Droplet Images: Smoothing Mask, Vertical Edge Detection Mask, and Horizontal Edge Detection Mask.

detection. These include image segmentation[7], and the use of other edge enhancing operators.[8-10] We may at some time wish to implement one of these techniques, or a variation thereof, but at present, the straightforward approach described above seems to suit our purposes well.

When an image is finally processed, it must be analyzed to determine its contents. Since images of droplets are monitored regularly, very simple qualitative tests may be made between individual images of the same droplet. By counting the number of white pixels present in an image, it is possible to determine whether or not objects are increasing in size. If the number of pixels remain constant between images, then the objects that those pixels outline are less likely to be crystals; if this number increases, then either the amount of precipitate or the number of crystals are probably increasing. A more quantitative and definitive test for the presence of crystals, however, is to determine if the outlines are composed of straight lines. Routines presently under development concentrate on the latter approach.

In order to locate straight edges in our processed images, we are currently developing a line-finding routine with our software system. The routine we plan on using will be adapted from a "context sensitive" line finder developed by Shirai.[11] Preliminary observations suggest that this procedure will be very effective in locating medium to large crystals (> 100 μm in diameter). For locating microcrystals or crystals just beginning to grow, or for discriminating between crystals and precipitate, it is likely that a pixel counting method such as the one described above will prove to be useful.

RESULTS

Preliminary results of image analysis of crystallization droplets are shown in Figures 5-9. The first figure shows a digitized image of lysozyme crystals grown using a prototype of the new crystallization plate. The crystals are approximately 500 μm in size. Figure 6 depicts the lysozyme image after it has been processed with a vertical edge detection mask and smoothed twice, while Figure 7 shows an image after a horizontal edge detection mask

FIGURE 5. Digital Image of Lysozyme Crystals.

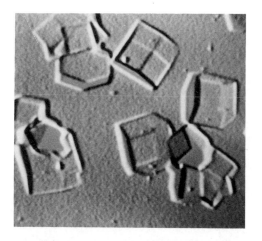

FIGURE 6. Image of Lysozyme Crystals After Undergoing a Vertical Edge Detection Convolution.

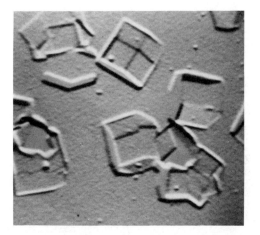

FIGURE 7. Image of Lysozyme Crystals After Undergoing a Horizontal Edge Detection Convolution.

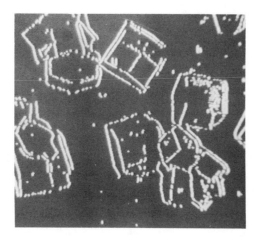

FIGURE 8. One Pixel-Wide Outlines of Vertical Edge Enhanced Lysozyme Crystals.

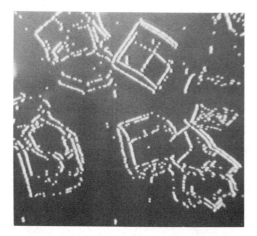

FIGURE 9. One Pixel-Wide Outlines of Horizontal Edge Enhanced Lysozyme Crystals.

has been applied and the resulting image has been smoothed. The last two figures show the enhanced edges outlined.

CONCLUSION

In continuing our efforts to completely automate vapor diffusion techniques for protein crystallization, we have begun integrating an image acquisition and analysis system into our existing laboratory robotics system in order to allow a host computer to monitor the crystallization volume and to make necessary changes in experimental conditions. Additionally, we have made changes in the robotics system and in experimental protocol to ease automation.

Automating protein crystallization experiments with laboratory robotics provides several advantages over manual methods. Liquid volume delivery is significantly more accurate with the robotics system, permitting routine and reproducible generation of experiments. Automation also permits an experimenter to create a large number of crystallization droplets over lengths of time which would not be possible manually. Furthermore, an automated system allows experiments to be easily conducted in hostile environments or with toxic substances. Automation of crystallization experiments ultimately will not only benefit our laboratory, but also other laboratories attempting to crystallize proteins.

Further development and testing of the image analysis system is required. In addition, we will soon begin combining image processing routines, robotics applications, and experimental calculations, in order to design an integrated, user-friendly software system. The ultimate goal of this project is to create an expert system which is capable of designing and executing new crystallization experiments based on information obtained automatically from previous experiments.

REFERENCES

1. Alexander McPherson, "Preparation and Analysis of Protein Crystals", (John Wiley and Sons, New York, 1982).

2. T. Blundell and L. Johnson (editors), "Crystallization of Proteins", in Protein Crystallography, (Academic Press, 1976).

3. R. Feigelson (editor), "Proceedings of the First International Conference on Protein Crystal Growth", J. Crystal Growth, (North-Holland, Amsterdam, 1986).

4. Keith B. Ward, Mary Ann Perozzo, and Jeffrey R. Deschamps, "The Automation of Protein Crystallization Experiments", in Advances in Laboratory Automation Robotics 1986, (Zymark Corp., Hopkinton, MA, 1987).

5. Noel Jones, Keith B. Ward and Mary Ann Perozzo, in preparation.

6. Shinya Inoue (editor), "Video Microscopy", (Plenum, New York, 1986).

7. Jack Sklansky, "Image Segmentation and Feature Extraction", IEEE Transactions on Systems, Man, and Cybernetics, SMC-8, 237 (1978).

8. Larry S. Davis, "A Survey of Edge Detection Techniques", Computer Graphics and Image Processing, 4, 248 (1975).

9. Manfred H. Heuckel, "An Operator Which Locates Edges in Digitized Pictures", J. Association of Computing Machinery, 18 (1), 113 (1971).

10. Jack Sklansky, "On the Hough Technique for Curve Detection", IEEE Transactions on Computers, C-27, 923 (1978).

11. Y. Shirai, in Artificial Intelligence, B. Meltzer and B. Raphael (editors), (North Holland, Amsterdam, 1973).

PCVISION is a trademark of Imaging Technology Incorporated.

IMAGETOOL is a trademark of Werner Frei Associates.

CRYSTAL PLATE is a trademark of the American Crystallographic Association.

LABORATORY ROBOTICS APPLIED TO TURBIDIMETRIC ENDOTOXIN ANALYSIS OF RECOMBINANT DNA-DERIVED PHARMACEUTICALS

R.H. Carlson, R.L. Garnick, M.M. Stephan,
D. Sinicropi, C.P. du Mee, and C. Miller
Genentech, Inc.
460 Point San Bruno Blvd.
South San Francisco, California 94080

ABSTRACT

The analysis of endotoxin samples from recombinant DNA-derived pharmaceuticals is one of the most commonly employed assays utilized by the biotechnology industry. A turbidimetric endotoxin analysis procedure has been successfully coupled with an HP Genenchem Robot to perform the sample preparation and complete analysis of the endotoxin content of a number of biochemical samples. The results obtained using the proposed automated method were comparable to the manual gel clot method, having an observed recovery of 98% with an RSD of 50%.

INTRODUCTION

Endotoxins are lipopolysaccharide components of the cell wall of gram-negative bacteria.[1,2] Because of their potency, stability, and ubiquity, endotoxins are of major concern to the manufacturers of parenteral products. Nanogram quantities can induce a febrile response in humans ranging from mild fever to shock or even death. Thus, a reliable method of detecting bacterial endotoxins in drug preparations is of vital importance to the pharmaceutical industry. In addition, manufacturers of recombinant DNA (rDNA)-derived products must be concerned with the effects of endotoxins on mammalian cell cultures during the fermentation stage of production.

The traditional assay for pyrogens since the 1940's has been the USP Rabbit Pyrogen Test ("pyro" = fire, "gen" = beginning) in which the occurrence of a febrile response in animals is monitored post-injection.[1] This assay, although reliable, is expensive, labor-intensive and nonquantitative. The Limulus Amebocyte Lysate (LAL) assay was developed in the late 1960's and 1970's as a semiquantitative method for the detection of endotoxins (endotoxins are pyrogens, ordinarily the only type of pyrogens ever encountered).[1,3-5] LAL is an extract made from the blood cells (amebocytes) of the horseshoe crab (*Limulus polyphemus*). It was discovered in the mid-1950's that this extract reacts with minute amounts of bacterial endotoxins by producing an insoluble gel (clot).[6] In 1977, the U.S. Food and Drug Administration (FDA) licensed the *in vitro* LAL assay as an alternative pyrogen test.[7] Since then, the LAL assay has been steadily replacing the Rabbit Pyrogen Test. Several studies have confirmed that the LAL test correlates well with the Rabbit Pyrogen Test, although the LAL test is more sensitive.[4,8,9] Thus, it is now possible to test solutions containing endotoxin concentrations below the pyrogenic response level in rabbits. This is extremely important in recombinant products because, by using this procedure, one can monitor the manufacturing process to ensure that it is essentially pyrogen-free.

There are four different LAL methodologies: gel clot, colorimetric, chromogenic, and turbidimetric assays. The LAL used must be obtained from an FDA-licensed manufacturer and must be designed specifically for the method chosen.

The Gel Clot Test: The gel clot test is performed by adding reconstituted LAL to an equal volume of liquid sample in a small glass test tube. The mixture is left to incubate at 37°C for one hour. If, after this time, a solid gel clot is formed in the tube that will remain in the tube when it is inverted, the test is considered positive for the presence of endotoxin. The mechanism of the LAL biochemical reaction is illustrated in Figure 1. The limit of sensitivity is a function of the lysate used but is, practically, 3 pg/mL or 0.03 EU/mL (EU = endotoxin unit).

The Colorimetric Test: The colorimetric test is performed by incubating samples and reagents as described in the gel clot test, then isolating the gel clot from the sample and subjecting it to Lowry protein analysis.[10]

The Chromogenic Test: In the chromogenic test, the LAL reagent is added to the sample and allowed to incubate. A yellow chromogenic substrate, which absorbs light at 405 nm, is added. After further incubation, the reaction is stopped by adding acetic acid and the completed reaction is read in a spectrometer. The degree of color formed (i.e., chromogenic substrate cleaved) is proportional to the amount of endotoxin or active clotting enzyme present. This reaction can be complicated by the presence of other interfering proteins, which are common products of the biotechnology industry. Chromogenic assays have been automated using robotics[11] and specialized commercially available instrumentation (Whittaker M.A. Bioproducts, Walkersville, MD).[1]

The Turbidimetric Test: The turbidimetric test, which is a refinement of the gel clot test, measures the increase in turbidity that precedes clot formation. The test is performed by adding a small amount of LAL reagent (i.e., less than for the gel clot method) to the sample. This is schematically presented in Figure 2.

LAL Reaction Mechanism

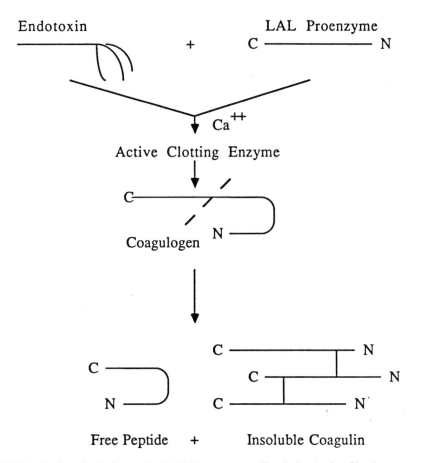

FIGURE 1. Endotoxin Activates the LAL Proenzyme to Form the Active Clotting Enzyme. The Active Clotting Enzyme Cleaves Coagulogen to Form Insoluble Coagulin (the Clot) and a Soluble Free Peptide.

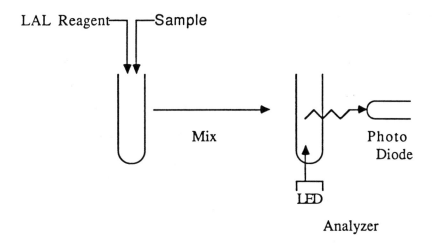

FIGURE 2. LAL Testing Schema.

The turbidimetric test was chosen over these other tests for automation based on the following considerations: [12]

    1. Cost savings - personnel and reagents

    2. Increased accuracy and precision - semiquantitative limit test (Gel Clot) *versus* quantitative determination (turbidimetric)

    3. Concern for employees - LAL testing is simple but repetitive and monotonous

    4. High number of samples for daily analysis

    5. Increased sensitivity - relative to gel clot method

    6. Computerized data reduction and analysis

    7. Robotic sample preparation for consistency of results

EXPERIMENTAL

The LAL-4000 Analyzer

The spectrometer used was the Pyrotell Benthos LAL-4000 Turbidimetric Analyzer. The LAL-4000 system of LAL testing is based upon the turbidimetric method. The instrument contains 20 optical readers, each consisting of a light-emitting diode (LED)-photodiode pair set in a temperature-controlled block. The LED's operate at a peak wavelength of 565 nm. The LAL-4000 incubates up to 20 LAL tests at $37^{\circ}C$ while continuously measuring the turbidity development in each test. The instrument records the time taken, which is termed the "onset time" for each reaction to reach a preselected turbidity level (the threshold in Figure 3 = 0.02 A). Using these onset time values, a standard curve is constructed from dilutions of an endotoxin solution of known concentration (Figure 4). The endotoxin content of unknown samples is then determined by reference to the standard curve. The LAL-4000 was controlled with an IBM PC/XT.

The Robot

The robot system used was purchased from HP Genenchem. The robot was the cylindrical workspace type, cable/belt driven, with digitally-controlled DC motors having optical encoders for servo control. The entire assay was performed with a dual function hand having tube grippers and a pipetter. Important specifications in selecting this robot for the assay were a position repeatability of plus or minus 1 mm while being able to function at different speeds (9 different speeds with speed 9 being very fast).

Auxiliary Equipment

The robot controller was the HP Vectra PC Model 45. Mixing of solutions was accomplished by using a vortexer (Thermolyne Maxi Mix II by Sybron) interfaced to the robot or by using a pipetting action (dispense, draw, dispense, draw, etc.). A dual range top loader balance (Sartorius) was interfaced into the system to calibrate (i.e., validate) the

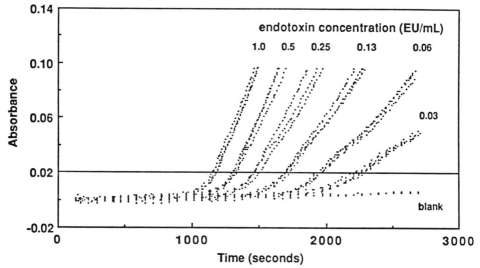

FIGURE 3. Kinetics of LAL Reaction. The turbidity of each sample is monitored simultaneously. In this example, six serial dilutions of a reference standard endotoxin were assayed inj triplicate. Onset time is the number of seconds required for the turbidity to reach a threshold value.

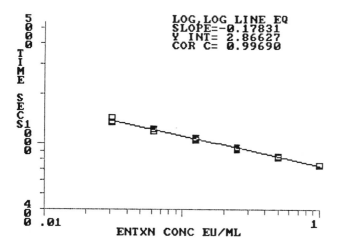

FIGURE 4. Standard Curve for Endotoxin in Water.

pipetting accuracy and precision. The pipetter was controlled with the HP Fluid Handling Modular Pump System with a valveless 1 mL syringe pump.

Reagents and Materials

The LAL reagent was Lot 099-52-395-GT purchased from Associates of Cape Cod. The endotoxin was USP Reference Standard Endotoxin Lot F. The purified water was purchased from Abbott.

RESULTS AND DISCUSSION

Qualification

The turbidimetric LAL test requires qualification of the analyst (i.e., robot) as well as the reagents and equipment. This is performed using guidelines recommended by Associates of Cape Cod. A six-point standard curve (0.031, 0.062, 0.125, 0.25, 0.5, 1.0 EU/mL) was tested in triplicate using USP Reference Standard Endotoxin. The qualification curve must be within 10% of the slope and 3% of the intercept of the curve as described by the manufacturer. In addition, the correlation coefficient (r) must be greater than 0.980. Qualification results for the robot are listed in Table 1. The slopes and intercepts from the qualification were averaged and these values were then used as the stored or archived curve.

TABLE 1. Qualification Results of the Robotic Analysis System for Endotoxin.

Run No.	r	Slope	Intercept
ACC Curve[a]		-0.181	2.875
1	0.985	-0.1672	2.8699
2	0.988	-0.1866	2.8365
3	0.991	-0.1727	2.8728
4	0.986	-0.1717	2.8591
5	0.997	-0.1682	2.8405
6	0.991	-0.1634	2.8424
7	0.987	-0.1629	2.8347
8	0.994	-0.1644	2.8506
9	0.987	-0.1738	2.8448
10	0.994	-0.1776	2.8318
11	0.988	-0.1742	2.8359
12	0.983	-0.1656	2.8472
13	0.997	-0.1783	2.8662
14	0.985	-0.1933	2.8669
	———	———	———
Average =	0.990	-0.1729	2.8500
RSD =	4.6%	5.1%	0.5%

[a] Curve supplied by manufacturer (Associates of Cape Cod) of LAL reagent

Accuracy and Precision

The accuracy and precision were evaluated by spiked placebo recovery studies using the archived curve generated in the qualification procedure. The results are listed in Table 2. The average mean recovery (accuracy) was 98.0% with an average RSD (relative standard deviation, precision) of 51.2%. These values demonstrate that the error of the analysis is limited to the precision of the assay. The error in the assay can probably be attributed to the variation in the kinetics of the LAL reaction. This error can be improved by using a single point standard, run with every group of samples, which modifies the stored curve to match the single point standard. This single point standard approach gave a recovery of 103% with an RSD of 22.4%. Because the gel clot test is a limit test with standards that are twofold increments of each other (i.e., 1.0, 0.5, 0.25, 0.125, 0.0625, and 0.03125 EU/mL), the test has an inherent error of plus or minus twofold (i.e., plus 100% to minus 50%). The accuracy and precision of the turbidimetric test using the robot were, therefore, substantial improvements over those obtained using the gel clot test.

TABLE 2. Results Obtained for the Spiked Placebo Recovery of Endotoxins in Water using the Robotic Analysis System.

Spike[a]	Percent Recovery	RSD (percent)	Replicates
0.031	104.8	46.9	20
0.062	97.3	33.2	17
0.125	112.3	52.6	20
0.250	93.7	56.9	20
0.500	90.4	74.1	21
1.000	89.2	47.9	20
	98.0	51.2	

[a] Values are in EU/mL

Correlation of the Turbidimetric and Gel Clot Tests

Water samples were analyzed in parallel by both the turbidimetric and gel clot procedures. The results (Table 3) indicate agreement between the two procedures well within the twofold concentration offered by the gel clot procedure. It should be noted that endotoxin could be determined at much lower levels by taking advantage of the turbidimetric capabilities of the robotic method than that possible using the gel clot method.

TABLE 3. Correlation of the Water Testing Results Using the Gel Clot Method and Robotic Analysis System

Sample	Gel Clot[a,b]	Turbidimetric[a]
1	< 0.049	0.0038
2	0.20	0.262
3	0.20	0.251
4	0.20	0.381
5	< 0.049	0.0008
6	< 0.049	0.0005
7	0.20	0.202
8	0.20	0.354
9	< 0.049	ND[c]
10	< 0.049	ND
11	0.20	0.164
12	< 0.049	ND
13	< 0.049	ND
14	0.20	0.140

[a] Units are in EU/mL
[b] Minimum gel clot sensitivity was 0.049 EU/mL
[c] Not detected

LAL Product Testing

Endotoxin was spiked into samples containing rDNA-derived product at levels of 0.031, 0.062, 0.125, 0.25, 0.5, and 1.0 EU/mL. These spiked samples were evaluated as a standard curve for the product (termed a product curve). Because of matrix effects caused by the presence of the product or excipients, deviations from the slope and intercept of the water curves were observed. The endotoxin curves for human growth hormone (Protropin[tm]) and Tumor Necrosis Factor (TNF)-Alpha are shown in Figures 5 and 6, respectively. These product curves demonstrate a linear response to endotoxin concentration as was observed in purified water alone.

SUMMARY

A robotic analysis system was developed for the determination of endotoxins in water and rDNA-derived product samples. The accuracy and precision of the method were observed to be 98% and 50%, respectively. The correlation between the gel clot method and the robotic analysis system indicated the methods gave comparable results, i.e., the same answer within a twofold endotoxin concentration. The robotic analysis system, using turbidimetric technology, was capable of significantly better sensitivity and quantitation than the gel clot method.

ACKNOWLEDGEMENTS

The contributions of A. Chen, E. Patzer, T. Arnerich, P. Bente, and P.A. Papa were greatly appreciated.

Standard Curve for Endotoxin in Protropin

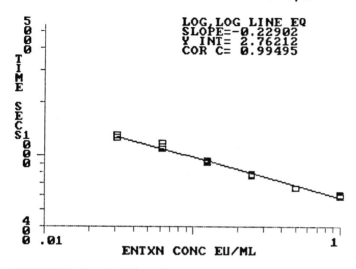

FIGURE 5. Standard Curve for Endotoxin in Protropin.

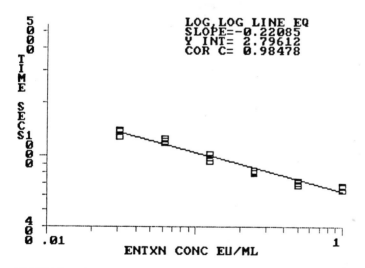

FIGURE 6. Standard Curve for Endotoxin in TNF-Alpha.

REFERENCES

1. M.J. Akers, "Pyrogen Testing," in Parenteral Quality Control, (Marcel Dekker Inc., New York, 1985), pp. 79-142.

2. C.M. Good and H.E. Lane Jr., "The Biochemistry of Pyrogens," Bull. Parenter. Drug Assoc. 31, 116-120 (1977).

3. J. Levin and F.B. Bang, "The Role of Endotoxin in the Extracellular Coagulation of Limulus Blood," Bull. Johns Hopkins Hosp. 115, 265-274 (1964).

4. J.F. Cooper, J. Levin, and H.N. Wagner Jr., "Quantitative Comparison of In Vitro and In Vivo Methods for the Detection of Endotoxin," J. Lab. Clin. Med. 78, 138-148 (1971).

5. F.C. Pearson and M. Weary, "The Significance of Limulus Amebocyte Lysate Test Specificity on the Pyrogen Evaluation of Parenteral Drugs," J. Parenter. Drug Assoc. 34, 103-108 (1980).

6. F.B. Bang, "A Bacterial Disease of Limulus polyphemus," Bull. Johns Hopkins Hosp. 98, 325-351 (1956).

7. Federal Register 42, 57749 (November 4, 1977).

8. H.J. Ronneberger, "Comparison of the Pyrogen Tests in Rabbits and with the Limulus Lysate," Dev. Biol. Stand. 34, 27-32 (1977).

9. G. Nyerges and S. Jaszovszky, "Reliability of the Rabbit Pyrogen Test and of Limulus Test in Predicting the Pyrogenicity of Vaccines in Man," Acta. Micro. Acad. Sci. Hung. 28, 235-243 (1981).

10. R. Nandan and D.R. Brown, "An Improved In Vitro Pyrogen Test: To Detect Picograms of Endotoxin Contamination in Intravenous Fluids Using Limulus Amebocyte Lysate," J. Lab. Clin. Med. 89, 910-918 (1977).

11. P.A. Martin and K. Tsuji, "Automation of Bacterial Endotoxin Testing with a Zymate Laboratory Automation System," in Advances in Laboratory Automation Robotics, G.L. Hawk and J.R. Strimaitis, eds. (Zymark Corporation Hopkinton, MA, 1984), pp. 219-236.

12. S. Borman, "Analytical Biotechnology of Recombinant Products," Anal. Chem. 59 (15), 969A-973A (1987).

Protropin is a registered trademark of Genentech, Inc.

THE APPLICATION OF ROBOTICS TO REACTIVE CHEMICALS HAZARD EVALUATION PROGRAM

M.R. White and G.V. Bettoney
Dow Chemical Company
Bldg. 1217
Freeport, TX 77541

ABSTRACT

Production of thermochemical data for hazard evaluation can be a tedious and time-consuming task. This is especially true in a laboratory that practices a reaction screening strategy where repetition increases tedium for the analysts.

To reduce the monotony of this exacting task, we have recently combined robotics with differential scanning calorimetry (DSC) to perform reactivity screening analyses. A Zymate I Robot was programmed to operate a Mettler TA3000 thermal analyzer system with a DSC oven. The robot performs steps that include manipulating oven lids, weighing and positioning glass ampoule samples, and entering sample information into the Mettler's TC10A processor. The system can run unattended for long periods of time and has proven quite reliable. As currently configured, the robot could accommodate, with some reprogramming, a second DSC or other analysis.

The benefits of this automation include freedom of the analyst for other tasks, potential increased sample throughput, and the ability to use longer but more accurate analysis methods.

INTRODUCTION

With the heightened awareness of society concerning safety issues, it is imperative that producers of commercial quantities of chemicals understand the reactivity of their materials. More importantly, such producers must have active programs to investigate the reactions which could occur under plant upset conditions or other unusual events. The Dow Chemical Company has had such a program for more than twenty years This program is known as the Reactive Chemicals Program, and is part of our overall Safety and Loss Prevention approach.

The Dow Reactive Chemicals Program requires participation by all production, research, and technical support functions. These units must also undergo periodic scrutiny, particularly when an operational change is being considered. In support of these requirements, many sites have established Reactive Chemicals Testing Facilities. The Texas Operations Reactive Chemicals Testing Team provides a thermal testing service for the largest chemical production facility within the company. This necessitates the analysis of several thousand samples each year.

Until recently, we utilized Differential Thermal Analysis (DTA) as our primary reactivity screening tool in Texas. However, the demand for more quantitative information led us to consider changing to Differential Scanning Calorimetry (DSC). Such a change would require considerably more analysis time than previously for several reasons. The rate of heating in a DSC is usually slower than for a DTA, often by a factor of two or more. In our case, reheating the samples in a DSC would be more meaningful, but this adds a factor of two to the time demand. Before we could implement this time-intensive effort, we needed to consider how we would automate our screening analyses.

One obvious possibility was to purchase an automated DSC. The difficulty here in our opinion was the state of the art in DSC, relative to our requirements. Since we handle many different chemicals in a variety of forms, we decided that we needed to use glass sample enclosures. We also liked the concept of a general-purpose robot, which would allow us the flexibility to do a variety of DSC-related tasks, or eventually to reassign the robot to other analyses. There were no systems utilizing a general-purpose, reprogrammable robot and a DSC on the market at the time we made our evaluations.

DESCRIPTION OF SYSTEM

The primary consideration for our screening analysis system involved the type and ability of data we regarded as necessary for making safety-related decisions. After a rather thorough survey of the market, we chose a Mettler TA-3000 Thermal Analysis System, comprised of a TA-10 Microprocessor, a TA-20 DSC oven, a dot-matrix graphics printer, and an IBM Personal Computer (PC/XT) for data storage and eventual archival. This system has demonstrated satisfactory analytical sensitivity and flexibility with very good reliability.

After choosing the DSC, we looked for a general-purpose robot that would meet our needs. In early 1985, the most attractive alternative was the Zymate I Robot, with a specially-designed hand for manipulating the small DSC ampoules. This unit was purchased in late 1985, and the task of programming the robot began in early 1986. As of this writing we have not upgraded the original robot, so the system is just as delivered, including a standard controller and a serial printer.

The robot hand serves three purposes: Lifting and placing sample ampoules, removing and replacing the DSC oven lids, and entering information into the Mettler microprocessor through the keyboard. The first two of these operations require the greatest precision and accuracy because of the size of the manipulated parts and the need to place the sample on the thermal sensor in reproducible fashion. The sample grip is a machined Teflon^{tm} piece which fits snugly into the DSC oven and has two holes drilled into it. One hole is inactive, being designed to fit over the reference ampoule which remains in the oven. The samples are picked up using slight vacuum and are released using air pressure supplied by an aquarium pump.

The remaining major components of the whole system are an electronic balance and the sample racks. The balance performs a checking function which confirms that a sample has been properly lifted, and that no leakage occurred during the analysis. The sample racks can hold up to twenty samples, a sequence that could take up to sixty hours to complete.

A sketch of the overall robot workstation area is included in Figure 1.

Steps in an Analysis

The analysis system is initially found in a resting mode, with the DSC oven closed and cool. After the samples have been sealed and weighed, the required sample information (weight, sample identification number, position on the racks, method number to be used) is given to the robot controller. A short input routine was written to accomplish this rapidly and also allow the analyst to check and easily correct this list. The samples are then placed on the racks and the analysis sequence started.

The first steps taken by the robot are to remove both lids from the DSC oven and place them on a stand. Next a sample is chosen from the rack and moved to the balance. Once assured that a sample is picked up, the robot moves to the oven and inserts the sample into it. The lids are replaced on the oven at this point, and the robot turns the hand

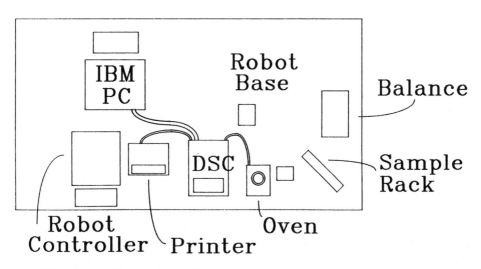

FIGURE 1. Robot Workstation for DSC Analyses.

over to retrieve the data entry tool. The requisite sample information is then entered through the Mettler keypad, and the DSC run is started. The robot returns to a rest position at this point until the oven is once again cool.

Once a DSC run is complete, the robot opens the oven, picks up the sample and weighs it again. If a significant weight change is detected, the test sequence is aborted at this point. Other conditions which will cause a termination of the analysis series include not detecting a sample at first weighing (missing sample or improperly lifted sample) and not detecting a sample after an attempted retrieval at the end of a DSC analysis (possible exploded sample).

Performance of the System

Since the complete screening analysis system became operational in midyear 1986, we have used it to run more than half of our screening samples. The utilization of hours outside of the normal working day allows us to readily meet our throughput demands. Although we have not performed a complete statistical analysis of the reproducibility parameters of the equipment, preliminary indications are that the position precision is more than adequate. The reliability of the whole system has been quite high, with very few outages or aborted runs. Power failure and exploded sample ampoules figure highly in the aborted runs. There are also other causes (DSC oven fan failure, vacuum loss) which have reduced the reliability slightly, but these are also not the fault of the robot. Indeed we have had only one outage which could be directly attributed to the robot in a year of operation.

CONCLUSIONS

We have demonstrated the utility of a general-purpose robot for automating a Differential Scanning Calorimeter. This combined analytical system has high reliability and throughput, allowing more thorough analysis of the reactivity of complex chemical systems without additional manpower. Although some features of the system are not optimal, our satisfaction with this automation methodology is such that no upgrades are currently under consideration.

ROBOTICS FOR THE AUTOMATION OF HPLC AND SPECTROPHOTOMETRIC PROCEDURES FOR AN ON-SITE CHEMICAL TESTING LABORATORY

Wayne A. Bates and John O. Young
Eastman Kodak Company
Chemicals Quality Services Division
Kodak Park
Rochester, New York 14650

ABSTRACT

A Zymate Laboratory Automation System has been implemented for the analysis of electrographic materials for a manufacturing quality services laboratory. The system integrates a Zymate I Robot with an IBM PC/XT^{tm}, interfacing the analyses from both an HPLC and spectrophotometer. The sample conditioning and introduction to the appropriate HPLC column/solvent set or the spectrophotometer is totally automated. The top level control of the system is accomplished through the IBM PC/XT, using various BASIC programs and a Nelson Analytical software package. Other functions supported by the IBM PC/XT are directing operational information to the robot, interpreting absorbance readings via a BCD port from the spectrophotometer, providing sample information to the Nelson Analytical software package, merging analysis reports, and performing sample management tasks. In addition, considering that this system was designed for production support, several factors had to be addressed. These include reliability, analysis speed, capability to perform multiple procedures, and adaptability to changing production priorities. These topics will be discussed, along with hardware/software designs and gains realized in quality and productivity areas.

INTRODUCTION

The use of laboratory robotics has been an effective way to increase the efficiency, productivity, and quality of analytical measurements. Our goal was to develop an automated analytical work cell for service in a manufacturing environment. For this application, HPLC and spectrophotometric procedures were merged into one automated method for the composition analysis of electrographic toner materials. As an on-site chemical testing laboratory, the robotic system required specific design considerations to address various attributes inherent in a production environment. These include high sample volumes, turnaround times of only a few hours, and around-the-clock service. Therefore, system requirements included high throughputs, minimal equipment down times and adequate backup capabilities. In addition, the system also needed to be flexible, adjusting smoothly to changes in production priorities, and meet the analytical needs of various material types. This paper describes the successful application of a Zymark Laboratory Automation System and the gains realized from it.

EXPERIMENTAL

Hardware

The IBM PC/XT with the Omega 10 + 10 Bernoulli box is used as the primary controller and communications link for the overall system (see Figure 1). The Zymate System currently being utilized includes a centrifuge, two Master Laboratory Stations (MLS), balance and computer interfaces, two Power and Event Controllers (PEC), a general-purpose hand, and a capping station (see Figure 2). Supporting the HPLC analysis is a 510 Waters pump and a Kratos 783 UV detector, which are both controlled through the PEC. The Rheodyne model 7066 tandem column selector and model 7126 HPLC injector are coupled and controlled pneumatically through the PEC. Solvent switching is accomplished by utilizing an Autochrom solvent selector, which is also controlled through the PEC. The HPLC integrator is initialized by a contact closer in the HPLC injector valve. The

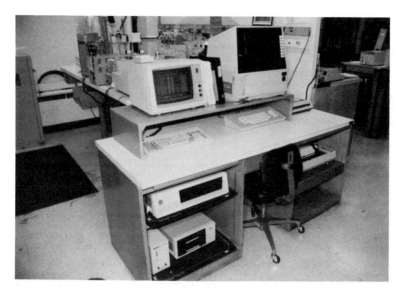

FIGURE 1. Control Center for Zymate System

FIGURE 2. Bench Layout for On-Site Chemical Testing Laboratory.

spectrophotometric method utilizes a Coleman (Perkin-Elmer) model 55 spectrophotometer. The absorbance readings from the BCD port are directed to the IBM PC/XT through a 24 bit parallel I/O interface card (model PIO012, Metrabyte Corp). A Cheminert R6000 low pressure injection valve has been adapted to obtain fixed aliquots for dilutions in the spectrophotometric method. A Mettler AE163 balance is used to obtain sample weights and Scan-O-Matic sensors and amplifiers were purchased as confirmation devices throughout the robotic work cell. Table 1 summarizes the equipment and software used in this system.

Software

A BASIC program is used to receive and direct information to the robot controller, spectrophotometer and the Nelson Analytical system. Samples are logged into the BASIC program and the analysis information is assembled (see Figure 3). The sample information is then sent to the robot controller and the analysis is started. If the sample requires an HPLC analysis, the appropriate column/solvent set is selected. The Nelson Analytical integration parameters are set by over-writing sequence files with information acquired from the sample login table and procedure. The ability to move automatically from the BASIC program to the Nelson software is accomplished by writing macros, using the Superkey software by Borland International. When the spectrophotometric procedure is in progress, the robot controller sends the sample weight and signals when to interpret the absorbance value from the spectrophotometer. For sample management purposes, the BASIC program also keeps track of the sample count by charge number (Figures 4 and 5).

Sample Preparation

Samples are manually loaded into preweighed test tubes. The corresponding identification numbers and analyses to be performed are logged into the IBM PC/XT computer. When initialized, the robot prompts the transfer of these files to an array. The sample tube

TABLE 1. Equipment and Software List

Zymark Corporation (Hopkinton,MA): Robotic Equipment

Mettler Instrument AG, (Greifensee, Switzerland): AE 163 Electronic Balance with Data Interface

International Business Machines Corporation (Boca Raton, FL): IBM PC/XT

IOMEGA Corporation (Roy, UT): Bernoulli Box

Millipore Corporation Waters Chromatography Division (Milford,MA): Waters 510 HPLC Pump

Rheodyne Inc. (Cotati, CA): 7126 HPLC Injecter Valve and 7066 Tandem Column Selector

Kratos Analytical A Division of Spectros (Ramsey, NJ): 783 HPLC Detector

Perkin-Elmer Corporation (Norwalk, CT): Coleman Digital Spectrophotometer

Laboratory Data Control, A Division of Milton Roy Company (Riviera Beach, FL): Cheminert R6000 Low Pressure Injector Valve

Hamilton (Reno, NV): Hamilton Valve Switchers and HV Valves

Skan-O-Matic (Elbridge, NY): Sensors and Amplifiers

Autochrom Incorporated (Milford,MA): 101-CM Solvent Selector

Nelson Analytical (Cupertino, CA): 3000K Software and 762SB Interface Box

Borland International Inc. (Scotts Valley, CA): Superkey Software Package

#	Method	I.D.	Charge	Operator	Comments	Contl.
1	Spec	Sample #1	$$$$$$$$$	Wayne Bates	Product Sample	N
2	Spec	Sample #2	$$$$$$$$$	Wayne Bates	Check Sample	Y
3	HPLC #1	Sample #3	$$$$$$$$$	Wayne Bates	Check Sample	Y
4	HPLC #2	Sample #4	$$$$$$$$$	Wayne Bates	Product Sample	N
5	HPLC #3	Sample #5	$$$$$$$$$	Wayne Bates	Product Sample	N

Sample Login Screen

Figure 3. Sample Login Screen.

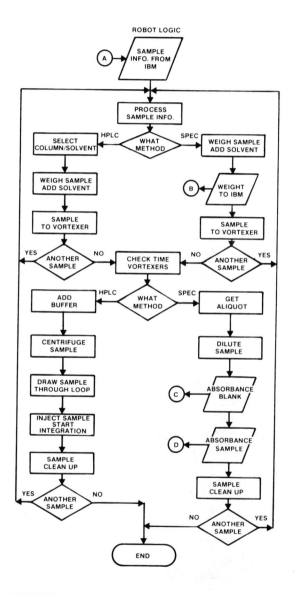

FIGURE 4. EasyLab Logic Flow Diagram.

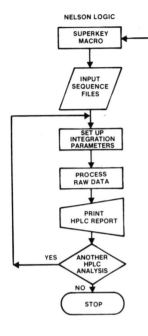

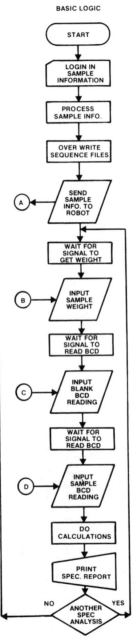

FIGURE 5. Basic Logic Flow Diagram.

is then taken from the rack and weighed, and the appropriate amount of solvent is added. After capping, the sample tube is placed in an available vortexer for mixing. The EasyLab^{tm} program then identifies the vortexer for method type, determines whether another analysis can be started and monitors agitation times. After agitation, the program then determines the method of analysis to be performed.

Spectrophotometric Procedure

For the spectrophotometric analysis, the sample tube is uncapped and an aliquot taken through a fixed-loop, low pressure injection valve. The original sample tube is discarded and a clean tube is positioned at the low pressure injector. The sample, along with the appropriate amount of diluting solvent, is dispensed into the clean tube and positioned under a draw needle. The diluted sample is then drawn through the spectrophotometer flow cell, via the MLS, and the absorbance reading is interpreted by the IBM PC/XT. The computer assembles the data and sends the calculated results to a printer. Upon completion of the analysis, the flow cell is flushed and the tube is discarded. The EasyLab program then checks whether another sample is waiting to be analyzed or if an analysis is already in progress.

HPLC Procedure

The HPLC procedure requires the addition of a buffer solution prior to centrifuging. After centrifuging, the sample is uncapped and positioned at the draw needle. The supernatant is then drawn through the HPLC injection loop, via the MLS. The Rheodyne injector valve is pneumatically turned and the Nelson Analytical integrator is activated. When the analysis is completed, the report is assembled, formatted by the Nelson Analytical software, and sent to the printer. The sample tube is then discarded while the EasyLab program continues its checking for additional analysis needs.

DISCUSSION & RESULTS

The success of this system has been primarily due to its reliability, analytical precision gains, and flexibility. As discussed earlier, these were necessary criteria to be met for implementation into a production environment. Although the ideal system has not been achieved, significant gains towards this goal have been realized. In particular, we have made improvements in the system's reliability through minimizing mechanical interactions and modifying or upgrading work stations. These changes include replacing the MLS valves with Hamilton drivers and Hamilton HV valves, elimination of hand switching, substituting a fixed-loop injector for the syringe hand, and utilizing the spectrophotometer BCD port as opposed to the A/D converter on the PEC.

This system, by design, requires a considerable amount of maintenance due to the variety of equipment integrated together. For the first few months, we identified trouble areas and established a preventive maintenance schedule. After the maintenance schedule was set and training completed, the system has been operating close to 90% efficiency (Figure 6). The maintenance schedule is documented an Equipment Performance Procedures Manual, and the lab staff performs most of these routine maintenance tasks.

In addition to reliability, the analysis turnaround time requirements for production have also been achieved. Since the agitation process is the rate limiting step of the procedure, maximizing the use of the vortexers helped us to realize this goal.

Figure 7 compares the precision gains through automating the spectrophotometric method using Shewhart Control Charts. Hypothesis testing was used to crossover the manual and automated analysis, using the procedure for correlated pairs. At the 95% confidence level and n=25, we found that there was no statistical difference between the two methods.

HOW OFTEN IS THE SYSTEM READY TO RUN?

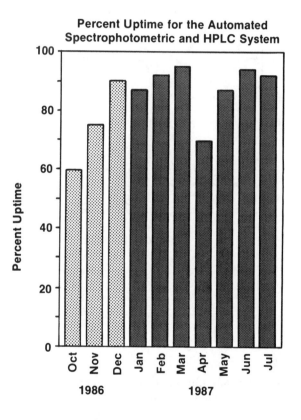

FIGURE 6. Percent Uptime for the Automated Spectrophotometric and HPLC System.

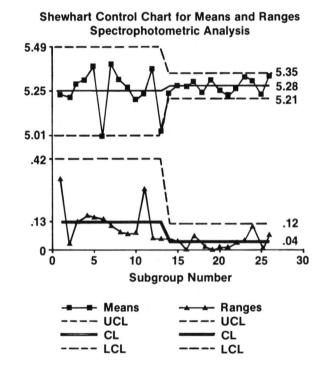

FIGURE 7. Control Chart of Spectrophotometric Analysis.

The HPLC analysis is less operator dependent and no significant gains in precision were found.

An additional gain for the area is in the quality of work life for the technicians. This has been greatly improved through less solvent exposure, more time available to perform development work and the elimination of tedious and labor intensive methods.

CONCLUSIONS

The robotics system has been in operation since July 1986. In general, it has proven to be a reliable and cost saving tool. As a direct result, we have been able to more effectively utilize our staff as well as reduce the overall cost of supplies for the analysis. The sample preparation and column switching capabilities will also allow the system to grow to support future analytical needs.

ACKNOWLEDGMENTS

The authors wish to thank the QSO and T&DM managements for their support without whose help this project could not have been accomplished. We also wish to thank the Laboratory Automation Group for their technical support and a special thanks to John Twist for his programming expertise.

IBM PC/XT is a registered trademark of the International Business Machines Corporation.

AN AUTOMATED ANALYTICAL LABORATORY

R. Keith Bergman, Louis R. Lofgreen,
Karla A. Hendrickson and David R. Koecher
Hercules Aerospace
PO Box 98, MS X3B1
Magna, UT 84044

ABSTRACT

An automated analytical laboratory for performing quality control (QC) analyses on rocket propellant is described. The facility includes three robotic work stations designed around the Perkin-Elmer Masterlab^{tm} system, a custom built automated strand burner, and a Perkin-Elmer 3203 minicomputer. The purpose of this paper is to discuss the integration of the various components to create a fully computerized, automated laboratory.

There are four work stations:

    A. Percent total solids by gravimetry and viscosity by Brookfield viscometry.
    B. Percent binder by IR spectroscopy, percent moisture by Karl Fischer titration.
    C. Method development.
    D. Burn rate, by acoustic emission strand burner.

A, B, and C comprise the robotic work stations; D is computer operated, but no robot has yet been incorporated.

The first two analyses identified above, along with the burn rate test, are required for QC; the moisture and viscosity analyses are for manufacturing information only.

The arrangement of the work stations was determined by the type of operations being performed, and by physical considerations. Each work station has its own controller (an IBM PC/XT)[tm], making the robots independent. However, they are all linked into the 3203 which is running LIMS 2000 software for data management.

When a sample arrives at the laboratory, its identification is logged into the 3203. The sample is then placed into special dispensers at each work station, and the robots are signalled to begin. After the tests are completed, the data and results are transmitted to the 3203 and compiled into a single report. This information is stored in the laboratory data base. A copy of the report is also transmitted to the central plant computer system for QC Department sign off.

The use of robotics to perform these routine analyses reduces labor costs and improves safety; the number of technicians required on a shift is reduced by 60%. Data is reported in a timely manner.

INTRODUCTION

Implementation of automated work stations is generally done in laboratories where they are intended to replace manual operations. This laboratory, however, was designed around automation with the intention that few manual operations would be performed. The thrust behind automating this lab was time and safety. A new manufacturing facility has been built which is capable of casting very large rocket motors. The large size of these motors makes it desirable to have a minimum of personnel present. Therefore, the entire facility makes use of state-of-the-art automation. An additional benefit is the inherent cost reduction obtained with automation.

Some of the propellant formulations which may be used in these motors have short pot lives, so analyses must be performed quickly and accurately. Real time data is required for quality acceptance. Because too much time would be required to deliver samples to the original analytical lab, a new laboratory was established at the manufacturing site. The purpose of this laboratory is to perform routine quality control (QC) analyses on uncured rocket propellants.

DESCRIPTION

There are three work stations for performing routine QC analyses. Two are built around Perkin-Elmer MasterLab robots with IBM PC/XTs as system controllers; the third work station also uses an IBM PC/XT, but there is no robot at this time. A third MasterLab robot is available for development work.

Along with the work stations, there is a LIMS system running on a Concurrent Computing (a Perkin-Elmer subsidiary) 3203 minicomputer. This machine is based on the Motorola 68000 CPU and runs Perkin-Elmer's LIMS 2000 software. The 3203 has two terminals, a printer, and three IBM PC/XTs connected to it, as well as a modem for communication with a VAX 11/750.

To ensure reliable operation, power to the robot work stations and the 3203 is provided via an Un-Interruptable Power Supply (UPS) with generator backup. Here is a brief description of the work performed at each station:

> The first work station tests per cent total solids by gravimetry[1] and initial
> viscosity by Brookfield viscometry. The second station determines percent
> binder by IR spectroscopy[1] and percent moisture by Karl Fischer titration.
> The third work station is a custom built automated strand burner which
> performs burn rate tests.

EXPERIMENTAL

Uncured solid propellant consists of oxidizers and fuels mixed with some type of liquid binding agent. In this state it is a thick slurry, reminiscent of peanut butter with sand mixed in it. Samples are delivered to the lab in various containers, according to the test which is to be performed. For the robot work stations, the propellant comes in 20 cc syringes; for the viscosity test, it is in a 600 mL plastic beaker; for the burn rate analysis, it is in a plastic Semco tube about 7 inches long and 1.5 inches in diameter.

After a sample is delivered to the laboratory, it is logged into the LIMS data base. The operator then places the syringes in special dispensers which extrude the material from the syringe at the robot's signal. The beaker is placed in a conditioning bath, and the Semco tube is put in a device which will force the propellant into straws similar to those served with soft drinks. After the samples are placed, the robots are started. While they are performing their tasks, the technician prepares the burn rate samples and performs that analysis.

When the robots have finished their analyses and calculated the results, the reduced data is written to an ASCII file. The robot then automatically logs onto the 3203 and initiates a transfer of the data file. LIMS utilities read the file, pull out the data, and place it in the proper fields associated with the sample. The burn rate data is transferred in much the same manner. After all the data for a sample has been received, the operator triggers a utility in the LIMS system which creates a report file containing it. This file is then transferred via modem to the VAX, where a QC engineer examines the data and approves the propellant for further use in the manufacturing process.

DISCUSSION

The connection between the 3203 and a PC is RS-232C. A LIMS communication program called LIMSCOMM, in conjunction with a group of communications modules which run on PC, eases the task of sending files. To establish a connection, the serial port on the PC must first be initialized with the MODE command. The command is:

    MODE COM1:9600,N,8,1

(for a connection on serial port 1 at 9600 baud with no parity, eight data bits, and one stop bit). At the DOS prompt, typing TOLIMS establishes the connection after which you are prompted to log on. By including various parameters after TOLIMS, logging on and transferring a file can occur automatically.

Perkin-Elmer Robot Language (PERL[tm]) supports a DOS shell, allowing MS-DOS programs to be run from within robot programs. Putting the following line in a PERL program will cause an automatic file transfer:

Dos Tolims /a ROBTA,75,STARWARS,ENV=NULL datafile limsfile

where "datafile" is the file name on the PC, and "limsfile" is the file name to be used on the 3203. The "/a" tells LIMS that some action is to be performed on the file, and the sequence "ROBTA,75,STARWARS,ENV=NULL" is the ID, acct num, and password of the robot. After the file transfer is complete, the PC is logged off and the PERL program continues.

Creation of a data file is performed by the "write" statement in PERL. The syntax for this command is:

write (var) to (filename)

This statement automatically opens the file and appends data to it until it is closed. More information can be added later with the "append" command. By using a series of "write" statements, a file may be built containing description information, sample identification, test identification, and data. Appendix A shows a sample program for creating a data file, and the file which is created. It should be noted that files created with this command are ASCII files.

In order for LIMS to successfully interpret the data file, two types of "forms" must be filled out. These are called the File Template and the Result Template. The File Template tells LIMS where the Test and Sample identifiers are in the file. A File Template is created for each type of file name extension. The Result Template tells LIMS where in the file the data is located. This template can be set up to look for a keyword (or words) which identifies the data. For example, if the file contains the line "MOISTURE = 2.36", the data parser can be set to look for the word "MOISTURE", then go over to the column where the data begins to read the value. One template is created for each type of data in a file.

As the data are received, they are placed in the database under the correct sample ID. After all data are stored, the file is marked complete and another utility is run to create a disk file containing the data. This file (also an ASCII file) exists outside the database, and may then be transferred to the VAX system. The file is read by a QC engineer who gives the go ahead for using the mix if it meets the specified requirements.

CONCLUSION

This automated laboratory provides reliable data within the time constraints of the manufacturing process, while maintaining a high level of safety. By using robotics, the number of required personnel is reduced by 60% on each shift. Linking the PCs to the 3203 allows data to be transferred reliably, without the threat of transcription errors. Performing these transfers automatically ensures that the data will be reported as quickly as possible.

REFERENCES

1. L. R. Lofgreen, R. K. Bergman, K. A. Hendrickson, "Application of Robotics for the Routine Determination of Percent Solids and Binder in Uncured Rocket Propellant", in Advances in Laboratory Automation-Robotics, Vol. 3, J. R. Strimaitis and G. L. Hawk, ed. (Zymark Corp., Hopkinton, MA, 1987), pp. 407-412.

APPENDIX A - EXAMPLE PROGRAM AND DATA FILE[*]

```
procedure LIMSCOMM
rem - this is an example program which automatically creates and
rem - transmits a data file to the LIMS 3203
clear               !clear screen
pad$ = "         "    !rqd so LIMS doesn't grab LF char by mistake
hdr1$ = "Test PC to LIMS Transmission File"
hdr2$ = "Test Id = TESTNAME"+pad$
d0$ = "SAMPLEID"+pad$
ts = 82.34      !total solids value
vs = 345.8      !viscosity value
ts$ = "AVG. TS = "+str$(ts)  !convert to string and add
vs$ = "VISCOS = "+str$(vs)  ! an indentifier
d1$ = ts$+pad$  !concatenate with pad
d2$ = vs$+pad$
write hdr1$ to "PCTEST.DAT"  !write data to file
write hdr2$ to "PCTEST.DAT"
write d0$ to "PCTEST.DAT"
write d1$ to "PCTEST.DAT"
write d2$ to "PCTEST.DAT"
close "PCTEST.DAT"          !close file, next line xmits
dos tolims /a ROBTA,75,STARWARS,ENV=N PCTEST.DAT LIMS.DAT
end procedure
```

This is what the file would look like:

```
Test PC to LIMS Transmission File
Test Id = TESTNAME
SAMPLEID
AVG. TS = 82.34
VISCOS = 345.8
```

*Source - Art Ambrose, Perkin-Elmer Corp.

THE DEVELOPMENT OF ROBOTICS FOR THE DETERMINATION OF ACTINIDE AND LANTHANIDE DISTRIBUTION RATIOS

H. L. Nekimken, B. F. Smith, E. J. Peterson, R. M. Hollen,
T. H. Erkkila and T. J. Beugelsdijk
Los Alamos National Laboratory
Los Alamos, NM 87545

ABSTRACT

A Zymate[tm] II PyTechnology robotic system was acquired to automate solvent extraction experiments. The system is designed to make the appropriate solutions, pre-equilibrate the liquid phases, perform the desired extraction, and detect and quantitate the metal ions in each phase. The solution preparation operations include weighing the solutes on a balance, adding the solvent, and mixing the resulting solution. Aqueous solution pH adjustment is automatically made by the robot. Extraction solutions are pre-equilibrated by mixing with the appropriate solutions and separating the phases. Aliquots of pre-equilibrated phases are dispensed into Teflon[tm] centrifuge tubes; the tubes are capped, mixed using a linear shaker, and centrifuged for phase separation. A sample of each phase is analyzed automatically with separate automated detectors (i.e., ICP) or with an on-line detection system. Advanced capabilities are under development for the robot. An IBM PC/XT is interfaced to the robot's controller so that data can be automatically obtained, tabulated, and plotted, and with the use of chemometrics computer programs and expert system software, decision making on experimental design will be possible.

In a precision and accuracy study, the robotics system performed well. Pipetting was very accurate and precise, with relative standard deviations (RSDs) of 0.17% and 0.31% and accuracies within 1% and 4% with water and toluene, respectively. However, aspirating and dispensing sample aliquots yielded poorer precision and accuracy than pipetting with

0.58% and 1.29% RSD with water and toluene, respectively. Back pressure from nitrogen gas allowed only 85% (water) and 72% (toluene) of the target volume to be obtained. The measurement of pH was very accurate and precise with an accuracy within 1% and an RSD of 0.09%. The sipper station with spectrophotometry detection was precise with 0.53% RSD (for the aqueous phase). Precision for weighing on a three-decimal place, open-top loading balance was 0.96% RSD and the accuracy was within 4% but was consistently low. The overall extraction procedure yielded a 7.37% RSD which is considered to be acceptable.

INTRODUCTION

Effective ways of performing various actinide (An) and lanthanide (Ln) separations are being researched at Los Alamos National Laboratory. Liquid/liquid extraction is one technique used for separating metal ions on an analytical or process scale. Organic extractants (ligands) are evaluated for their ability to complex and solubilize Ln and An metal ions under a variety of conditions. To effectively evaluate new extractants and correlate structural features with extraction capabilities, many liquid/liquid metal distribution ratios (D) must be determined as a function of such variables as ligand and metal ion concentrations, pH, acid type, and organic solvent. Information about the composition of the extracted species is commonly obtained from slope analysis.[1] Because of the labor intensive nature of obtaining the large amount of D data necessary to fully evaluate a new ligand system, a laboratory robotics system has been developed for the automatic acquisition of this data.

Laboratory robotics is generally used to automate sample preparation procedures,[2] occasionally performing solvent extractions automatically.[3,4] The laboratory robotic system described in this manuscript is designed to acquire data for the Actinide Separations and Coordination Chemistry research program at Los Alamos National Laboratory. Because this robotic system is designed for research experiments, it should be flexible. The system can perform several tasks including preparation and pre-equilibration of the extraction solutions, solvent extraction, phase separation, and metal quantitation. Advanced capabilities, including automatically acquiring, tabulating, and plotting data and decision making on experimental design are being developed for the robot (using an IBM PC/XT interfaced to the robot controller). A precision and accuracy study of the robotic extraction procedure is included in the discussion.

EXPERIMENTAL

System Configuration

A modified Zymate II PyTechnology robotic system is used to perform solvent extractions. Figure 1 shows a schematic diagram of the present hardware configuration for this system. The robot arm is located in the center of a circle mounted to a bench top with a locator plate numbered 1 through 48 and is surrounded by various working stations. The prewritten software and address for each working station are easily loaded into the Zymate II Controller, enabling these stations to be rapidly moved from one location to another.

This robotic system presently includes three racks: Rack 1 holds 150-mL fleakers that contain the initial extraction solutions and the wash solutions (ethanol and water) for the sipper station; Rack 2 holds empty 10-mL Teflon centrifuge tubes (with screw caps) with which all solvent extractions are performed; and Rack 3 holds empty 13x98 mm polypropylene test tubes, used to store aliquots of each solution phase before analysis. For future applications, three additional racks are available (additional centrifuge tube and fleaker racks and a scintillation tube rack). Two hands are required to handle these vessels, Hand C to carry the fleakers and Hand E to carry the centrifuge and test tubes. A pipet hand is required to dispense aliquots of each solution phase into a centrifuge tube.

The screw capper caps and uncaps the centrifuge tubes, and the linear shaker and centrifuge are used to mix and separate the two immiscible phases, respectively. Aliquots of each phase are obtained with the liquid/liquid extraction station. The pH station (with

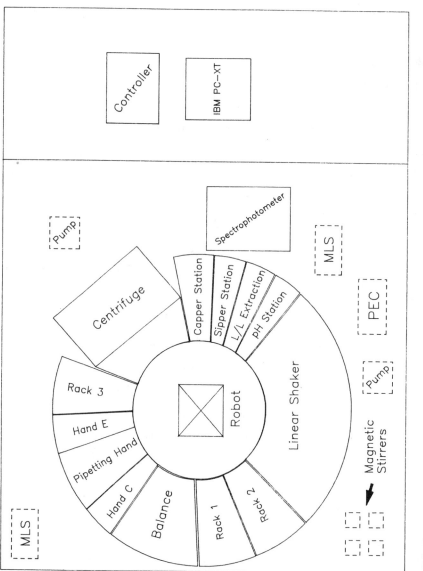

FIGURE 1. A Schematic Diagram of the Hardware Configuration for the PyTechnology, Solvent Extraction Robotics System. Dotted line denotes equipment located beneath the lab bench.

an Orion semimicro combination pH electrode) is available to determine the pH of the aqueous phase following the extraction and to adjust the pH of an aqueous solution (as described later in this manuscript. A metal ion determination for each solution phase is initiated by aspirating an aliquot of each solution with the sipper station. A Hewlett-Packard (Model 8452) diode array spectrophotometer (with an 80-mL flow cell) is used for the metal detection of each solution phase. Spectra are acquired and stored by an external computer (IBM PC/XT) interfaced to the robot controller. A PM-400 Mettler top-loading balance, capable of weighing fleakers, is not required for the solvent extraction; however, it will be utilized in making the extraction solutions (as described later in this manuscript). Other equipment located below the bench top (denoted by dotted lines in Figure 1) includes two master laboratory stations (MLS) for dispensing solution and aspirating aliquots of the two immiscible phases, one power and event controller (PEC) to control the various switches and inputs, two ISCO (TRIS) peristaltic pumps to aspirate samples at the sipper station and to provide water to wash the pH probe, and four Troemner magnetic stirrers (Model 700) for solution mixing as discussed later in this manuscript.

Procedure

Before the robotic system could be used, a few hardware adjustments and some software reprogramming of the PyTechnology system purchased from Zymark Corporation were required to accommodate different vessels (10-mL Teflon instead of 15-mL polypropylene centrifuge tube and 150-mL instead of 300-mL fleaker). When this task was completed, an application program was written to perform solvent extractions.

A 10-mL centrifuge tube is first uncapped and returned to Rack 2. The pipet hand (which uses a 1.0-mL syringe) is used to pipet 2 mL of the aqueous solution and 2 mL of the organic solution from the appropriate fleakers into a 10-mL centrifuge tube. This tube is then recapped and placed on the linear shaker. The solution is shaken for 30 min and then centrifuged for 5 min. Following centrifugation, a 1-mL aliquot of the top, organic (toluene) layer is aspirated into the liquid/liquid extraction station's holding loop. This solution is then dispensed into a clean 13x98 mm test tube. The cannula and holding loop of the extraction station are rinsed with 5 mL of methanol. By actuating a three-way valve located immediately after the extraction station's MLS syringe, 2 psi of nitrogen is blown through the holding loop and cannula for 90 seconds to dry the entire system. A 0.85-mL aliquot of the bottom, aqueous layer is then aspirated. As the cannula proceeds through the remaining volume of the organic layer, the first three-way valve, described above, is again actuated, as well as a second three-way valve located after the nitrogen gas tank regulator, which provides access to 0.1 psi instead of 2 psi nitrogen gas. This slight positive pressure of nitrogen is enough to slowly bubble nitrogen through the solution until the bottom layer comes in contact with the cannula tip, therefore preventing contamination of the aqueous aliquot.

The aqueous sample is transferred from the holding loop to a clean 13x98 mm test tube. The pH of the aqueous phase is measured and the final value is printed on a Thinkjet printer (Hewlett Packard, Palo Alto, CA) The organic phase is aspirated into the spectrophotometer's flow cell by turning on the sipper station's peristaltic pump. After the pump is turned off, a delay time of 45 seconds is executed to ensure that there is no longer any solution flowing through the flow cell. A spectral measurement is obtained upon command from the IBM PC/XT, and this spectrum is assigned a number and stored on the computer's hard disk. The flow cell is then thoroughly rinsed with ethanol. To the aqueous phase, 5.1 mL of arsenazo III is added near the balance with a MLS syringe. The resulting solution is mixed by placing the liquid/liquid extraction station's cannula near the bottom of the test tube and actuating both three-way valves to bubble 0.1 psi of nitrogen throughout the solution. After 45 seconds of bubbling the solution with nitrogen, it is well mixed. This solution is aspirated by the sipper station, and a spectral measurement is obtained as described for the organic solution above.

Precision and accuracy studies were completed by repeating a given process or measurement 10 times (unless otherwise noted) at each PyStation. The pipet hand's precision was the first study completed. Two mL of water were pipetted into 10 separate centrifuge tubes and each tube was weighed manually before and after the liquid was dispensed to determine the exact volume pipetted. The same experiment was repeated with toluene instead of water. For each of 10 centrifuge tubes that contained 2 mL of toluene and 2 mL of water, 1.2-mL aliquots of toluene and water were aspirated and dispensed into 13x98 mm test tubes as described in the procedure above. The extraction station was washed between the acquisition of each organic and aqueous phase aliquot (as described above), and each of the twenty 13x98 mm test tubes in this experiment were weighed manually before and after the liquids were dispensed to determine the exact volume of each aliquot. This experiment was also repeated for target volumes of 1.0, 1.4, and 1.6 mL (for each of these volumes, four measurements were obtained).

To test the precision and accuracy of the pH station measurements, the pH meter was calibrated with pH 4 and 10 buffer solutions before measuring the pH of 10 separate test tubes of a pH 9.0 borate buffer solution. After each measurement, the pH probe was washed with water. The precision of the sipper station and spectrophotometer were evaluated by adding 3 mL of a 1% red dye solution to 3 mL of water in 10 separate 13x98 mm test tubes. Each of these solutions was mixed by bubbling nitrogen throughout the tube and subsequently was sipped into the spectrophotometer's flow cell, where a spectral measurement from 190 to 820 nm was obtained, assigned a number, and stored on the computer's hard disk. The ability of the balance station to weigh 1.0 g of sodium acetate repeatedly was evaluated by pouring the powder from a 13x98 mm tube into a 150-mL fleaker with vibrating hand E, 10 consecutive times.

Finally, the precision of the overall extraction procedure was evaluated by completing 10 separate, yet identical, extractions, one after another, and recording the resulting D values. The extraction of $5x10^{-4}$ M $UO_2(NO_3)_2$ (in a solution of 0.01 M chloroacetate buffer and 0.1 M $LiClO_4$, adjusted to pH 1.5) by 20 mM 4-benzoyl-2,4-dihydro-5-methyl-2-phenyl-3H-pyrazo-3-thione (HBMPPT) and 2 mM trioctylphosphine oxide (TOPO) (in toluene) was studied. Measurements of D have previously been obtained by other methods for the extraction conditions listed above.[5]

RESULTS AND DISCUSSION

Hardware Modifications

The majority of hardware modifications were required because the 10-mL Teflon centrifuge tubes used in this application are significantly smaller than the standard 15-mL centrifuge tubes for which the PySystem was originally designed. The height of the rack for the 10-mL Teflon centrifuge tubes was shortened; an additional Teflon wall was inserted on the linear shaker's rack to hold the centrifuge tubes firmly in place; and rubber stoppers were placed in the centrifuge's tube holders to enable the robot hand to retrieve them. A Teflon guard around the liquid/liquid extraction cannula was installed to prevent any solution from splattering when a wash is in progress. Space limitations around the robot's arm required a 60% reduction in the size of the balance PySection. The fleaker rack was elevated to provide adequate space for magnetic stirrers to be placed beneath the fleakers (as discussed later in this manuscript).

Software Modifications

The smaller Teflon centrifuge tubes required some software reprogramming for all the PyStations involved in the solvent extraction procedure. Similar programming changes were required for all operations involving the 150-mL fleakers because these fleakers are shorter than the standard PySystem 300-mL fleakers, and the height of the fleaker rack also was modified to provide room for magnetic stirrers. Software modifications were required for the liquid/liquid extraction station to provide access to the 0.1 and 2 psi nitrogen lines (controlled by the three-way valves).

Other minor programming changes were required to improve the efficiency for obtaining aliquots of the organic and aqueous phases. To aspirate the organic layer, the centrifuge tube was tipped to access more of this solution phase and to decrease the chances of contamination by the aqueous phase. The dispensing routine was modified so that the organic solutions dispense slowly and the aqueous solutions dispense rapidly and deeper within the test tube, and low-pressure (0.1 psi) nitrogen was programmed to blow through the holding loop and cannula at the end of this routine. These software modifications were incorporated to prevent any droplets from being retained in the holding loop or cannula or from being lost on the sides of the 13x98 mm tube.

Additional software was written for the sipper station to allow aspiration of a sample from a 13x98 mm test tube or a rinse solution from a 150-mL fleaker. The peristaltic pump was programmed to turn on and off before a solution is aspirated to produce an air gap between sample solutions large enough to prevent sample contamination or air bubbles from being trapped in the flow cell. Programming of the IBM PC/XT computer was also required to provide control of the diode array spectrophotometer synchronized with the robot's actions. The majority of the hardware and software modifications made for this robotic system were completed within three months after most of the system was received.

Precision and Accuracy Studies

Table 1 gives a summary of the data acquired for evaluation of the precision and accuracy of the robotic system. The pipetting study showed excellent precision and accuracy, similar to pipetting precision and accuracy reported for other robotics systems.[2,3] The aqueous pipetting was more accurate and precise than the organic pipetting (since the organic solutions tend to stick to the pipet tip more than the aqueous solutions); however, in both cases the RSD was below 0.5% and the accuracy was within 5%.

Aliquots obtained with the extraction station were not as precise or accurate as with the pipet hand. RSDs of 0.58% for the aqueous phase solutions (based on eight measurements) and 1.29% for the organic phase solutions were calculated (again, the organic solutions yielded poorer results than the aqueous solutions). The volumes aliquoted were significantly lower than those actually obtained, which is probably the result of back pressure from the nitrogen present within the holding loop. The actual volume obtained for the aqueous solutions was consistently 85% of the target volume, whereas the volume of organic solution obtained was consistently 72% of the target volume. Using these correction factors, it is possible to deliver the desired volumes.

The pH station was both precise, with an RSD of only 0.09%, and accurate, with an accuracy within 1%. The sipper station study (which included the addition of color reagent) yielded an RSD of about 0.5% (based on nine measurements and calculated from absorbance values at 502 nm) and an accuracy within 10%. The balance station study yielded less than 1% RSD, a good precision considering the balance reads to only three decimal places. The actual weights obtained were always lower than the target weight because the pouring program routine ensures that the target weight is not exceeded. However, this is not a major problem because the exact sample weight is transferred from the balance to the robot controller through the balance interface.

TABLE 1. The Precision and Accuracy of the Robotic System by Station (Based on 10 Measurements).

Station	Chemical	Target Value	Avg.Value	Accuracy (%)	RSD (%)
Pipetting	Water	2.0 ml	2.01 ml	+ 0.5	0.17
Pipetting	Toluene	2.0 ml	2.07 ml	+ 3.5	0.31
L/L Extraction	Water	1.2 ml	1.01 ml[a]	-15.8	0.58
L/L Extraction	Toluene	1.2 ml	0.86 ml[b]	-28.3	1.29
L/L Extraction	Water	1.0 ml	0.84 ml[b]	-16.0	--
L/L Extraction	Toluene	1.0 ml	0.71 ml[b]	-29.0	--
L/L Extraction	Water	1.4 ml	1.20 ml[b]	-14.3	--
L/L Extraction	Toluene	1.4 ml	1.00 ml[b]	-28.6	--
L/L Extraction	Water	1.6 ml	1.35 ml[b]	-15.6	--
L/L Extraction	Toluene	1.6 ml	1.16 ml[b]	-27.5	--
pH	Borate Buffer	9.0	8.92	- 0.9	0.09
Sipper	Red Dye	A=0.8-0.9	A=0.845[c]	<$\pm$7.0	0.53
Balance	Sodium Acetate	1.0 g	0.965 g	- 3.5	0.96
All	UO_2/HBMPPT/ TOPO	D=1.1[d]	D=0.65	--	7.37

[a]Based on eight measurements.

[b]Based on four measurements.

[c]Based on nine measurements.

[d]Based on value from Ref. 5.

The precision of D values for the overall extraction study was 7.4% RSD. Any number below 10% RSD is considered good because there are so many steps during the extraction that contribute to the overall error. A D value 1.7 times as great has been reported previously for this same extraction;[5] however, the difference in these D values are not statistically significant.

FUTURE RESEARCH

Extraction Studies

Validation of the solvent extraction procedure using this laboratory robotic system will be completed before routine use of the system will begin. Additional D data for the UO_2/HBMPPT/TOPO extraction system will be obtained with the robot and compared with corresponding data using other methods.[5] This automated system will be used to evaluate various extraction systems, primarily using radiotracers, where detection can be performed by gamma counting. Gamma counting can be completed by manually transferring samples to a counter, by using the sipper station and a radioactivity flow monitor, or by using a well detector that can be accessed by the robot arm. The determination of how fast an extraction system reaches equilibrium can also be performed with this robotic system with the use of a remote probe. Rate studies will be especially useful when determining the uptake of metals by chelating resins.

Future Capabilities

As a research tool, a robotic system should be flexible, and therefore, this extraction robotic system's capabilities will be expanded. Solution preparation is the initial, time-consuming step in the procedure for determining D values. Solutions can be prepared by the robot in 150-mL fleakers by placing these fleakers on the balance and adding solids (poured from a 13x98 mm test tube) and stock solutions (dispensed from a MLS syringe) by weight. The solvent is added with a MLS syringe or a large volume dispensing station, and the solutions are mixed with magnetic stirrers at the stirrer fleaker rack (Rack 1). Aqueous solutions have their pH adjusted at the pH station by titrating these solutions to the desired pH value. This station has its own magnetic stirrer, pH feedback written into its software package, and access to acid and base solutions from a MLS.

A second, time-consuming feature in the measurement of D values is pre-equilibrating the extraction solutions. Pre-equilibration of the solution phases is necessary for completing certain dynamic processes that do not directly correlate to the actual metal extraction ahead of time and for making interpretation of the actual extraction simpler. Saturating the aqueous phase with the organic solvent and equilibrating the hydrogen ion concentration between the two phases are examples of pre-equilibrating processes. The robot can perform a pre-equilibration by adding the appropriate reagent to the extraction solution (with a MLS syringe or a large volume dispensing station), mixing the two phases with a magnetic stirrer, and then storing the resulting solution in Rack 1 for settling. The pre-equilibrated solution layer may then be transferred to another fleaker with a MLS syringe or a large-volume dispensing station, or in some cases, it may not be necessary to remove the second layer before dispensing the extraction solution into a centrifuge tube.

The capabilities of the robotic system can be improved by effective utilization of the external IBM computer. The IBM PC/XT already automatically stores spectra acquired from the spectrophotometer. This computer can also easily take the raw data generated by the robot and automatically calculate and plot the corresponding D values (using Lotus 1,2,3 or a similar software package). Using chemometrics computer programs to carefully choose the correct experiments to perform should also be possible. Expert system software such as 1st-class can be utilized to make the robotics system more intelligent. The use of artificial intelligence could be employed to solve simpler problems, such as determining if an extraction has reached equilibrium or a solution phase is pre-equilibrated, or more complex problems, such as having the robot make decisions regarding experimental design based on previously acquired data.

SUMMARY AND CONCLUSIONS

In a relatively short time (3 months), a robotic system was developed to perform solvent extractions. The extractions performed by the robotic system are similar to those done manually. The robot is at least as precise and usually as accurate as the manual method. Improvements in the robotic extraction procedure and in the overall system will continue to be made, and the incorporation of the additional features discussed above will make it an even more powerful and flexible tool for evaluating a variety of extraction systems. The ability of the robot to prepare and pre-equilibrate solutions will be invaluable, and as this system becomes more automated, it will be easier for chemists to obtain useful information from the system. Minor hardware modifications and reprogramming PyTechnology software for different applications can be carried out easily. The robot is already capable of performing solvent extractions and should eventually become an all-purpose, powerful laboratory research tool. The robot will save the Laboratory human resource time, effort, and money.

ACKNOWLEDGEMENTS

The authors would like to thank the many contributors to the Laboratory's actinide separation and coordination chemistry program.

REFERENCES

1. T.C. Lo, M.H.I. Baird and C. Hanson, Handbook of Solvent Extraction (Wiley, New York, 1983).

2. G.L. Hawk and J.R. Strimaitis, eds., Advances in Laboratory Automation-Robotics 1986 (Zymark, Hopkinton, MA, 1986).

3. G.F. Plummer, "The Automation of Analytical Methods for the Determination of Drugs in Biological Fluids," in Advances in Laboratory Automation-Robotics 1986, G.L. Hawk and J.R. Strimaitis, eds. (Zymark, Hopkinton, MA, 1986).

4. C. Tillier, H. Allegret and Ph. Devaux, "Application of Robotics in Residue Analysis," in Advances in Laboratory Automation-Robotics 1986, G.L. Hawk and J.R. Strimaitis, eds. (Zymark, Hopkinton, MA, 1986).

5. H.L. Nekimken, B.F. Smith, G.D. Jarvinen, E.J. Peterson and M.M. Jones, "Computer Controlled Flow Injection Analysis for Rapid On-line Determination of Distribution Ratios," submitted to Anal. Chem., August 1987.

TOTAL AUTOMATION OF THE FLEXURAL TESTING OF PLASTICS USING INSTRON'S ROBOT-BASED TEST SYSTEM INTERFACED WITH A PDP 11/84

C. Driscoll, J. DePaolis, J. Azzoli
G. Brenn, and F. Haimbach
Hoechst Celanese Corporation
R. L. Mitchell Technical Center
86 Morris Avenue
Summit, New Jersey 07901

ABSTRACT

A totally automated procedure to perform the flexural testing of plastics has been implemented in our Physical Testing Laboratory. It is based on a system consisting of a Zymate II robot and peripherals, a vertically loaded sample holder, dual micrometers for thickness and width measurements, and the Instron Electromechanical Testing Machine. In addition, a PDP 11/84^{tm} is used not only to control the flex tester and the Zymate, but also to perform a variety of data analysis and storage functions through the use of sophisticated customized software. Our new robotic-based protocol is less labor intensive, consistently exceeds the precision of an experienced operator, exhibts no bias in results, and has been made completely compatible with our pre-existing DEC^{tm} computer.

This paper will describe and compare the flex procedures before and after the introduction of the robot, outline the major changes/additions which were made to the software to make a fully-reliable package, and present experimental data validating this automated approach. Finally, an overall strategy is proposed for automating techniques requiring specialized or custom products.

INTRODUCTION

The Hoechst Celanese Physical Testing Department at the R. L. Mitchell Technical Center in Summit, N.J. evaluates the mechanical properties of a broad spectrum of materials-from single fibers to large molded pieces. The molded samples range in flex modulus from 10,000 to 5,000,000 psi depending on rigidity. Most of the material analyses are performed on standard shaped specimens. The lab has sixteen Instron Electromechanical Testers in addition to a wide variety of other instrumentation. The laboratory group provides mechanical testing services to the Hoechst Celanese Corporation and to the Summit site which houses the Celanese Research Company and Celanese Engineering Resins R&D groups. This location employs approximately 450 technical and support staff. In addition to providing material test information, this Department serves as a technical leader for the Corporation in evaluating new technologies relevant to our lab areas of expertise.

A major part of the Physical Testing Department is the DEC PDP 11/84, interfaces, peripherals (terminals, printers, etc.), and customized software. It is used for controlling the Instron testers and calculating and storing data. The stored information can be accessed for further analysis if desired. All test results are archived on the system regardless of whether they were generated automatically (Instrons) or manually (e.g. Izod Impact Test, ASTM D 256). Several upgrades have occurred since the original purchase and the current version provides the Department with a modern LIMS-type system.

The ASTM D 790 Method,[1] "Flexural Properties of Unreinforced and Reinforced Plastics and Electrical Insulating Materials", is routinely performed by skilled physical testing operators. The test is labor intensive and may take up to 45 minutes to complete a single sample (5 specimens, minimum). The manual procedure is performed as outlined on the following page. The operator loops through these tasks until all specimens in the job have been tested.

- the job is logged in via a utility on the PDP 11/84;

- thickness and width measurements are taken and
   entered into the appropriate file;

- the specimen is placed on the flex fixture;

- the test is performed under the control of the 11/84;

- upon completion, either break or no-break, the stress
   and/or strain data are stored in the database;

- the tested specimen is removed from the fixture.

The stress/strain information in the database can be accessed/extracted via FORTRAN programs or Datatrieve^{tm} procedures. The extracted data can be transferred across the network to a node in the VAXCluster^{tm} for further analysis if desired. A typical example would be to graphically display the data for inclusion in a report or paper.

DEFINITION OF THE SYSTEM

Justification and Evaluation

There are several attractive benefits to be gained through the introduction of a laboratory robot into this environment. These are broadly categorized as economic, service, and technical. First among these advantages (indicated in bold) is the placing of the company in **a more competitive position.** Thus, test results for either research or quality control can be obtained at a lower price than one's competitors. With the strong impetus towards holding the line on total costs, the dollars saved on testing can be used to effectively support research, product improvement, marketing, manufacturing, etc. A second economic benefit is the **improvement gained in personnel utilization.** Since the robot frees an individual to perform other tasks, more jobs can be completed in the same amount of time, and the head-count guidelines existent in most companies impose less of a constraint. Another benefit comes from **expansion in capacity,** that is, more tests can be run in a shorter time since the robot could be operated around-the-clock with minimal attention. This would also translate into **faster turnaround of results.** Since the intervention of the operator in the handling and testing of samples would be diminished using robot-assisted analysis, **precision should be improved.** There is also the **quality** concept to be considered, whereby one strives to do the analyses correctly the first time and thereby decrease the number of repeats. Finally, the use of the robot will **eliminate undesirable tasks.**

The reasons for combining the flex method and a robotic system were as follows:

(1)   there was a pre-existing, well-defined manual method

(2)   all operations and their order of performance were understood

(3)   a computer system was already in place, which not only ran the testing equipment, but also reduced the data using proprietary software and archived the results

(4)   the overall test was labor intensive

(5)   a large number of flexural tests were performed

(6)   Physical Testing is a projected growth area for robotics due to equipment replication and similarity of interfacing.

The first two items listed above are obvious and considered vital for success, especially for a first application. As to the pre-existing computer system, it is advantageous to have one already in place; however, we had to be certain that the robotic controller/computer was compatible with the 11/84 in our configuration. It was also clear that if modifications to the software/hardware were required, other operations in the laboratory including the generation of high quality data could not be affected. Obviously, if the cost to execute these changes were excessive, the cost effectiveness of the robotic system would be overridden. Reasons four and five were important since they significantly affected the overall efficiency of the laboratory. Thus, the unattended, extended operation feature was particularly attractive. Finally, it was felt that if this first application were successfully introduced into the Physical Testing Laboratory, installation of additional systems would follow with a savings in start-up costs.

System Specifications

The search to match a robotics system with an application at the Hoechst Celanese Research Company began in late 1984. As preliminary steps, possible profiles were developed, brief feasibility and economic studies were conducted, and safety issues were investigated. Upon completion, we were convinced of the benefits of robotics and had sound reasons for selecting flexural testing as the first project. It should be pointed out, however, that its introduction would not be possible unless certain specific criteria were satisfied. These included complete compatibility with our computer and the accompanying customized software, precision and accuracy comparable to the manual system, and less labor intensive than the existing procedure.

Next, a prototype flexural test system was proposed. The specific components were: (a) a rack capable of holding a minimum of 100 specimens; (b) an automatic thickness and width measuring device which is sensitive to 0.001" and can transmit the dimensions to an external computer; (c) a robot which is readily programmed and can preferably be controlled by our in-house computer; (d) an Instron Universal Testing Machine; and (e) the PDP 11/84 computer. Since this combination was not commercially available, two options were considered in order to implement this approach. The first was to have the job completely customized - at a cost close to $200K, considering the software modifications that were required. In addition, since the code is company-owned, there was a secrecy issue to resolve. A second approach would be to purchase the items separately and do the assembling and interfacing ourselves. Neither choice was cost effective.

Instead of canceling the project, it was decided to form a robotics team within the company consisting of Analytical, Computer, and Physical Testing personnel. Its primary purpose was to compile a specification document for distribution to vendors. If an agreement were subsequently made, the team would have the responsibility for successfully implementing the robotic application. It took until mid-1986, following the arrangement between Instron and Zymark, before concrete progress was made. After considerable discussion of our acceptance criteria, all concurred that the now commercial flex test system was not labor intensive, and there was a firm understanding of what must be done to assure compatibility with our existing DEC computer. There was still, however, the question of data validity. Since results from the fully-configured, robot-assisted procedure could not be compared with the manual test prior to shipment, it was decided that a check on the accuracy of the thickness and width gauges would satisfactorily answer our concerns since their accuracy would have a profound effect on the calculated results. This is illustrated in Figure 1 where the total testing error is plotted vs. the error in thickness measurement. The reason for the increasing severity of the error going from strain to stress to modulus is due to the incorporation of the thickness measurement in these specific calculations as the first, square, and cube power, respectively. The 5% total error line is shown to emphasize that differences greater than that are considered significant.

The actual criterion for validating the gauge measuring devices was that data generated automatically should be equivalent to those obtained by an experienced analyst performing the operation manually with a micrometer. The results of this experiment are shown in Table 1. During this pre-shipment test eleven specimens were tested, which included elastic as well as stiff materials. The average difference in thickness or width was only 0.001".

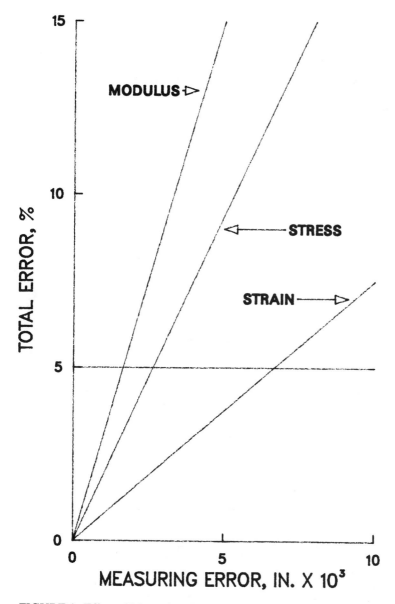

FIGURE 1. Effect of Measuring Error - Thickness.

Although this was encouraging, two observations needed further investigation - the two mil difference between techniques in the thickness mode for samples 2 and 3, and the consistently higher width values obtained by the operator on all samples. The first problem was explained by the compressibility of these elastic specimens due to the excessive pressure applied by the automatic device. It was adjusted, however, to match the stiffness of the material under test. The second problem was resolved when the width of the specimens was measured at the same place along the length of the bar both manually and automatically.

TABLE 1. Validity Check of Measuring Devices (All data in mils).

	Thickness		Width	
Specimen	Manual	Auto	Manual	Auto
1	119	119	490	488
2	119	117	490	488
3	119	117	490	487
4	120	121	489	488
5	120	121	489	488
6	120	120	487	485
7	121	122	492	491
8	123	123	490	490
9	124	125	492	492
10	124	125	493	492
11	138	137	500	502
Average $\triangle$		1		1

EXPERIMENTAL

Instron's Automated Material Testing System

The robotic system, purchased from Instron, closely matched our initial conception. It consisted of the following components:

- custom-made dispenser with a 110 specimen capacity for 1/8" flex bars;

- Mitutoyo Digimatic Indicator (2), Model 543-423, digital measuring device with control unit;

- Zymate[tm] Laboratory Automation Robotics System which includes the Zymate II robot, GP hands and custom grips, a power and event controller, and the Z845 Remote Computer Interface;

- Easylab[tm] programs for the flex test and to exercise the system;

- mounting plate which secures the robot, the sample dispenser, the measuring device and the flex fixture;

- Instron, Model 1122 Material Testing Instrument.

A schematic of the total system layout is shown in Figure 2.

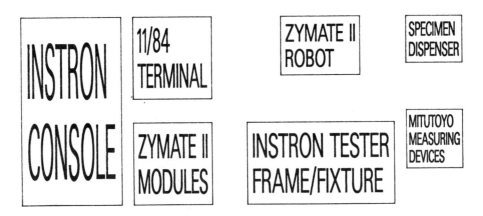

FIGURE 2. Layout of the Robotic System.

As a check on the overall operation of the robot and to fine tune the programs, an exercise procedure written by Instron was used. All basic tasks can be evaluated without interaction with the Instron or the computer. The exercise consists of having the robot remove a specimen from the dispenser, present it to the Digimatic Indicators and record the measurements, load it onto and then remove it from the test fixture, and finally dump it to waste. When this preliminary evaluation of the system was carried out in our laboratory, the robot was able to process 100 samples without error. In addition, the measuring device, with a resolution of 0.0001", exhibited a standard deviation of <0.1% in thickness and width. When an operator took the measurements using a micrometer, which has a resolution of 0.001", the same average values were obtained; however, the precision was poorer.

DEC/Zymate Interfacing

The next part of this project involved writing the software to incorporate the robot into the existing plastic flexural test procedure. The system before the introduction of the robot consisted of the test control and the data acquisition software which now required modification. In addition, two other programs had to be written. The three tasks comprising the robotic system are: the Communication Interface Task (CIT), the User Interface Task (UIT) and the Robotic Plastic Flex Task (RPF). See Figure 3 for a diagram of the communication flow between the three tasks.

The robotic testing procedure begins with the operator entering jobs in the queue via a menu driven program, the UIT. A job includes its identification number and n sample identification numbers, with each sample having x number of specimens. The specimens are placed in the rack with a separator (double thickness bar) after each sample. Jobs can be added to the queue at any time, which means more jobs can be added once the robot has started. After the operator enters the information in the queue, the test is started. The

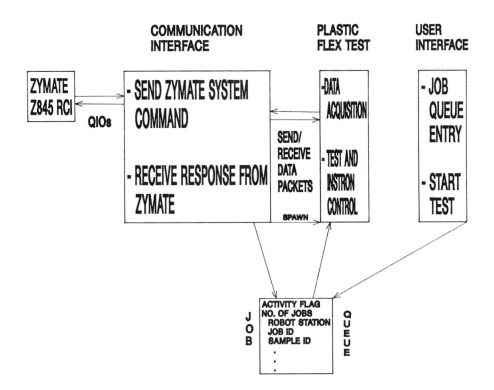

FIGURE 3. Communications Flow Between Tasks.

job. When a nominal thickness is sensed by the robot, the flex test is allowed to proceed normally. When a oversized bar is retrieved, the results for all specimens of that sample are averaged and statistics calculated. When all samples have been run, the system shuts down.

The CIT is the heart of the robotic system and handles all communication with the Zymate. It is used to start the appropriate test task and step the Zymate through its internal programs which will retrieve a specimen, obtain the thickness and width, and load and unload the flex fixture. While interfacing the Zymate to the PDP-11/84 the speed of the remote interface was found to work best at 600 baud. See Figure 4 for additional parameter settings. The communication between the Zymate and PDP[tm] involves sending a Zymate command to the controller via QIO's, which initiates an action, and getting back a response from the controller. The controller's lack of sophistication is evident in the communication. The simple task of measuring the thickness and width of a specimen takes three commands and three responses which should only take one command and one response, thus making more work for the host computer.

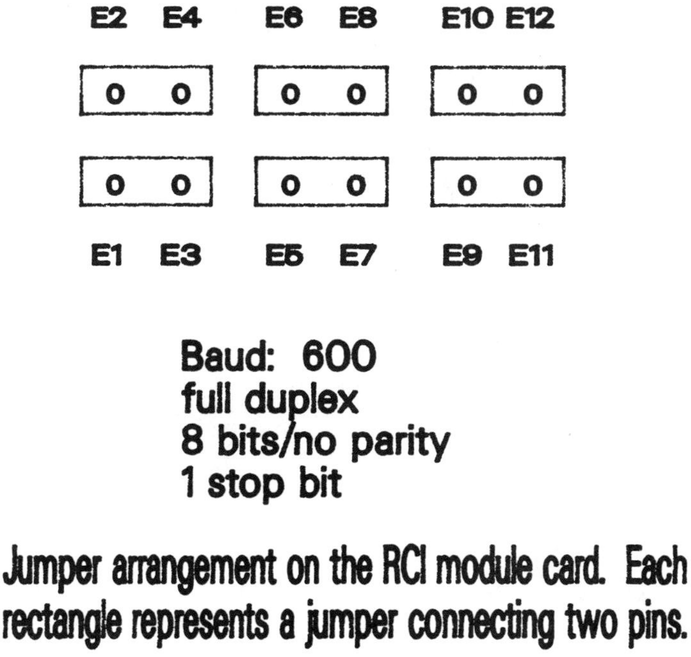

E2   E4   E6   E8   E10 E12

o o		o o		o o
o o		o o		o o

E1   E3   E5   E7   E9 E11

Baud: 600
full duplex
8 bits/no parity
1 stop bit

Jumper arrangement on the RCI module card. Each
rectangle represents a jumper connecting two pins.

FIGURE 4. Communication Configuration.

The manual plastic flexural test was modified for the robotic application. All operator intervention had to be removed and the flow had to be adapted for automation. This included getting samples form the queue and talking to the CIT. Previously, the data acquisition stopped automatically when a break was detected or it was stopped by the operator when 5% strain or full scale was reached. The full scale load is detected during the test. Rather than detect the 5% strain "on the fly" during the data collection, it was decided to accumulate sufficient data to calculate the 5% strain during the analysis. The time necessary to reach 5% strain was calculated based on the crosshead speed and specimen thickness. Thus, the data acquisition will continue until one of three event flags is set - the timer runs out for 5% strain, a break or full scale load is detected, or operator intervention is required.

The totally configured system and the accompanying communication and operation sequences are shown in Figure 5. From this figure and Table 2, it is evident that the purchased Instron package plus our host computer act as an "operator emulator". That is, all the basic steps from the manual procedure are carried over to the automated approach; however, the operator has been eliminated, except for the initiation of the job.

RESULTS AND DISCUSSION

Several sample types have been run on the fully-interfaced, robot assisted flex system to check its versatility and integrity. A typical data set obtained on materials covering a wide range in stiffness is shown in Table 3.

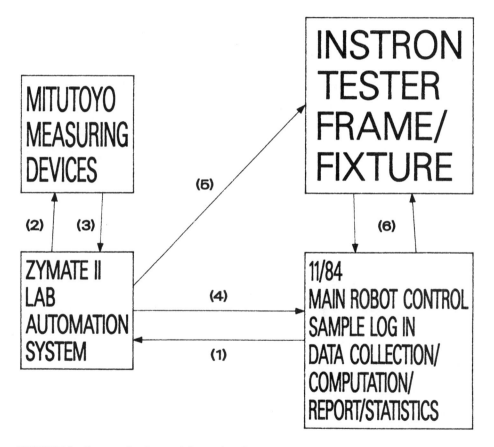

FIGURE 5. Communication and Operation Sequences - Total System.

TABLE 2. Communication and Operation Sequences for the Total System.

Route of Communication	Operation
1	the job is logged in by the operator via a utility on PDP 11/84 and the test sequence is initiated;
2->3->4	the thickness and width measurements are taken by the digital micrometers and transmitted to the 11/84;
5	the specimen is placed on the flex fixture and the Instron crosshead is brought down rapidly to the test position;
6	the test is performed under the control of the 11/84;
1->5->4	upon completion of the test, the crosshead is raised to its start position, the specimen is removed from the test fixture, and a ready signal is transmitted to the host computer.

TABLE 3. Comparison of Results, Manual (M) and Robotic (R).

	1-M	1-R	2-M	2-R	3-M	3-R	4-M	4-R
Thickness, (in.)	.125	.125	.117	.116	.121	.121	.127	.126
σ	-	-	-	-	-	-	-	-
Width, (in.)	.495	.494	.490	.491	.490	.490	.491	.490
σ	-	-	-	-	-	-	-	-
Strength, (psi E-3)	35.3	35.4	23.9	23.9	13.2*	13.5*	1.29*	1.01*
σ	0.4	0.3	0.9	0.8	-	-	-	0.23
Modulus, (psi E-6)	2.03	2.10	1.18	1.21	.396	.400	.028	.030
σ	.01	.04	.02	.01	-	-	-	-

* 5% Strain

The test conditions used manually and automatically were similar, and the number of specimens per sample were the same for statistical comparison. The results show that the precision of the robotic test is at least equal to that of the manual procedure, with one exception. Also, there is no bias exhibited based on the limited number of sample sets tested. The reasons for the strength difference and the poor test precision for sample #4 is due to the fact that the robotic system is presently equipped with only one load cell and the testing for this sample was done on the lower 0.5% of the cell's range, while the manual testing was done with a load cell on a range setting of 5.0% of its full range.

All the economic, service, and technical benefits, described priviously, were realized with this robotics application. In addition, there were several bonuses derived from the project. First, it forced us to thoroughly understand our hardware and software. In its six years of operation, familiarity with the system had decreased due to either personnel changes or changing job responsibilities. This project also forced us to be up-to-date in the robotics area and to be conversant with the offerings of several vendors. The information gathered by the Summit team has been distributed company-wide. Our overall confidence in robotics has increased and we are more comfortable in extending a manufacturer's capabilities. A final "plus" not considered before purchase was the fact that the automatic micrometer has eliminated operator bias.

On the negative side, there are still several deficiencies to be addressed. The most serious is the inability to access some of the utilities on the 11/84 when the robot-assisted flex test is in the data gathering mode. It is anticipated that this can be overcome with software. Also in the computer area, an improvement in the Zymate controller and the communication interface between the Zymate and the PDP would be highly desirable. This would shift a considerable work load away from the host computer. To increase the flexibility of the system, electronic autoranging of the Instron is necessary. At present, the single load range limits the utility of the equipment. A new dispenser, which would eliminate a sample preparation step, should be designed. In future versions of this system, it is suggested that sturdiness of the fingers be upgraded and the 5-250# load cell become standard on the plastics testing equipment.

The necessary time and effort were spent on the initial phase of this project (from conception of the application to the purchase of a system). It was fortuitous that a commercial system was not available after our first evaluation since it forced a review of our position and the formulation of a strategy - a general strategy that may be applied when automating techniques requiring specialized or custom products. As a final section to this paper, it is worth sharing this information, especially with those actively evaluating their first system.

Our strategy consisted of a fifteen point plan as shown below. The effort spent on each item will vary with the technical/administrative organization and the strengths of the participating individuals.

(1) Develop application profiles and select one or more to actively work on. A complete survey of the Analytical and Physical Testing laboratories was carried out and a priority list for uses of robotics was compiled with inputs form each research supervisor and the department manager. The prime candidate to chair this task force is someone with a firm knowledge of the areas, who is a good communicator, and is up-to-date in robotics.

(2) Select a robotics team consisting of members with the appropriate expertise who will work together to evaluate, specify, justify, recommend a "best" system , and have the responsibility for its implementation, if purchased.

(3) Conduct a detailed feasibility study. This will allow the identification of potential problem areas and the setting of timetables for their resolution.

(4) Perform a preliminary cost justification. It is advisable to do this at an early stage to establish whether continued effort is warranted. Consider such issues as additional services, equipment, and personnel necessary to support the application.

(5) Do a safety audit.

(6) Get management commitment. After items 3-5 have been satisfactorily completed, it is suggested that the site management be brought "on board". In our organization it was a matter of keeping the immediate supervisors informed and rely on them to carry the message higher.

(7) <u>Prepare a specifications document.</u> This is a critical step and could become a time-consuming process. It should describe, in detail, the application, the responsibilities of the buyer and the seller, any pre-shipment test(s), and criteria for acceptance. If constructed correctly, this document will leave room for movement by either party and will not prohibit creative thought for assembling and operating the system. You want to reflect the view that all are working towards the same goal with a high probability of success.

(8) <u>Select a vendor.</u> If your needs are not commercially available, you must decide whether it is more cost effective to buy turn-key equipment or to absorb set-up expenses internally.

(9) <u>Get operator buy-in.</u> If probable operators were not part of the team, now is the time to get them involved. It is also important to inform the employees that the use of robots is not threatening.

(10) <u>Conduct demo(s) and accept.</u> Usually the specification document contains a pre-shipment demo. If practical, all team members should attend and agree to accept/reject.

(11) <u>Train personnel.</u> At least one person in the organization should have a concrete understanding of the system and be designated as the primary operator.

(12) <u>Install, debug, and test.</u> After installation, at least a simulated procedure involving all components of the system should be performed before final acceptance from the seller. Any major bugs will be eliminated at this time. Finally, a testing protocol is executed to assure that the results from the robot-assisted technique are equivalent to the previous procedure(s).

(13) <u>Document, maintain, support.</u> Similar to other pieces of laboratory equipment, documentation of performance and failures is a must. Retaining copies of previous methods, within reason, and back-ups of the present program is recommended. It is further suggested that an inventory of critical spare parts be maintained.

(14) <u>Optimize procedure.</u> After you have become comfortable with the system, optimization to provide increased cost savings is possible.

(15) <u>Look for expansion.</u> Now that the first application has been installed, continue to evaluate other areas and procedures where a robot can be justified. Re-examine the priority list in item #1.

SUMMARY

Instron's robot-based flexural testing system has been interfaced with a PDP 11/84 computer. The results generated to date have demonstrated good precision and accuracy relative to the manual approach. Its use has resulted in better utilization of equipment and personnel and has permitted us to provide better service to our clients at a reduced cost per analysis.

The approach taken has provided us not only with an increased awareness in the area of robotics but also with the opportunity to expand the capabilities of the DEC computer. The formulation of an overall strategy before purchasing specialized or customized equipment and the recommendations for second generation systems were a natural extension of the basic project.

ACKNOWLEDGMENTS

The authors wish to thank those individuals at Instron - P.Blanchard, P.Borsari, and A.Stein and at Zymark - J.Little, J.Malley, and F.Zenie who played significant roles in the success of this endeavor.

REFERENCE

1. American Society for Testing Materials Method No. D-790, "Standard Test Methods for Flexural Properties of Unreinforced and Reinforced Plastics and Electrical Insulating Materials," ASTM Book of Standards, Section 8, Plastics, American Society for Testing and Materials, Philadelphia, PA (1983).

DEC, PDP, PDP 11/84, Datatrieve, and VAXCluster are trademarks of Digital Equipment Corporation.

AUTOMATED GRAPHITE BREAK LOAD ANALYSIS

Karla A. Hendrickson, Louis R. Lofgreen,
R. Keith Bergman
Hercules Aerospace
PO Box 98, MS X3B1
Magna, UT 84044

ABSTRACT

A common strength test performed on graphite fibers is the break load analysis. The fibers are gathered into bundles about the size of broom straws, treated with resin, and allowed to harden. These bundles are called tows. The tow is placed in a mold which has depressions at each end, where a thermoplastic resin is poured. When the resin sets, the sample, complete with end tabs, is ready for testing. At our facility, thousands of tows are tested each year. It is a boring, tedious test and well- suited for automation.

The break load analysis was automated by using a custom built sample rack and a Zymate[tm] I robot. A magazine type rack was designed which holds 60 specimens in a horizontal orientation, stacked one on top of the other. An air actuated cylinder is used to push one specimen at a time from the rack. When one rack is empty, a full one can simply be put in its place. The robot is programmed to pick up the sample, rotate it 90 degrees to a vertical position, and place it into the machine grips. An IBM PC/XT then initiates operation of the test machine and collects the data.

Investigation is being done on automation of strain measurement for tows. To date, this test has not been successfully automated with currently available strain gauges or extensometers. A discussion of our efforts in this area may help other investigators. When applied, the gauges must not be restrained in any way; however, if the robot has no contact with them, they cannot be retrieved after the test. An optical system appears to be the best solution, but nothing suitable has yet been found on the market.

INTRODUCTION

Approximately 150,000 graphite tow samples are tested each year at the Hercules fiber line at Bacchus Works. Tow samples consist of graphite fibers gathered into bundles approximately the size of broom straws. These bundles are treated with resin and cured in an oven. Thermoplastic resin is then molded onto the end of the tows so that the grips have end tabs to clamp onto. The samples are placed one at a time in an Instron Universal Tensile Testing machine and pulled to failure. The maximum load data is reduced from a strip-chart and recorded.

Obviously this test is highly conducive to fatigue, boredom, and distraction. Therefore, it lends itself nicely to automation. In the process, the use of robotics will free skilled laboratory personnel for more challenging and productive duties. Although a human is able to test the samples slightly faster than a robot, the robot exhibits a single-mindedness which translates into repeatable results, consistent techniques, and improved data accuracy.

A Zymate[tm] I, manufactured by Zymark[tm] Corporation, was used as the sample manipulator and interacted with several "in house" custom design modules such as sample gravity feed racks and pneumatic grips.

The robot retrieves a sample from the rack, rotates it 90 degrees, and introduces it into the grips of the Instron. When it is confirmed, by photoelectrics, that the sample is in place, the Instron starts the test and the data is acquired by an automated data acquisition system.

EXPERIMENTAL

The rack designed for this test is a gravity feed magazine type. Sixty samples are placed in a horizontal orientation in the magazine. An air actuated cylinder pushes the specimen, with a guide plate, out into the pickup position. When it retracts, the next sample falls into place. When the rack is empty, an alarm on the robot signals an operator to load another magazine. The robot retrieves the tow from the pickup point, rotates it 90 degrees to the vertical position and moves it into the pneumatic grips. An air actuated cylinder is signaled via the Zymark Power and Event Controller (PEC) to open the plexiglass safety guard in front of the grips. Photoelectric sensors, also connected to the PEC, scan to ensure that the previous sample was ejected. When it is confirmed with a signal to the PEC that the grips are clear, the robot inserts the tow into the grips. Again the sensors check for confirmation and the grips automatically close on the sample. If the sample is not in place, the robot will try to insert it again. If it is still not confirmed, the alarm will sound and the robot will wait for assistance. Once the grips are closed, the PEC signals the air cylinder to close the safety guard, then signals the Instron controller, an IBM PC-XT, to initiate the test and acquire the data. Upon failure, the crosshead returns to its initial position and the pneumatic grips release the failed sample, which falls into a chute. The chute is necessary to keep the lower platen of the Instron free of broken tow specimens, as they collect rapidly. The cycle is repeated until all samples in that test series are complete.

DISCUSSION

The development of this automated tensile system for break load analysis went smoothly. The only difficulties encountered were those involved with automating the strain measurement. Initially, the possibility of utilizing an optical extensometer was researched for this. However, nothing was available on the market that could meet our needs of extremely small (2%) strain measurements. Therefore, it was decided that the existing extensometer would be automated.

In the manual method the knife-edged extensometer is placed directly onto the sample and held in place by clips applying spring tension. This method could be automated easily by using an air cylinder to move the extensometer onto the sample, and then using another cylinder to hold the sample onto the knife blades. It was determined; however, through countless efforts and configurations, once attached to the sample, the extensometer has to be allowed to hang in "free-space". It can not be connected to anything except the sample. As the sample is being pulled, the entire extensometer has to be able to move with the sample. Even though this movement is slight, the modulus reading is very different if the extensometer is held or attached in any way. Placing the extensometer on the sample automatically and then letting go causes a problem in that when the sample fails, the extensometer rapidly moves away from the sample. It does not move to a repeatable position and therefore cannot be retrieved by the robot. Due to the problems encountered, another method to measure strain had to be sought.

Instron Corporation has an automated extensometer on the market on a limited basis. This extensometer looked like it might meet the needs of the test. Several dozen samples were sent to their facility to see how the extensometer would perform. They reported that the results looked favorable, and an order has been placed at this time.

The implementation of the extensometer should go quite smoothly. The robot will go through the cycle as before. Once the sample is in place and pre-loaded to about 25 lbs, the extensometer, operated by its own controller, will close onto the sample, and the test will begin. After each sample has failed, the extensometer calibrates and prepares for the next sample. Since the strain data is simply calculated from the stress-strain curve, and only 75% of the strain data from the chart is necessary, the extensometer will be taken off of the sample seconds before failure. This will also save the extensometer from unnecessary fatigue caused from the impact of the failing sample.

To date, the break load analysis is complete and working smoothly.   The strain measurement will be worked into the system in early 1988.

SUMMARY

The break load analysis for the graphite tow tensile test was automated successfully. Automation of this test frees skilled technicians from a tedious task, and allows them to pursue more challenging tasks.   Also achieved are more repeatable results, consistent techniques, and improved data accuracy.

The success of this project has opened doors for other automation projects involving graphite test preparation and analysis.   Preparation of the resin end tabs for the tow samples is currently being investigated, as well as other tests involving graphite.

LABORATORY ROBOTICS: MAKING THEM WORK

Joe Cross
Phillips Petroleum Company
Bartlesville, OK 74004

ABSTRACT

Analysts, like most workers in today's society, are looking towards automation to help them be more productive. Laboratory robotics is a unique tool to automate the most manpower intensive portions of the analyst's job - sample preparation and manipulation. The future for robotic automation is good, with robots performing tasks as simple as weighing and dilution to robots working in an automated laboratory where computers are processing data supplied by a robot analyst, decisions are made by the computer on the progress of the experiment, and the robot responds with the appropriate procedure changes.

To be successful, any robot application, requires considerable planning, a good working knowledge of the method being automated, creative solutions to key problems that might hinder the robot in performing required tasks, and endless patience to debug and customize programs to meet the laboratory needs. This paper deals with the different aspects of making robots work successfully in the laboratory.

INTRODUCTION

Laboratory robotics is becoming a very valuable tool for laboratory automation. Applications are numerous, evidenced by recent symposia proceedings.[1,2,3] There are, however, road blocks holding the technology back from its potential usefulness. Almost every application attempted has some unique aspect about it. Very few procedures are performed in exact detail at any two locations. To reproduce and sell, in quantity, robot systems that are pre-programmed to perform analytical tasks would mean the purchasers, and their sample requirements, would have to conform to the methods provided.

Companies offering robots, specially set up for laboratory work, and system companies providing custom robot systems are now beginning to compete in the market place. Usually these robotic systems are the result of customer and vendor interaction to meet individual requirements.

The most common approach for robot implementation is for each individual laboratory to purchase robotic equipment (i.e. robot, work stations, racks, software, etc.) and adapt it for their own applications. Many common laboratory applications can be automated using robots, and commercial workstations designed to aid the robot to complete laboratory tasks are available.

The success of a robot application is not strictly dependent upon the analyst being able to program the robot to do the tasks desired. Its success is also dependent on how well, or how error free, the robot is capable of performing. The time and money invested must be offset by benefits such as reduced labor costs, increased capabilities, improved accuracy, etc.. Other items, which contribute to the success or failure of a system include laboratory space and utility requirements, operator training, acceptance by laboratory personnel, speed of the robot, etc.. Thus, many factors are important to robotic automation success.

Criteria which help make robot applications successful are considerable planning, a good working knowledge of the procedure being automated, creative solutions to key problems that might hinder the robot in performing required tasks, and endless patience to debug and customize programs to meet the laboratory needs. When using laboratory robotics to automate any task, whether simple or complex, following a basic process, such as outlined below, can reduce the time required and increase the chance of success.

1. Method Investigation
2. System Planning
3. Workstation Development
4. Workcell Layout and Construction
5. Robot Programming
6. System Evaluation and Modification
7. Installation (and Training)
8. System Validation and Quality Control

This automation process combines planning, development, validation, implementation, and continued quality control. The following report discusses various aspects of this automation process.

METHOD INVESTIGATION

Method investigation has two important aspects 1) method selection and 2) determining procedural unit operations.

Selecting a method can be one of the most important steps in an automation project. A procedure that works very well may not be amenable to automation. In the same way, one that is tailor-made for automation may not have the justification to pay the cost involved. With today's technology and enough time and money, just about any lab procedure can be automated with laboratory robotics, but not necessarily economically. As a member of an automation group responsible for helping other chemists automate their laboratory projects, I find it extremely important for both the automation people and the lab chemists to share in this selection.

There are many items to consider in selecting a method. The workload of the laboratory may dictate what needs to be automated. Complexity of the manipulation tasks may make some projects more difficult to accomplish than others. Any method or procedure being considered for automation should be a good one, capable of producing quality results when applied properly. If the method has interferences or steps that require judgment on the part of the operator, then alternate mechanisms may need to be developed to take the place of the analyst's judgment. Are items such as consumable supplies (ie. pipet tips, vials, filters, etc) available and adaptable to automation?

Next in line is to break the method or procedure down into unique steps or unit operations such as sampling, weighing, diluting, etc. Programming a robot system and developing workstations to aid it in its tasks are best thought out from this unit operation process.

A simple example of the unit operation process can been seen from a dilution procedure for oils outlined below.[4] The automation process can begin from this list of steps:

1. Load balance with vial and syringe with pipet tip
2. Pick up next sample
3. Shake sample and uncap
4. Take an aliquot of the sample with syringe
5. Deliver sample to vial on balance
6. Take weight and record
7. Dispose of pipet tip, cap and return sample
8. Calculate solvent volume for proper dilution
9. Deliver solvent
10. Weigh dilution and record
11. Cap dilution and store in rack
12. Print dilution data on label

From this list of steps the automation process can begin.

AUTOMATION PLANNING

This part of the process might also be labeled system specification. Whatever the title, a systematic plan to assemble and implement a robot system is essential to be successful routinely in robot automation.

From the unit operations listed above, determine which tasks a robot must have help in completing. For example, a one arm robot can not take the cap off a vial by itself. Thus, capping stations were introduced to grasp the vial and turn it while the robot grasps the cap and lifts it off the turning vial. Robot suppliers offer workstations to aid robots with many common laboratory tasks. Selection of a robot system to do a job often depends upon the workstations each supplier has available to aid the robot in its work.

It is not uncommon in automation projects to encounter tasks that a robot can not perform by itself and no workstation is available to provide the necessary assistance. It is important to address these problems early. Solutions may come by modifying common laboratory apparatus to allow a robot to work with it. Or a more creative solution, such as the development of a new workstation, may be necessary. Lab work at this stage pays off. More detail on workstation development is given in following sections of this report.

As each step in the process is being investigated, consideration should be given to what will happen if the robot fails to complete a task properly. Task completion testing can be done with devices such as microswitches, photosensors, weight readings, etc. Software routines can then be written to detect failure and to allow the robot to re-try the task, clear the work area and go on to the next sample, or to shutdown the system if the failure could result in damage or incorrect results.

Workcell designs can be made by ordering the steps listed above. Often optimum layouts can be arranged by drawing workcell layouts and placing the workstations in different positions. By making the drawings to scale, bench and room space allocations can be made before workcell construction begins.

There are a number of other considerations to be made in planning workcell layouts:

    1) safety hazards and the need for hoods, sinks, etc.,

    2) supplies needed such as vials, pipet tips, reagents, etc. (how to arrange and how the robot can keep track of them),

    3) utilities needed and the locations for each (water, air, vacuum, sewer, etc.),

    4) data and laboratory environment communications (what additional computer capabilities are needed).

WORKSTATION DEVELOPMENT

In almost every project I have been involved in with laboratory robotics, the job, as it was done in that particular lab, could not be done with a robot and existing commercial accessories. It was necessary to design and construct a workstation to aid the robot.

As represented above by the device to assist robots to cap and uncap vials, workstations are devices that perform specific tasks within a robot system. Other examples of commercial workstations include laboratory balances, syringe pumps, pH meters, etc. Other types of workstations developed by researchers and reported in literature include; ovens with pneumatic piston operated doors,[5] cap dispensers,[4] etc. It would be impossible to give a detailed approach that would allow you to develop workstations to solve any laboratory automation problem. Therefore, I will describe examples of how we solved problems we encountered.

Reagent Powder Dispensing Example: Phillips' X-Ray Fluorescence Group prepares many of its samples by fusing them under heat with reagents such as lithium tetraborate or potassium pyrosulfate. The manual procedure calls for a preset amount of the fluxing reagent to be weighed into a vial and then the appropriate amount of sample weighed into the fluxing reagent. What we wanted to do was develop a robotic system to pre-weigh the fluxing reagents. The existing robots could manipulate reagent vials, interface to laboratory balances, etc., but could not dispense powdered reagents. We finally found a device used in pharmaceutical and food industries to dispense preset amounts of drugs or food items such as tea.[6] We were able to interface the device to the robot so that the robot could load a vial on a balance and initiate the powder dispenser.[7] The system is shown in Figure 1.

Cap Dispenser Example: We robotically dilute hydrocarbon samples with xylene for metals analysis by Inductively Coupled Plasma (ICP) Analysis. The hydrocarbon is weighed into a vial, xylene is dispensed, the vial capped and mixed. We close the vial with a polyseal cap to keep the sample from leaking. A dispenser was needed to supply the robot with the caps. An obvious solution was found by copying a dixie cup type dispenser. The gravity feed dispenser that resulted is shown in Figure 2.

X-Ray Fluorescence Robot Example: An early project using robots at Phillips was to automate the X-ray fluorescence analysis of sulfur in hydrocarbons. Preparation of the samples is not difficult for a person, but a one armed robot needed considerable help with the job. The sample is prepared by aliquoting the sample into a sample cup, diluting it with solvent if needed, covering the sample cup with a very thin (.25 mil) Mylar window, mixing the sample and solvent, and inserting the sample cup into the X-ray spectrometer. There was no robot system available that would perform any of these functions as supplied, nor were there any commercial workstations available to assist the robot with them.

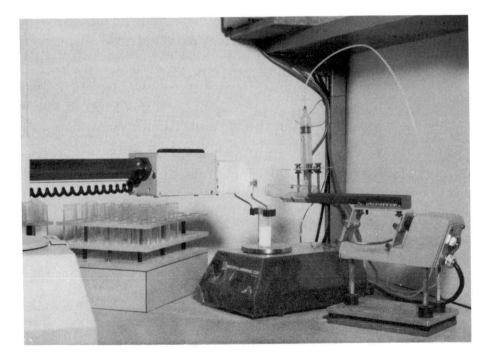

FIGURE 1. Robotic Powder Dispenser

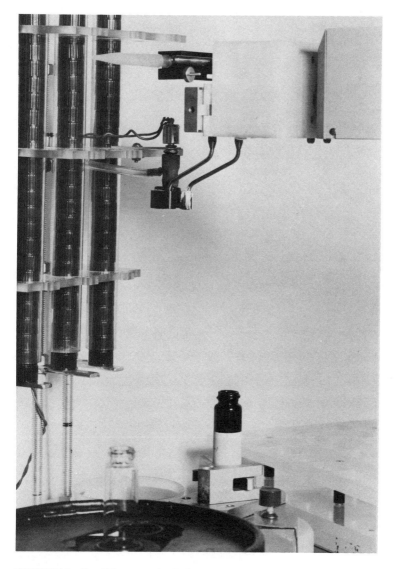

FIGURE 2. Cap Dispenser for Laboratory Robot.

A detailed discussion of the solutions to these problems was published previously.[8] The way we arrived at the solutions was to take ideas from past experiences and put them into practice. For example, the major hurdle to solve was handling the Mylar film. We looked at many methods of gripping such as vacuum, sharp hooks, foam rubber grippers, etc. before deciding that the vacuum method was the best and went about perfecting a vacuum gripper to pick the film up and unroll it. Similarly, we investigated several methods to cut the film before deciding upon using a heated nichrome wire. We performed these experiments before we started setting up a workcell to do the entire job. We knew that if we could not accomplish these tasks manually, we could not use robotics for the method. Figure 3 shows many of the workstations used in this procedure.

Many of the workstations operate on positive air pressure or vacuum, such as the vacuum gripper or the pneumatic pistons for attaching the collar, inserting the sample into the spectrometer, and ejecting the sample cup core. The air and vacuum were controlled through solenoid valves operated by the robot's computer. In the case of the Zymate System, the power and event control (PEC) module provides easy control of such devices. For PC type controllers, similar interfaces can be used or interface boards such as those available from companies like Metrabyte (Taunton, MA).

Other tools of the trade include: 1) microswitch and photo cell sensors to insure each workstation is able to complete its assigned task, 2) pneumatic pistons and grippers to move objects that the robot can not move because of strength, time or position, 3) switches to turn instruments that use AC power on and off, and 4) software routines to allow the robot to keep up with hand changes, consumable supplies, etc.

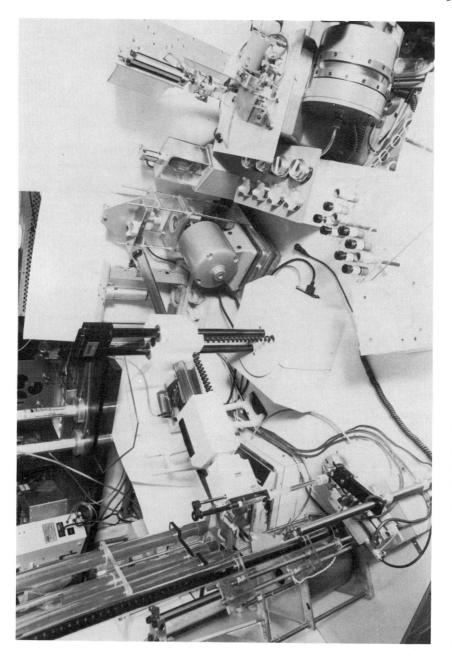

Figure 3. Robotic System For Sulfur In Oils.

WORKCELL LAYOUT AND CONSTRUCTION

Although it may not seem important, robot efficiency in performing an assigned task often determines if the application is successful. System efficiency can be greatly enhanced with a well-conceived plan of the workcell layout. The speed of an application is often determined by the number of movements a robot must make. Constructing a workcell so that a robot's movements are relatively short distances with easy access to workstations will enhance speed.

One aspect of laboratory robots that is particularly useful is their ability to log and perform multiple tasks. By use of internal timers or polling loops in the robot software, tasks can be performed at the right time or better use of the robot can be made during slack time. Performing multiple tasks requires additional thought in laying out workcells. Other considerations have to be made in planning a workcell layout including laboratory space requirements, utilities and services needed (electrical, air, vacuum, water, sewer, hood, etc.), maintenance and human service access, etc.

Workcell construction is best begun by first testing each workstation independently before the total workcell is constructed. This is particularity true for new workstations being developed for the specific application. As each workstation is tested and added to the workcell, access points are determined and added to the controller memory. Thought is also needed in determining how the robot will go from one workstation to another. It is often necessary to add clear points to avoid collisions.

ROBOT PROGRAMMING

The sections above lead you through analyzing and planning a method for robotic automation. At this point, it is time to create the computer program which will perform the application. For this discussion we will cover programming only for the Zymate Laboratory Automation System.

A technique that I have found useful in setting up robot programs is to first outline the overall method by listing the tasks the robot must perform in the proper order. Then teach the robot each task it is to perform (getting vial from rack, placing vial on balance, mixing sample, etc.). Teaching a task involves guiding the robot through the coordinates it must follow and naming the coordinates or storing them in the computer memory for retrieval during the application. Coordinates can be named as absolute points or as relative points to another absolute coordinate.

Once the robot has been taught the task coordinates, a task program can be written. The task program should provide instructions for the robot's manipulations and for operation of the workstations involved with the task. Provisions are to be made for sensing task completion such as microswitches, photocells, grip force, proper weight, etc. Recovery routines can be added for task failures.

Once the task programs have been written, the method can be built by stringing the task programs together in an application program or task scheduler. This program is usually preceded by a parameter input and initialization program to set-up the robot system properly.

References 9 and 10 provide good discussions on techniques that are applicable to programming. Reference 9 pays particular attention to failure detection and recovery routines. It is usually good to insert these type of routines into the program after it has been tested and the common types of failures detected.

SYSTEM EVALUATION AND MODIFICATION

There are multiple aspects to evaluating how well a system performs. First, each task is evaluated to determine how reliable the robot can perform it (how often will failures occur). Second, the overall procedure is evaluated in terms of set objectives such as analysis speed and through-put, data accuracy and precision, etc. Third, the procedure is evaluated to determine if modifications can be made to improve the system performance.

During individual task evaluations, the system is checked for mechanical reliability. Sensors and verification procedures are added for steps that the robot may find difficult or for steps where failure is fatal to the procedure. Examples of sensing techniques are the tactile sense of the robot's grip to assure the presence of a sample vial, microswitch closure to verify that a door is closed properly, photocells to verify that a capping procedure worked before the sample is inverted, weight readings from a balance to insure that the robot is working with enough sample, etc.

Data quality can be evaluated by analyzing routine samples using both the robot and manual procedures and comparing the results. The system should be evaluated to determine if it can provide suitable data on a continuing basis. It is also good to provide quality assurance for any method by analyzing certified standards such as National Bureau of Standards (NBS) materials, if they are available.

The analyst must make the final decision as to how well the system performs. Items discussed above, such as speed, sample through-put, data quality, etc, are to be considered. In analyzing the system the analyst should look at how much speed is really needed. The system may have more than sufficient sample through-put, although it may be slow. The analyst should also estimate the mean time between system failures and determine how that will effect the laboratory. If the system is not sufficient in any of these areas, modifications to improve the system or to provide software routines to anticipate system failures must be made before the system is installed or turned over to the operator.

INSTALLATION

Laboratory robot systems are often developed in locations other than where the system will reside. It is important to involve the system operator in the entire process of developing the automated system. When it is time to transfer the system the operator should perform as much of the transfer as possible. It is also important that the laboratory be prepared as determined in the planning stage before the transfer is made. One other important note on system transfers is that the system is not installed until the new operator is trained to operate the system and trouble shoot system failures.

Trouble shooting system failures is a very important aspect of operating a robot. Part of justifying a robot usually is determined by reducing labor costs. This means that people should not be involved any more than needed. However, robots, like most machines, need attention to function smoothly. Small changes in position coordinates of critical steps can mean increased system failures. These critical steps need to be inspected periodically and verified that they are still being performed adequately.

SYSTEM VALIDATION AND QUALITY CONTROL

Much of the work for system validation is accomplished in the system evaluation step. However, any time changes to the system are made or particularly if the system is transferred to a new lab for set up, the system should be validated again. The techniques remain the same.

An important part of any automation process is to insure that quality analytical results are obtained on a continuing basis. The best way to provide this assurance is to set up a routine quality control program for the method. If the manual method was already involved in such a procedure, then the same samples and test standards can be used for the automated procedure. If standards are not already available, it is well worth the effort to prepare and use routine quality assurance standards to keep check on the method. Examples of QA procedures can be found in reference 11.

CONCLUSIONS

Developing and implementing successful robot applications in the analytical chemistry laboratory requires careful planning, a good working knowledge of the procedure, creative solutions to key problems, and systematic evaluations. A systematic approach to the automation process can lead to faster system installations and to improved performance. Cooperation of all parties involved in automation is critical to its success.

REFERENCES:

1. "Advances in Laboratory Automation, Robotics-1984", edited by G.L. Hawk and J.R. Strimaitis, Zymark Corp., Hopkinton, Ma, 1984.

2. "Advances in Laboratory Automation, Robotics-1985", edited by G.L. Hawk and J.R. Strimaitis, Zymark Corp., Hopkinton, Ma., 1985.

3. "Advances in Laboratory Automation, Robotics-1986", edited by G.L. Hawk and J.R. Strimaitis, Zymark Corp., Hopkinton, Ma., 1986.

4. R.D. Jones and J.B. Cross, ibid #2, p 293-312.

5. L. Lester, T. Lincoln and H. Donoian, ibid #2, p509-529.

6. Hierath and Andrews Corp, Wheat Ridge, Co., ISO-G Systems.

7. J.B. Cross and E.J. Marak, "Advances in Laboratory Automation, Robotics-1984", edited by G.L. Hawk and J.R. Strimaitis, Zymark Corp., 1984, p181-192.

8. J.B. Cross, L.V. Wilson, E.J. Marak and R.D. Jones, "Advances in Laboratory Automation, Robotic-1985", edited by G.L. Hawk and J.R. Strimaitis, Zymark Corp., 1985, p 347-366.

9. R.D. Jones, H.R. Pinnick,Jr., and J.B. Cross, "Making Laboratory Robots Smart", in Advances in Laboratory Automation - Robotic 1987, ed G.L. Hawk and J.R. Strimaitis, Zymark Corp., Hopkinton, Ma. 1987.

10. W. Jeffery Hurst and James W. Mortimer, "Laboratory Robotics, A Guide To Planning, Programming and Applications",1987, VCH Publishers, New York, New York.

11. G. Kateman and F.W. Pijpers, "Quality Control In Analytical Chemistry", John Wiley and Sons, New York, N.Y., 1981.

ROBOTIC AUTOMATION OF SOME COMMON ORGANIC LABORATORY TECHNIQUES

Gary W. Kramer and Philip L. Fuchs
Department of Chemistry
Purdue University
West Lafayette, IN 47907

ABSTRACT

The Purdue Automated Synthesis System (PASS) is being created to allow reaction development, analysis, and optimization to be carried out by a machine. PASS couples a distributed computer control network with dual Zymark laboratory robot arms, automated reactors, fully automated gas and liquid chromatographs, and other computer-controllable devices.

Development of the PASS project has necessitated automating several common organic synthesis techniques. Among these are the slow addition of liquid reagents (automated addition funnel), the precise addition of gaseous reagents (automated gasimeter), liquid-liquid extraction (automated separatory funnel), and pre-chromatographic purification (automated plug filtration). Techniques for dispensing molecular sieve beads and automated solvent evaporation have recently been added to the system.

INTRODUCTION

The Purdue Automated Synthesis System (PASS) is a harbinger of the way experimental synthetic organic chemistry will be done in the next century. Reaction condition control and selection is carried out by a computer, experimental manipulations are accomplished by robotic arms and other automated devices, and analyses are performed by totally automated chromatographs. Since many of the details of PASS have been described previously[1-4], only a brief introduction is given here.

PASS is divided into two main components as shown in Figure 1. Reactions are carried out on the synthesis table, and samples from these reaction mixtures are transported via autosampler vial to the other table for analysis. The reaction scale is small, 0.1 to 1 mmol in reaction volumes of 3 to 5 mL. The reactors and most other ancillary devices are self-cleaning, allowing a large number of reactions to be carried out unattended. PASS is controlled by a hierarchical computer network. A central executive computer directs 8-bit managerial processors which, in turn, control the remainder of the devices that make up the system. To improve the system time response, Zymate robot arms are used to automate only those operations which would otherwise be difficult.

DISCUSSION

As we develop PASS, we find that we must continually formulate additional automated techniques to allow the study of a desired reaction. Bringing new chemistry "on-line" becomes much simpler as our repertoire of standard unit operations increases. However, because the practice of synthetic chemistry is so rich in experimental methodology, we anticipate that nearly every new chemical system that we examine will require devising a way to automate some new situation. Some of these schemes will be useful only in totally automated systems such as PASS. However, many techniques will be more general and can find application on traditional laboratory benches.

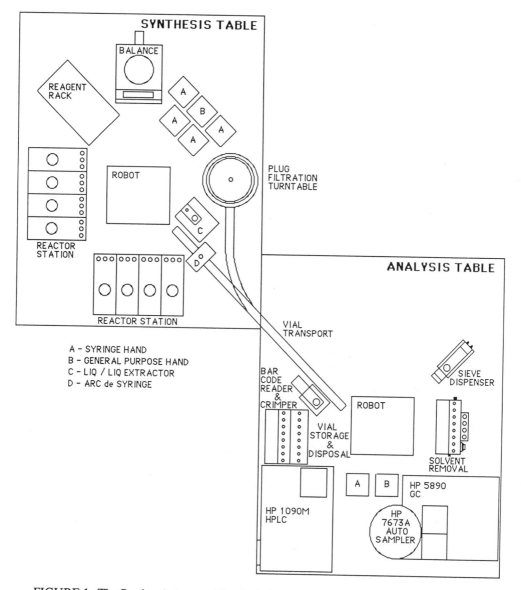

FIGURE 1. The Purdue Automated Synthesis System Table Layout.

An Automated Addition Funnel

The general problem of slowly adding a liquid reagent to a reaction mixture using a controlled rate has plagued organic chemists for over a century. This difficulty is exacerbated when the reagent is corrosive or air-sensitive, when small amounts must be added, or when more than one reagent must be added in a controlled fashion. Traditional devices such as "constant addition" funnels, even when fitted with stopcocks containing needle valves, are difficult to adjust to provide constant addition rates. Syringe pumps allow easy flow-rate control but suffer from "freeze up" problems with air-sensitive reagents or with solutions of solids dissolved in volatile solvents. Metering pumps, while usable with larger volumes, are not suitable for delivery of small volumes of expensive reagents.

PASS currently has three modes for delivering liquids to its reactors: common solvents can be added by the pumping stations used to clean the reactors; reagents and other solvents can be added using one of the robotic syringe hands; and the slow adder (Figure 2) can be used to add liquids at slow, controlled rates.

The slow adder is an automated addition funnel consisting of a pressurized reagent reservoir, a computer-controlled solenoid valve, and a liquid presence detector. By accurately controlling the time that the valve is open, the rate at which the valve is opened, and the pressure drop across the system, a precise delivery of reagent can be achieved.

The heart of the slow adder is a miniature, Teflon^{tm} solenoid valve (Series 2 two-way valve, General Valve Corp., Fairfield, NJ) which has a dead volume smaller than 50 uL and an activation time about 8 ms. An adjustable bubbler is used to set the pressure drop across the system in order to provide a pressure slightly higher than that of the exit bubbler

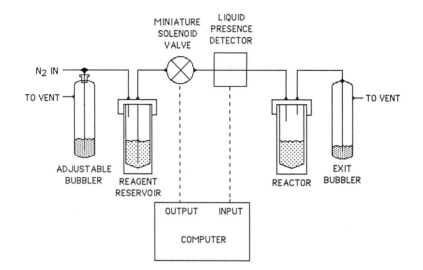

FIGURE 2. Schematic of the Automated Addition Funnel.

so that liquid will flow from the reservoir to the reactor when the valve is open. A liquid presence detector[4], placed close to the reactor, is used to determine the beginning and end of addition and to uncover certain error conditions. The system plumbing is 0.063-in OD Teflon tubing with ChemInert flare fittings. Reagents only come in contact with glass and Teflon.

The rate of reagent addition is determined by several variables: (1) the pressure drop from the reservoir to the reactor, (2) the length of time that the valve is open, (3) the rate at which the valve is opened, (4) the length and inside diameter of the delivery tubing, and (5) the viscosity of the liquid being transferred.

The apparatus is assembled as shown in Figure 2. The pressure differential between the reservoir and the reactor is adjusted along with the valve open-time to produce the required drop size. A simple computer program pulses the valve open and closed while these manual adjustments are made. For accurate work, the system must be calibrated under conditions as close as possible to those of the actual delivery. A known volume of the reagent is placed into the reservoir, followed by pulsing the valve until the liquid presence detector senses the liquid. The computer then counts the number of pulses issued until the detector signals the absence of liquid. A calibration factor is calculated from the known volume of reagent and the number of pulses required.

The utility of the slow adder can be extended by driving two or more valves from the same computer signal. If each valve subsystem is properly calibrated, a true simultaneous addition of the reagents can be achieved. For best results the reservoirs of each valve system should be pressurized from the same adjustable bubbler. The delivery tubing, reagent concentration, and solution viscosity of each system should be as identical as possible.

The applicability of the slow adder system is not limited to simple timed reagent additions. By incorporating other computer-readable sensors, such as reaction temperature or pH probes, the computer can be programmed to deliver reagents at rates dependent on other factors.

Use of the slow adder is not restricted to automated systems. This device can be used on a traditional synthesis bench to deliver liquids from milliliter to liter quantities under the control of a standard microcomputer.[5]

An Automated Gasimeter

Like the addition of liquids, the delivery of known volumes of gas to reaction mixtures under controlled conditions has long been a problem in synthetic chemistry. Traditional methods involving gas burettes, condensing gases in cold traps, etc.[6] are not easily automated. Syringe dispensers offer a reasonably general method for small volumes. Our alternative method is shown in Figure 3.

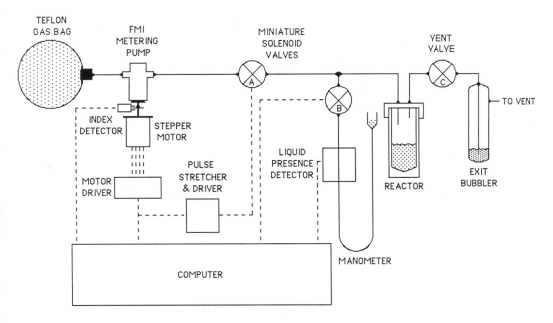

FIGURE 3. Schematic of the Automated Gasimeter.

The gas supply is stored in a Teflon gas sampling bag with a septum inlet. This type of bag, normally used to collect environmental samples, enables introduction of nearly any type of gas directly on the PASS synthesis table. The bag is charged with gas from a cylinder in a fume hood. The permeability of Teflon film toward water vapor, and air prohibits long term storage of gas in the bag. For less reactive gases, bags made with Halar films or multilayer films with metallized mylar provide improved resistance to gas diffusion.

The central ingredient of our gas adder is the stepper-motor driven, reciprocating-piston pump (Fluid Metering Corporation, Oyster Bay, NY). Its 1/4 inch ceramic piston, housed in a carbon liner, permits pumping gas without damaging the pump. Due to the reciprocating piston design, the pump delivers gas during slightly less than half of the rotation of the pump motor. This corresponds to roughly 180 of the 400 motor steps per revolution. An optical interrupter index sensor is mounted on the pump drive shaft. It is adjusted to become active exactly when the delivery of gas begins. By counting the number of drive pulses issued after the index sensor activates, the computer can monitor the amount of gas delivered.

The miniature Teflon solenoid valve, labeled A, is necessary to prevent the gas from leaking back through the pump. This valve must be open while the pump is displacing gas and for a short time thereafter. The computer could oversee the opening and closing of this valve; however, we find it convenient to control the valve with a pulse stretcher/driver triggered by the step pulse to the pump motor driver. The pulse stretcher opens the valve as soon as the step pulse is issued and then holds the valve open for about a second. The pulse stretcher is retriggerable so if the step rate is more rapid than 1 Hz, the valve remains open.

The delivery of gas at constant pressure is accomplished by using the automated manometer. When solenoid valve B is open, the manometer fluid is exposed to the gas and its level, monitored by one of our standard liquid presence detectors[4], reflects the pressure in the reactor. When the pressure falls below the set point, the detector signals the computer to step the motor/pump to provide more gas. In this way gas is delivered on demand to the reactor. Selection of the manometer fluid is determined by the gas being used. Solenoid valve B can be closed to prevent gas from leaking out through the manometer when the reactor is purged.

Like all gas delivery systems, our gas adder can be impaired by leaks. By using the 1.0-mL syringe hand on the robot, our system can be quickly calibrated and leak tested. With vent valve C open, the computer first rotates the pump to flush the reactor with gas. The syringe needle of the robot hand is inserted through the septum inlet on the reactor. The computer then rotates the pump to its index mark. The manometer valve, labeled B, is opened, and the vent valve is closed. The robot syringe is filled in 0.01-mL increments while monitoring the liquid presence detector until the system is at the reference pressure (manometer liquid is detected). The syringe then removes a known volume of gas, and the computer steps the pump until the reference pressure is restored. If the number of steps required matches a predetermined reference value, the system is deemed to be both calibrated and leak free. If not, an error condition exists.

An Automated Separatory Funnel

Liquid-liquid extractions are often used in synthetic chemistry for the separation of reaction products from reactants and by-products on the basis of their differential solubilities in two immiscible liquids. In the process, reactions are often quenched since the reactants are separated and often one or more of the reactants is destroyed by reacting with one of the extraction liquids.

We have previously described a simple device using a vortex mixer for automating the liquid extraction procedure.[7] Figures 4a-c show a second generation version of this apparatus. The reservoir, fashioned from 10-mm OD glass tubing, has a capacity of about 3 mL. A length of 4-mm OD glass tubing is fused to the inner wall of the reservoir to hold a 0.063-in OD Teflon eductor tube in place. The eductor tube is used to drain the reservoir during cleaning. The top of the reservoir is held in place by an O-ring mounted in an aluminum bracket on the vortex mixer. A cap fastened above the O-ring mount serves as a holder for the three tubes entering the reservoir and a guide for the needle on the robot syringe hand. A Teflon collet couples the vortexer cup to the bottom of the reservoir.

The separatory funnel reservoir is cleaned by filling with a suitable liquid through one of the two extractant liquid inlet tubes, vortexing, and then draining through the eductor tube. Samples to be extracted are added via syringe through the center guide hole in the cap as shown in Figure 4a. Extraction fluids may be introduced by syringe or pumped in through the inlet tubes. After vortexing and settling, an aliquot of the appropriate layer can be removed by syringe.

In our previous work, the separation process was always well planned before the system was run unattended. Since there was no way to determine the exact position of the liquid-liquid interface after vortexing, only a portion of the desired liquid phase was removed by syringe to ensure that there would be no contamination by the other liquid. Following vortexing, arbitrarily long settling times were employed to insure that phase separations always would be complete. These restrictions are wasteful of reaction sample and system time, two commodities always in short supply in PASS. Accordingly, we have attempted to overcome these constraints with an automated separatory funnel accessory that allows the system to locate the liquid-liquid interface.

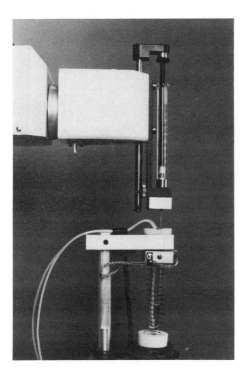

FIGURE 4a. Adding a Sample to the Automated Separatory Funnel.

The concept for the liquid interface detector arose from the observation with our standard liquid presence detectors[4] that it is often necessary to adjust the detection threshold when liquids with different refractive indices are used. A version of the liquid presence detector was built to accommodate the 10-mm reservoir tube (Figure 4b). The large amount of stray ambient light that impinges on the phototransistor precludes using the simple comparator circuit that we normally employ with our liquid presence detectors[4]. By using a pulsed LED and synchronous detection, the stray light problem is eliminated as long as the photodetector does not become saturated.

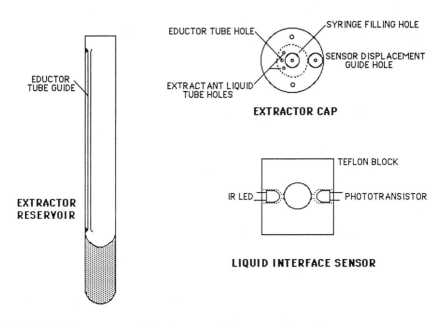

FIGURE 4b. Components of the Automated Separatory Funnel.

In practice, when the system wants to sense the position of the liquid interface, or to verify if a phase separation has occurred, the robot inserts the needle of one of its syringe hands through the guide hole in the rear-most position of the cap and pushes the detector down the tube as shown in Figure 4c. (The spring mounted around the tube pushes the detector back up.) When the detector senses the liquid interface its level is calculated from the position of the robot arm. At the present time, the detector requires manual adjustment to accommodate different liquids. Future modifications which allow the computer to adjust the detector circuitry hopefully will overcome this limitation.

An Automated Plug Filtration Apparatus

PASS relies on gas and liquid chromatographs for quantitative analyses of its reaction samples. In order to carry out the analyses as rapidly as possible, the chromatographs are equipped with high speed, high resolution columns (10 m X 0.530-mm capillary columns for GC and 5 cm X 4.6-mm 3-micron columns for HPLC). These columns and the high speed analytical methods we employ are not tolerant of polar or high molecular weight materials which require long elution times. To prevent such materials from being injected into the chromatographs, it is customary to elute the analytical samples through a short plug of solid adsorbent. This process is known as a plug filtration. Lower molecular weight materials are rapidly eluted while the tars, polymers, and highly polar materials are trapped on the plug. If the adsorbent is anhydrous, it also removes traces of water dissolved in the sample.

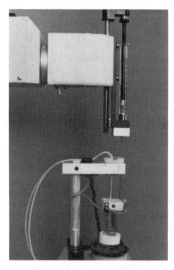

FIGURE 4c. Lowering the Liquid Interface Sensor.

FIGURE 5. Automated Plug Filtration of an Analytical Sample.

Figure 5 shows the PASS apparatus used for plug filtration. The unit consists of a carousel holding up to 200 disposable pipettes in two concentric rows. Each disposable pipette is fitted with a glass wool plug and loaded with about 1 cm of silica gel, alumina, or Florosil adsorbent. The carousel is mounted on a stepper-motor driven base. An optical interrupter index sensor is mounted on the motor drive shaft. This allows the computer to find the home position of the carousel at tube slot 00. The other tube locations are found by counting step pulses from the home index at 4 pulses per tube position.

PASS analytical samples are transferred from the synthesis table to the analysis table in autosampler vials. The transport mechanism is an O-gauge model train engine specially equipped to carry the vials between the robot arms. Figure 5 shows the train, carrying an uncapped sample vial in its "smokestack," parked under the home position of the plug filtration station. The robot syringe hand injects a sample onto the plug filtration column. After changing to a second syringe hand, the robot adds a "chase" solvent to elute the sample. When the elution is complete, the train carries the sample to the analysis table.

Automated Molecular Sieve Bead Dispenser

Many chromatographic analyses are adversely affected by having water in the samples. Analyzing wet samples can lead to peak tailing, changes in retention times, and even physical damage to the columns. One way to dry such samples is to employ a solid desiccant such as molecular sieves. To maintain their capability to absorb water, molecular sieves must be protected from the atmosphere before use. This precludes simply placing the sieves in uncapped sampler vials. Figure 6 shows a dispenser for round molecular sieve beads.

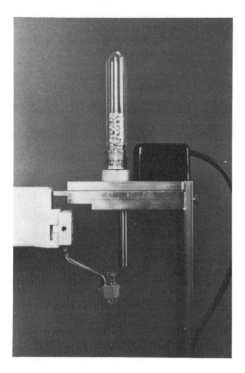

FIGURE 6. The Molecular Sieve Bead Dispenser

The sieve beads are stored in a sealed tube affixed to a slide dispenser. When the slide is in the rest position a single sieve bead can enter the hole in the slide. As the robot hand, bearing an uncapped autosampler vial in its gripper, attempts to position the vial under the dispenser tube, the face of the hand depresses the slide. This moves the sieve bead over the dispenser hole where it falls into the waiting vial. As the hand is withdrawn, an internal spring returns the slide to the rest position where a new sieve bead falls into the slide hole.

The sieve beads used in the dispenser must be carefully graded in size to match the hole in the slide. If the sieve bead is too large, it can plug the entrance hole. An undersized sieve bead will allow more than one bead to enter partially into the slide hole. In this case, the upper bead is usually crushed as the slide is depressed. An electrical buzzer mounted under the black box on the rear of the dispenser is activated by a microswitch whenever the slide is depressed. The vibrations facilitate moving the sieve beads in and out of the slide hole. A second buzzer mounted directly on the storage vial (not shown) can be used to expedite the sieve bead movement. The autoinjectors on the chromatographs must be adjusted to insure that their needles do not hit the sieve bead residing in the bottom of the sampler vials.

Automated Solvent Evaporator

The high speed chromatographic analyses on which PASS depends can also be adversely affected by the presence of certain solvents. Since these solvents are often utilized in the synthesis stage, but are undesirable during the analysis phase, some method must be employed for removing them.[8] Figures 7a-c show our solvent removal subsystem.

The unit consists of a heated block into which the robot can place up to eight autosampler vials (Figure 7a). Above the heated block is a hinged lid that swings down to cover the mouths of the vials. This lid has a cavity above each vial position. In the center of the cavity, a tube directs a jet of nitrogen directly into the vial aperture. This greatly increases the rate of solvent evaporation. The cavity above the vial serves as a small fume hood. A opening in the rear of this cavity is connected to a vacuum line enabling aspiration and disposal of solvent vapors in an actual fume hood.

One of the problems in automating a solvent evaporation process is knowing when it is complete. If a single solvent of known quantity is to be removed, then a timed operation can be made to work. Timing the removal process becomes very cumbersome when different solvents are being used. We have solved this problem by constructing what amounts to an electronic nose. A model 822 Taguchi Gas Sensor (Figaro Engineering, Inc., Wilmette, IL) is mounted in a sealed chamber in the cabinet below the heated block. The sensor chamber is attached to a vacuum source and to tube leading to a sniffer probe (shown stored on the left front side of the case in Figure 7a). A Taguchi Gas Sensor is a heated metal oxide semiconductor which changes its resistance in proportion to the type and amount of gas molecules adsorbed onto its surface. TGS sensors are commonly found in sniffers used to detect natural gas leaks and breathalyzers used to detect breath alcohol. The response of TGS sensors can tailored somewhat for detecting specific gases. The model 822 sensor is especially sensitive toward common organic solvents.

When the system wants to test one of the vials, the analysis robot hand picks up the probe and inserts it into an opening in the cavity above the vial (Figure 7b). The vacuum pulls some of the vapor from the headspace above the vial across the sensor. If the vapor concentration is below a threshold value, the evaporation process is considered complete, and the vial can be removed for further processing.

Figure 7c is a rear view of the solvent removal subsystem showing the pneumatic cylinder which opens and closes the lid under computer control. One set of eight tubes can be seen leading to the vacuum manifold. A second set of tubes emanates from the eight valve nitrogen manifold which switches the nitrogen evaporation jet to each evaporation position. In front of the nitrogen manifold is a small pressure regulator which controls the pressure to the nitrogen jets.

FIGURE 7a. Inserting a Sample Vial into the Automated Solvent Evaporator.

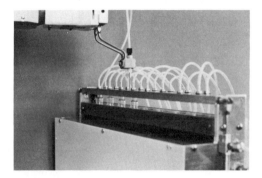

FIGURE 7b. Checking for Complete Removal of Solvent.

FIGURE 7c. A Rear View of the Automated Solvent Evaporator.

CONCLUSION

The Purdue Automated Synthesis System continues to evolve. New devices and techniques provide it with ever-increasing abilities to handle different chemical situations. Although the techniques described here were developed for a totally automated system, several of them, especially when driven by a personal computer, can be very useful on traditional synthesis benches as new solutions to old problems.

ACKNOWLEDGMENTS

We would like acknowledge the assistance of Roger Frisbee with the development of the automated addition funnel and the automated gasimeter. It is also our pleasure to recognize the efforts of Doug Lantrip, Courtland Sears, Jose Hanquier, and Glenn Sabadosa in making the PASS concept come alive. Financial support by Rhone Poulanc, Eli Lilly and Co., PPG Industries, Inc., Hewlett-Packard Co., Hoffmann-LaRoche Inc., The Dow Chemical Co., and the National Science Foundation (CHE-8406115) is gratefully acknowledged.

REFERENCES

1.   G. W. Kramer and P. L. Fuchs, "Robotic Automation in Organic Synthesis" in Advances in Laboratory Automation - Robotics 1986, J. R. Strimaitis and G. L. Hawk, eds. (Zymark Corporation, Hopkinton, MA, 1987) p 361.

2.   G. W. Kramer and P. L. Fuchs, "Robotic Automation in Organic Synthesis" in Advances in Laboratory Automation - Robotics 1985, J. R. Strimaitis and G. L. Hawk, eds. (Zymark Corporation, Hopkinton, MA, 1985) p 417.

3.   A. R. Frisbee, P. L. Fuchs, and G. W. Kramer, "Robotic Optimization of Organic Reactions - Phase I" in Advances in Laboratory Automation - Robotics 1984, G. L. Hawk and J. R. Strimaitis, eds. (Zymark Corporation, Hopkinton, MA, 1984) p 47.

4.   G. W. Kramer and P. L. Fuchs, "Automation in Organic Synthesis," Byte, 11, 263 (1986).

5.   G. W. Kramer, A. R. Frisbee, and P. L. Fuchs, "A Simple, Automated Device for the Precise Addition of Liquids," submitted for publication.

6.   G. W. Kramer, A. B. Levy, and M. Mark Midland, "Laboratory Operations with Air-Sensitive Substances: Survey," in Organic Synthesis via Boranes, H. C. Brown, (Wiley Interscience, New York, 1975) p 191.

7.   A. R. Frisbee, M. H. Nantz, G. W. Kramer, and P. L. Fuchs, "Robotic Orchestration of Organic Reactions: Optimization via an Automated System with Operator-Specified Reaction Sequences," J. Am. Chem. Soc., 106, 7143 (1984).

8.   A related system for solvent evaporation has been described by E. C. Lewis, D. R. Santarelli, and J. O. Malbica in Advances in Laboratory Automation - Robotics 1984, G. L. Hawk and J. R. Strimaitis, eds. (Zymark Corporation, Hopkinton, MA, 1984) p 237.

Zymark is a registered trademark of Zymark Corporation.

Teflon is registered trademark of E. I. DuPont de Nemours & Co.

COMPARISON OF FIRST GENERATION AND PYTECHNOLOGY ROBOTIC SYSTEMS FOR LABORATORY OPERATIONS

W. Jeffrey Hurst, Kendra C. Kuhn, and Robert A. Martin, Jr.
Analytical Research and R&D Analytical Services
Hershey Foods Corporation
P.O. Box 805
Hershey, PA 17033-0805

ABSTRACT

In the past year, PyTechnology has been introduced by Zymark allowing a robotic system to be installed and running in several days with a series of selected applications. When contrasted to Zymate I systems the difference is substantial. This presentation will be divided into three areas: PyTechnology vs. Zymate I technology, Data Correlation of PySystem vs. Manual Methods and Perceived Future Directions for Robotic Systems. In the first area the PyTechnology based systems will be compared with earlier Zymate technology as it pertains to centralized methods development and robotic implementation. As a continuation of these discussions, validation data will be presented showing a comparison with manual preparation and robot sample preparation for a variety of methods. The third area will address some perceived future directions for older Zymate systems that will add another possible dimension to robot implementation via work task dedication.

INTRODUCTION

Laboratory robotics has recently celebrated its fifth birthday and is continually developing, and maturing with over 1000 robots of various types in place in various parts of the world.[1] Zymate I and some of the Zymate II robots, while very productive in some applications, suffered from a lack of flexibility since they were purchased and placed in service for a dedicated application. In those laboratories where these dedicated applications could be accomplished routinely these units are still in operation, but many laboratories purchased and programmed units to accomplish operations that have been altered due to changes in analytical methodology or product line. These units might now be sitting fallow since the time required to reconfigure and reprogram these units is considerable. Some have said that it could take from 8-10 weeks of concentrated programming time to revalidate a new method.[2] The other alternative is to contract for external programming support which could easily be more than the original purchase price of the robot. Many laboratories have neither the time nor the money to accomplish either goal. Additionally, while equipment purchases can be capitalized, software costs sometimes cannot and therefore software costs are taken from the operating budget which in many cases is also not a feasible alternative due to limitations on this budget. In the fall of 1986, Zymark introduced PyTechnology.[tm]

PYTECHNOLOGY

PyTechnology is a new type of system architecture that allows laboratories to install and implement a specific laboratory procedure by the selection of PySections. Each of the PySections has the necessary hardware and software to allow the rapid installation and eventual operation of a particular Laboratory Unit Operation, (LUO).[2] Since the assorted PySections can be installed and removed with relative ease, it is extremely easy to reconfigure a system allowing the laboratory to be much more flexible in its robotic operations. Table 1 shows an example of some of the PySection commands for the section named Weighing-Solid Addition.

TABLE 1. Sample PySection Commands.[3]

COMMAND

GET.CONTAINER FROM.BALANCE

PUT.CONTAINER.ON.BALANCE

POUR.CONTENTS

POUR.POWDER

This manuscript will compare first generation and PyTechnology robotic systems that are in use in many labs. It will discuss the various advantages/disadvantages and compare the data developed during the validation of the PySystem.

The most obvious advantage to the PySystem is the fact that the unit is complete with hardware and the associated software necessary to accomplish a particular laboratory task. This combination allows the elimination of one of the roadblocks to successful robotic implementation - large blocks of "quality" time which must be dedicated to the new robot. This time requirement is the necessity for large blocks of a robot programmer's time. Without this time available, the time required for implementation and eventual operation occurs in small blocks and becomes excessively large. Sometimes, the entire operation can fail. With PyTechnology, once the hardware is physically installed, the software is loaded into the controller. Using a series of simple commands, the operator indicates the location of the particular PySection to the robot, and the section is then ready to run. With this technology, the necessity to teach the robot a particular position and movement is virtually eliminated.

Another advantage is that there are a large number of safety features built-in to the system. Earlier units used Confirm[tm] techniques to accomplish this action. These techniques could include the operation of a switch or the interruption of an electrical eye. However, if they were not user installed, then they were not used. Additionally, sometimes the operator would not be aware of these techniques and would not install them until a catastrophic event occurred. In PyTechnology, many of these safety provisions are built-in, making collisions almost impossible. For example, after initializing the system it then knows the location of the various peripheral items such as hands. Additionally, it knows which hand it has and where it is so, it could not do anything that would cause a collision with the hand. These features allow the elimination of another concern associated with the implementation of robotics - safety. Since safety in PyTechnology is built-in, concerns in this area are greatly minimized.

Probably the greatest advantage in this new system architecture is the concept of centralized methods development and transfer. While earlier systems would allow the transfer of methods, they required that such systems be identically configured. If such was the case, then methods transfer could then occur as might be envisioned with one laboratory sending another lab its diskette, the receiving lab installing the program and completing the methods transfer. On the other hand, if the sending and or receiving labs had differing layouts or even different workloads, then such methods transfer would not work. Either laboratory might have to invest substantial time and effort into altering the existing programs and reconfiguring the robot to allow installation in the particular lab. The time required to accomplish these tasks might outweigh the advantages and therefore such methods transfers would not occur.

In a PySystem, the "dream" of centralized methods development and transfer becomes a reality, since one is not limited to a particular hardware or environmental arrangement. In such a scenario, as long as both labs have the same PySections, then it is relatively easy to program a particular operation on one robot and then transfer its operation to another system. The rigorous physical requirements that were previously necessary to allow the transfer are now no longer required since the PySections can be placed at any location in the robot's work envelope, and the robot then told the location and the necessary programs loaded. When these actions have been accomplished, the robot can be placed into operation.

In a recent episode with Hershey Foods Corporation (HFC) laboratories, methods transfer happened immediately between a central and a division laboratory with comparable PySystems. The program disk was given to the division laboratory and installed in the system to run the application. Another related advantage in this same area is that organizations can use modestly equipped robots to develop basic methods and use this basic program as a basis for building more sophisticated programs.

In addition to the other advantages, the PySystem is very easy to use by non-technical personnel. The operator indicates the type of analysis and answers the setup prompts added by the programmer. Then the robot waits for input before continuing. Additionally, the system allows the use of the system by two different programmers; however, after programs are written with either PyTechnology or standard robotics the ease of operation of both systems is similar.

As with any new concept, no matter how attractive it might sound the proof is in its implementation. In the HFC labs, PyTechnology was implemented and used to validate a series of HPLC sample preparation methods. When compared to first generation robotics five methods were validated in a much shortened time frame. The data from one of these validation tests is summarized in Table 2.

TABLE 2.   Summary of PySystem Validation Data.(% Glucose in a Laboratory
Manufactured Sample)

Manual Extraction	Robotic Extraction
4.82	5.01
4.83	4.78
4.89	4.93
4.96	4.98
4.84	5.01
4.83	4.78
4.89	4.93
4.96	4.98
$\bar{x}$ 4.88	4.92
%CV 1.02	1.8

A review of the data from this series of studies indicates that the robot prepared samples give data that is in excellent agreement with manually prepared samples. No attempt was made to compare the time necessary to prepare both sets of samples since this concept has been discussed in several other studies.

LIMITATIONS OF PYTECHNOLOGY

While the concept is very attractive it is not without its own disadvantages.   The disadvantages are not major concerns but should be mentioned to provide a clear set of information to those considering PyTechnology or comparing standard robotics to PyTechnology. There are a limited number of PySections available, so there are a limited number of operations that can be accomplished. As more PySections become available this problem should disappear. Also, space utilization is not as efficient as earlier units. This can be considered a trade-off when gaining the hardware-software combination.

In the area of software concerns, if an operator wishes to abort an operation, in mid-operation, then all actions must be "undone" in one of two ways. The first way is to type in the individual commands required to undo the actions. For example, if it became necessary to remove the tube from a hand and place it back in its rack, then each step of the procedure must be typed individually   The second concern is since the section comes preprogrammed, then the system programmer must try to figure out Zymark commands. Additionally, since the software was not locally written written you do not always have access to variables that have been used elsewhere. While this is not a fatal flaw it is of some concern.

Since there are a limited number of PySections, then there does exist the possibility that one might need other sections. One is then left with three possible decisions: (1) develop the method on a non-Py system (2) attempt to custom design your own PySections (3) contract for a custom designed PySection. In our opinion, the most attractive of these alternatives is to attempt the second option. If one does attempt this option then the inability to obtain information about the Zymark programming and syntax is a concern. Additionally, should one have an item of equipment such as the centrifuge that is currently underutilized in a standard system then it might be suitable for inclusion in a PySystem. If it has been purchased prior to Py then the interfacing becomes extremely difficult since the "custom designing" of a section becomes a reality.

NON-PY SYSTEMS

As the final component when comparing the dedicated and PyTechnology approach to robotics, one is sometimes faced with what to do with a first generation non-Py robot. In many cases, an earlier robot cannot be upgraded or modified to allow its use in a PySystem, so the choice must be made to either purchase a totally new system or not purchase anything and attempt to go it alone. A first approach is to allow it to go fallow which is of course politically unwise and not the best of resources. The second and more attractive approach might be convert these systems to a series of dedicated workstations.

One could conduct a use survey of the operations in a laboratory that are considered time-consuming and boring. Many of these operation might have even been considered for automation but were not adopted due to other priority needs for the robot. It might be an appropriate time to consider the workstation approach to robotics. For example, after such a use survey one might realize that weighing for oven moistures is a most labor intensive operation in the laboratory and that if this operation could be automated the laboratory would realize a substantial time savings. This approach could most probably be applied to any number of LUO's, such as liquid-solid extraction, liquid-liquid extraction, or centrifugation. A potential group of these workstations can be seen in Table 3.

SUMMARY

PyTechnology has an obvious advantage over a dedicated system in the area of methods transfer and centralized methods development, but this type of usage might leave another robot underutilized by the laboratory. These robots could then be converted into workstations for other uses in the lab and both types of system could then be used to their ultimate potential. That potential is increased laboratory throughput and productivity and the resulting improvement of the work environment for laboratory personnel.

TABLE 3. Potential Dedicate Workstations

Application	LUO(s)
Weigh station for oven moistures	Weighing and manipulation measurement, control
Liquid/Solid extraction	Liquid handling, separation
Liquid/Liquid extraction	Liquid handling, separation conditioning
Serial dilution	Liquid handling, manipulation

REFERENCES

1. Personnel Reference.

2. Zymark Corporation, Instruction Manual, Vol. I.

3. Zymark Corporation, PyTechnology Catalog.

ANALYSIS OF BLOOD AND SALIVARY CHOLINESTERASE ACTIVITY USING AN AUTOMATED MICRO-RADIOMETRIC TECHNIQUE

Anthony G. Roccograndi, Jr., Eric W. Kaldy,
Robert A. Miller, Jay A. Chepanonis, Aaron J. Jacobs
US Army Institute of Dental Research
Walter Reed Army Medical Center
Washington, DC 20307

ABSTRACT

Blood cholinesterase activity levels are used to monitor exposure to organophosphates (insecticides) and to diagnose both liver disease and megaloblastic anemia. In order to minimize the hazard of handling both biological samples (which may be pathogenic in nature) and radioisotopes, the enzymatic assay was automated using laboratory robotics. The Zymate^{tm} Laboratory Automation System has been programmed to prepare the samples in less than 10 minutes. This decrease in preparation time allows the liquid scintillation counter to be operated at maximum throughput (1 sample/10 minutes). The cholinesterase assay requires the pipetting of microliter quantities of blood, blood components and highly viscous saliva. The blood is separated into three components (whole blood, plasma, and packed cells) by centrifuging prior to the enzymatic assay. This pipetting is done with a electronically controlled 25 microliter positive displacement syringe. Water, 0.05M phosphate buffer at pH-8 and the tritiated acetylcholine substrate are added to the sample which is incubated for 5 minutes at 37^0C. Stop solution (1M $CICH_2COOH$, 2.0M NaC1, pH-2.5) is immediately added and the mixture is transferred to a scintillation vial. Scintillation cocktail is added, the vial capped, the sample-cocktail solution is mixed and placed in scintillation counter rack. The rack must be placed into the scintillation counter by a technician/analyst.

The developed robotic system provides increased sample throughput, precise and accurate results, and requires no hands-on technician involvement during the preparation process.

INTRODUCTION

A micro-radiometric assay was being performed manually to determine the different levels of cholinesterase activity in blood and saliva for individuals exposed to organophosphates. Clinically, serum cholinesterase levels have been used to monitor exposure to organophosphates (insecticides) and have been associated with a number of human disease states. Low levels of serum cholinesterase are found in patients with liver disease, malnutrition, and anemias.[1] Moderately elevated serum levels are found in patients with nephrotic syndrome and some increase may be found in hyperthyrodism.[1] Many common insecticides depress cholinesterase activity in serum, indicating over-exposure to these compounds.

The levels of activity can be attributed to the two groups of cholinesterase, acetylcholinesterase and pseudocholinesterase. There are two specific acetylcholinesterases which hydrolyze only acetylcholine; however, there are eleven non-specific cholinesterase enzymes (or pseudocholinesterases) which hydrolyze the esters of benzoylcholine, butyrylcholine, tributyrin and alpha-naphthylpropionate.[2] Acetylcholinesterase is found in brain, nerve cells, muscle, lung, erythrocytes and has been reported in saliva.[3] Pseudocholinesterase is found in serum and also has been reported in saliva.[4] The comparison of salivary cholinesterase to blood cholinesterase levels requires dividing the blood into three fractions (whole blood, plasma and RBC's) and comparing their enzyme levels to the enzyme levels of both parotid and extraparotid saliva.

The cholinesterase activity can be determined by any of several techniques: manometric measurement, electronic measurement of the change in pH, photometric measurement, and radiometric measurement. High levels of reproducibility are difficult to attain and maintain since the techniques and small sample sizes require extreme precision. There was an obvious need for a more consistent, reliable method of running the assay that was independent of human technical consistency.

The radiometric method was selected for automation because the extreme sensitivity of the technique would provide the best test for the precision of the automated preparation techniques. Preparation techniques are based on the method of Johnson and Russell[5] with modifications made to volumes of samples and reagents. This technique uses a tritiated acetylcholine substrate which liberates tritiated acetic acid upon hydrolysis. The tritiated acetic acid is then extracted from the aqueous phase into the scintillation cocktail and counted in the liquid scintillation counter. Additional concerns that led to the decision to introduce automation were the desire to decrease exposure of laboratory personnel to radioactivity and biohazards and the desire to increase sample throughput.

MATERIALS AND METHODS

Equipment; Table Setup

The robotic system is a Zymate II Laboratory Automation System. The equipment is listed in Table 1 and table layout is depicted in Figure 1. All chemicals used are from Fisher Scientific, Fairlawn, NJ, unless otherwise noted.

TABLE 1. Robotic Equipment.

1.	Zymate robot	19.	Empty vial rack
2.	250 uL syringe hand	20.	Radioactive tip waste
3.	2 mL pipet tip rack	21.	Heating block
4.	Centrifuge	22.	Master laboratory station(MLS)
5.	Vacuum motor	23.	Empty vial rack
6.	Vacuum flask	24.	Saline reservoir
7.	Vacuum flask	25.	Wash station reservoir
8.	Suction cannula	26.	Zymate controller & printer
9.	Centrifuge rack	27.	Mettler balance
10.	Tip waste	28.	Wash station
11.	Sample vial rack	29.	Capping station
12.	Substrate blood rack	30.	Cap dispenser
13.	250 uL pipet rack	31.	Sample conditioning station
14.	Dual function hand	32.	MLS dispense station
15.	Positive displacement syringe	33.	Scintillation rack
16.	Vortex station	34.	Stop solution reservoir
17.	Capping station	35.	Scintillation reservoir
18.	Power and event controller(PEC)	36.	Master laboratory station

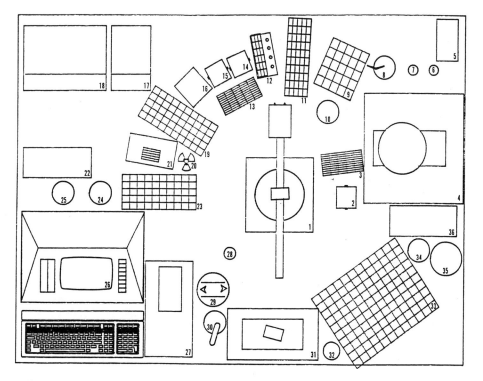

FIGURE 1. Bench Layout for Automated Micro-Radiometric Technique. (not drawn to scale).

STANDARD ASSAY PROCEDURE

The manual procedure is carried out in batch form, processing all samples in sequence throughout each step of the assay. The automated procedure is a serialized process which carries out the same steps of the manual process although not necessarily in the same order. This difference had no effect on results.

The sequence for the automated cholinesterase assay is broken down into the following procedures- sample preparation, assay, and scintillation preparation. To visualize the assay refer to Figure 1. The bracketed numbers after each step indicate the sequence of stations.

Sample Preparation of Blood

1. With the dual function hand, remove an aliquot of whole blood, 1 mL, from a 2 mL vacutainer (Becton-Dickinson, Rutherford, NJ) and place in a 10 mL centrifuge tube (Nalge Company, Rochester, NY). Discard tip (Elkay Products, Inc., Shrewsbury, MA. [14,3,12,9,10]

2. Transfer sample with general purpose hand to centrifuge. Centrifuge sample at 3,000 rpm for 2 minutes to separate RBC's from plasma. [9,4]

3. After centrifuging, place centrifuge tube in rack. Then remove plasma layer with dual function hand and place in a microbute (PGC Scientifics, Gaithersburg, MD) held in a cooling block for later use. Discard tip. [4,9,3,9,11,10]

4. Wash remaining RBC's with 0.9% saline, vortex and recentrifuge. Remove saline layer via suction and repeat step 4 once. [9,16,4] [8,16,4]

5. After second washing and removal of subsequent saline layer return packed RBC's to centrifuge rack. [4,8,9,]

6. Transfer an empty vial to the balance and tare. With positive displacement syringe, pipet 10 uL whole blood, plasma or packed cells into a microtube and weigh in balance (Mettler Instrument Corporation, Hightstown, NJ). With the general purpose hand, place microtube in heating block. [19,27,15 (12,11, or 9) 27,14,21]

7. Dilute with 30 uL of distilled H_2O using 205 uL syringe. Discard tip. [2,13,12,21,10]

Sample Preparation of Saliva

For saliva, omit pipeting blood and H_2O, and pipet 40 uL of saliva into the microtube.

Assay

1. Add 40 uL of 0.5M potassium phosphate buffer with the 250 uL syringe and discard tip. [13,12,21,10]

2. Add 40 uL of tritiated 0.165mM acetyl choline substrate (New England Nuclear, Boston, MA). Mix thoroughly by drawing ingredients in and out of the pipet and stirring. Discard tip. [13,12,21,20]

3. Incubate in heating block (Microtube Incubator Denville Scientific, Denville, NJ at room temp. for 11 minutes [21]

4. With the dual function hand immediately add 120 uL of stop solution containing 1M chloroacetic acid, .5M NaOH, and 2M NaCl, pH 2.5. [14,3,12,21,10]

Scintillation Preparation

1. Transfer the microtube with the dual function hand into a scintillation vial (Wheaton Scientific, Fairlawn, NJ). [21,33]

2. Transfer scintillation vial to MLS dispense station and add 10 mL of scintillation cocktail consisting of isoamyl alcohol, toluene, and liquifluor (New England Nuclear, Boston, MA, (300:700:50). [33,32]

3. Cap scintillation vial. [29,30]

4. Shake vial and return to scintillation rack for counting in the scintillation counter (Beckman Instruments, Inc., Irvine, CA). [31,33]

The robot will perform the procedure in duplicate for each blood component for each of a set of four samples for a total of 24 samples, (e.g. start with four 2 mL vacutainers of whole blood, end product equals eight reacted whole blood samples, eight reacted plasma samples, and eight reacted RBC samples, or a total of 24 samples per run).

The three procedures of the automated cholinesterase assay consists of several subprograms that allow the sample to be processed in groups of four. This was initiated by spinning of the blood in four centrifuge tubes, which allows the robot to integrate the subprograms while waiting for a portion of the process to be completed. For example, when blood is placed in the centrifuge and started to spin, the robot then attaches another hand and adds reagents to the already weighed whole blood. This interprogramming allows the robot to be highly efficient because many subprocesses get done concurrently.

Saliva is analyzed independently of blood using a subroutine of the cholinesterase procedure also in sets of four.

RESULTS AND DISCUSSION

The reproducibility of the results obtained with the robot controlled syringes was determined by pipetting 10 aliquots of water with each syringe and then weighing each individual volume on the analytical balance. The results are illustrated in Figure 2.

The graph demonstrates that the smallest volume which is acceptable to be pipetted is 10 uL, 35 uL and 120 uL for the 25 uL positive displacement syringe, the 250 uL syringe, and the 1 mL syringe, respectively. The acceptable level of variation for the 25 uL syringe and 250 uL syringe is 5%. The quantity of stop solution added does not affect the enzyme activity so a higher percent variation is acceptable for the 1 mL syringe. A 10% variation was measured for 120 uL syringe.

The positive displacement syringe was acquired because it was observed that a residue was left inside the pipet tip when pipetting blood. Therefore, weighing of the blood aliquot was added to the assay to insure that the sample was pipetted precisely. This allows for an accurate calculation of enzyme activity per unit volume.

The precision of the method is described in Table 2. In this comparison, both the manual and robotic determinations used equivalent volumes and reaction times. Repetitive analysis of 10 Rhesus monkey blood samples resulted in coefficient of variations of 7.4% for packed cells, 2.9% for whole blood, and 6% for plasma by the manual technique. Similar analysis by the robot (see Table 2 section II., without mixing + 5 sec shake) resulted in coefficient of variations of 28.9% for packed cells, 25.5% for whole blood and 12.3% for plasma.

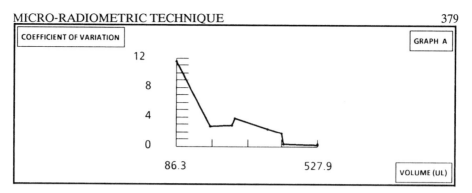

PRECISION OF 1000 ul SYRINGE

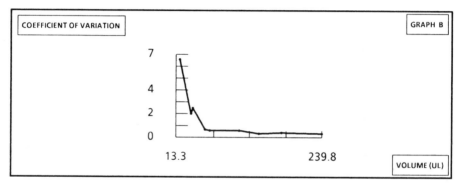

PRECISION OF 250 ul SYRINGE

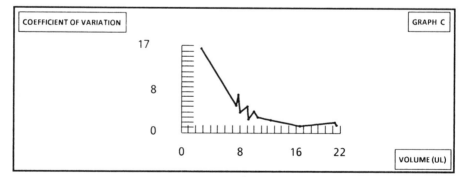

PRECISION OF 25 ul POSITIVE DISPLACEMENT SYRINGE

FIGURE 2. Syringe Reproducibility.

TABLE 2. Precision of the Method.

SAMPLE	AVERAGE ENZYME ACTIVITY (Unit/Min/Ml)	% VARIATION
I. Manual Assay		
Packed Cells	2.39	7.4
Whole Blood	2.53	2.9
Plasma	2.43	6.0
	Average	5.4
II. Without mixing & 5 second shake		
Packed Cells	1.64	28.9
Whole Blood	1.87	25.5
Plasma	1.92	12.3
	Average	22.2
III. Mixing & 5 second shake		
Packed Cells	2.14	9.6
Whole Blood	2.24	5.2
Plasma	2.32	1.7
	Average	5.5
IV. Mixing & 15 second shake		
Packed Cells	-----	-----
Whole Blood	2.43	3.6
Plasma	2.49	1.1
	Average	2.3

This difference between the manual and robotic techniques was attributed to the sample mixing. In the manual technique, mixing occurs as one rapidly dispenses the substrate from the pipet directly on the sample. Unfortunately, this did not occur with the robot. Therefore, a modification to the subprogram of adding the tritiated acetylcholine substrate was introduced. The program now mixes the sample, H_2O, buffer, and substrate by drawing the ingredients in and out of the pipet tip while rotating the tip around the inside of the vial. This combined mixing and stirring technique reduced the coeeficient of variation to 9.6% for the packed cells, 5.2% for the whole blood, and 1.7% for the plasma. The same mixing and stirring technique increased the enzyme activity from 1.64 units/min/mL to 2.14 units/min/mL for packed cells, from 1.87 units/min/mL to 2.24 units/min/mL for whole blood, and from 1.92 Units/min/ml to 2.32 units/min/mL for plasma. While the average percent variation of the robotic technique section III (5.4%) was similar to that of the manual technique I (5.5%), the enzyme activity was lower for the robot.

At this point in the assay, a portion of the reaction mixture remained in the microtube during the extraction, unlike the manual technique. By increasing the extraction time (5 sec shake to 15 sec shake) the entire reaction mixture was dissipated from the microtube yielding cholinesterase levels of 2.43 units/min/mL for whole blood and 2.49 units/min/mL for plasma. The similarity in the results from the manual and robotic techniques demonstrates that both techniques have the same accuracy. Since there are no cholinesterase standards available, additional tests for accuracy were not performed.

The present bench layout allows for a total sample capacity of 16 vacutainers of blood (96 analyses) or 50 saliva samples (100 analyses). The sample throughput on the lab automation system exceeds the 10 minute count on the liquid scintillation counter because the robot processes a sample in 7.5 minutes. Currently, the layout is limited by the number of small syringe tips. When the number of tip racks is increased, the robotic technique will analyze 192 samples/24hrs routinely compared to 168 samples which can be maximally processed manually in an eight hour day.

An automated system for enzyme analysis (cholinesterase) has been developed by incorporating a microsyringe with standard laboratory robotic stations. The automated assay initiates with raw samples and concludes with scintillation vials in racks ready for counting. There is an excellent correlation between the data produced by robotic and manual analytical methods with a smaller coefficient of variation for replicate analysis using the Zymate System. This laboratory robotic system allows investigators and technicians time to perform other laboratory and administrative duties.

ACKNOWLEDGEMENTS

The authors would like to thank Debra R. Oehler and Kay A. Cornwell for their administrative assistance; Martin A. Dempf III and Wayne Verost for their technical support; and the consultants Dr. Lewis Lorton and Dr. Alvin Williams in the preparation of this study.

REFERENCES

1. A.L. Latner, Cantarow and Trumper, Clinical Biochemistry, 7th Ed. (W.B. Saunders Co., Philadelphia, 1975, pp. 552.

2. H.U. Bergmeyer, Methods of Enzymatic Analysis, 2nd Ed. (Academic Press, Inc., New York, 1974), pp. 831.

3. K. Ueda and K. Yamaguchi, "Cholinesterase Activity of Human Saliva Types of the Enzymes", Bull. Tokyo Dent. Coll., 17(4),231 (1976).

4. R. Ryhanen, M.E. Puhakainen, O. Hanninen, and V. Kontturi-Narhi, "Pseudocholinesterase Activity and its Origin in Human Oral Fluid", J. Dent. Res., 62 (1) pp.20 (1983).

5. C.D. Johnson and R.L. Russell, "A Rapid, Simple Radiometric Assay for Cholinesterase, Suitable for Multiple Determinations", Anal. Biochem 64, 229, (1975).

TRENDS IN LABORATORY AUTOMATION - 1987

Francis H. Zenie
Zymark Corporation
Hopkinton, MA 01748

INTRODUCTION

The Automation Dilemma is posed through two key questions:

Are the benefits worth the work, investment and possible risk?

Will competition gain a strategic advantage by acting faster than me?

Business Week magazine recently published a comprehensive analysis of office automation. To emphasize the key findings, they summarized their recommendations in a brief editorial.

> "Office automation fulfills its promise only when organizations are reshaped by top management to take advantage of the benefits it offers. Even though business is still in a period of experimentation with electronic tools, managers are using them to boost competitiveness, not just productivity. No company can afford to be left behind."[1]

Laboratory automation is often seen in the limited role as an economic alternative to manual operation. Recently, however, effective laboratories have recognized automation as an opportunity to create a strategic advantage.

The economic alternative to manual operation approach is typically in response to immediate needs to increase capacity or to make people available for other work. Generally, there is no requirement for improved results. Fast installation and start-up is essential because the need may be urgent. Justification is based on a direct cost comparison between manual and automated alternatives.

The key in the strategic advantage approach is better decisions - that is, timely, quality decisions based on valid data. Better decisions should lead to:

1. More effective Research & Development - i.e., innovative new products, often tailored or optimized for a defined (specialty) use, ready for timely commercialization.

2. Higher quality products for improved customer satisfaction and greater market share.

3. Improved organizational productivity.

4. Reduced risks to employees and the environment.

Our leading chemical, pharmaceutical, food, energy and biotechnology companies face intense, world-wide competition. Today, improving laboratory quality and productivity has reached a strategic urgency in many of these organizations. Justification for strategic advantage is made by comparing the present value of the future benefits to the cost or investment required to implement the project. While the risks associated with strategic advantage are usually higher than those associated with economic alternative, the potential benefits are far greater!

Remember, however, the easy advances in laboratory automation are behind us. The next step brings increased risk and requires greater commitment, but the potential benefits are well worth the investment and are essential to meeting the organization's technical, marketing and corporate strategies.

THE LABORATORY'S STRATEGIC ROLE

Strategically, laboratories provide information for business decisions. Competition demands that laboratories apply technology in the "Determined Pursuit of Corporate Strategy". Since strategy must be dynamic, laboratories must constantly improve. High value-added products lead to outstanding profitability and need superior laboratory support to insure meeting customer needs and expectations.

To be outstanding, organizations must create:

MORE PRODUCTIVE LABORATORIES with
MORE EFFECTIVE PEOPLE producing
HIGHER QUALITY RESULTS.

Century Oils Ltd. of Stoke-on-Kent, England illustrates a creative approach to using laboratory services as a key strategic contributor. Century Oils supplies premium lubricating products. Strategically, however, their unique added value is wear protection of valuable customer equipment. Rather than differentiate the chemistry of their oils, they provide a comprehensive testing service to alert customers of approaching wear problems and to recommend corrective action.

Century Oils operates a highly automated laboratory with modern instruments, computerized data handling and documentation and a laboratory robotics system to subdivide and distribute customer samples for various analytical procedures. Contamination and wear trends are recognized quickly by comparing current results with prior results stored in the customer data base. Strategically, Century Oils has created a competitive advantage using laboratory automation to assure customers of timely, quality warnings of potential wear or contamination problems.

A NEW LOOK AT JUSTIFICATION

We now know that justifying laboratory automation must include both economic and strategic factors.

Economic Justification

"It is unreasonable to ask that a lab guarantee a reduction inpersonnel upon introduction of a robotic system. Such a reduction should not be expected, at least during the first 6-12 months after the system has begun functioning. What I do guarantee is the fact that over a period of time, the use of lab robotics will result in significant technician time savings and increased lab efficiency. These time savings will lead to a reduction of personnel involved in routine procedures, or allow the lab to take on additional projects.[2]

Since laboratory robotics offers an alternative to manual procedures, economic justification is based on a comparison of automated versus manual approaches. Laboratory robotics is flexible automation, thus economic justification considers all the procedures for which the system will be used. An Economic Justification Index (EJI) can be estimated as follows:

$$EJI = \frac{\text{Annual Hours Saved} * \text{Average Cost per Hour}}{\text{Total Installed Cost}}$$

Where:

Annual Hours Saved =   Total number of hours saved for all procedures automated by the system

Average Cost per Hour =   Analyst cost per hour including fringe

Total Installed Cost =   Total cost of robotic system including instrumentation, accessories, methods development and programming

Table 1 illustrates guidelines for evaluating the Economic Justification Index for a proposed automation project.

TABLE 1. Economic Justification Index Guidelines.

EJI	Evaluation	Comment
>1.0	Compelling	Proceed with project
0.75 - 1.0	Good	Proceed with project
0.5 - 0.75	Acceptable	Check strategic justification
0.3 - 0.5	Marginal	Requires compelling strategic justification

Strategic Justification

Although harder to quantify, strategic benefits are often more valuable than simple cost savings compared to manual techniques. Faster new product introductions and higher quality, more competitive products can change the entire business outlook. Laboratory automation offers the following potential benefits which, in turn, create strategic advantages.

High Quality Results - Better precision than manual results leading to higher quality products, more effective research and faster new product introductions.

Multiple Application Flexibility - Ability to do multiple procedures, transfer proven procedures between laboratories, and the flexibility to reconfigure when needs change.

Faster Turnaround of Results - More rapid availability of information leading to more timely decisions in research, product development, quality control and process control.

Safety - Isolate people from hazardous environments or protect critical experiments from human contamination.

TABLE 2. Strategic Justification Index Determination.

Factor	Rating*
High Quality Results	_____
Multiple Application Flexibility	_____
Faster Turnaround	_____
Safety	_____
Total	_____

*Rating Guidelines: 0 = Not very important, 1 = Beneficial but not compelling, 2 = Very important

The Economic Justification Index (EJI) and Strategic Justification Index (SJI) may be represented in the two dimensional monograph, shown in Figure 1, to indicate the combined justification for a proposed project.

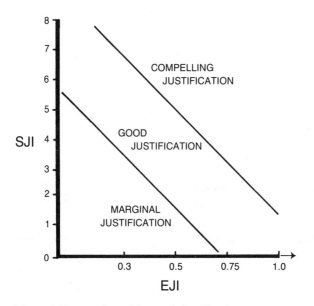

Figure 1. Economic and Strategic Justification.

ROBOTICS - FLEXIBLE, SYSTEMS TECHNOLOGY

A system is defined as a group of interdependent, interacting elements combined to perform a unified purpose. The term Laboratory Robotics overemphasizes the robotic arm rather than the integrated system of Laboratory Unit Operations (LUOs). The robotic arm is a system element for materials handling and simple manipulation. A more useful definition is: laboratory robotics is the extension of programmable computers which allows computers to do physical work as well as process data.[3] System flexibility is vital; three levels of flexibility are available in the ideal situation.

Experimental - Programmable method parameters.

Multiple Procedure - Programmable procedure selection from a program library.

Reconfiguration - Efficient system reconfiguration for new applications.

Laboratory robotics must build on an architecture that provides a foundation for continuing technology development and achieves the required systems flexibility. The key elements of this architecture are:

1. **Modular Structure** - Modularity is required for flexible adaptation to a wide range of laboratory procedures. New or improved capabilities should be compatible with earlier systems so that pioneers, willing to assist in the early applications, are protected from obsolescence as the technology develops.

2. **Built-in Technique** - Quality laboratory results require the consistent use of the best available techniques. Wherever possible, each laboratory robotics module should incorporate valid, tested techniques to eliminate human or procedure variability.

3. **Easy Programming** - Complex computer applications, which require sophisticated programming support, reduce control of laboratory operations by the laboratory staff. Since laboratory robotics must be flexible in order to perform a wide range of procedures, programming is best performed by the laboratory staff.

4. **Computer and Instrument Compatibility** - Laboratory robotics must function as an integrated system with general purpose laboratory computers and a wide selection of analytical instruments. Optimum performance is possible when the user is free to use the best available computer and instrument capability.

ROBOTICS - A BETTER WAY

Real automation innovations occur when we challenge old ideas and release our minds to create new approches which utilize the unique strengths of modern technology. The best innovations will be elegant in concept but simple in execution. If we only need a quick economic alternative, we will tend to grasp the smallest increment from where we are. If we seek a strategic advantage, however, we need to stretch for a more creative approach.

Separate the goal from the current procedure - think of totally new ways to achieve the goal using the best available technology and ideas. For example, James E. Curley and his colleagues at Pfizer, Inc. Central Research in Groton, CT needed to automate pharmaceutical tablet dissolution to meet ever increasing demands for dissolution rate data. In the Fall of 1984,[4] they reported the use of a Zymate System to perform dissolution rate tests on six tablets according to USP Method II. The dissolution procedure was performed by the robotic system, but a person was still required to add testing medium to each vessel at the beginning of each run and to clean the vessels afterwords.

In the Fall of 1985,[5] Curley and his colleagues reported fully automated dissolution testing where the robotic system cleaned and filled vessels between each run permitting testing of up to twelve sets of six tablets without manual intervention. This enhancement required a creative breakthrough. In current procedures, vessels were manually removed from the dissolution baths and washed, scrubbed and dried. The vessels were then manually returned to the bath and filled with medium. Emulating this procedure would have been difficult and, therefore, unreliable for the laboratory robot. Curley formed the question, "Could the vessel be pumped dry, cleaned in place with a spray nozzle and then filled with medium by the robotic system?". Simple experiments showed that this approach worked as well as the prior techniques and could be performed reliably by the robotic system. This new approach permitted them to report "By running overnight, the robot can perform in a 24-hour period what a person would accomplish in the usual 40-hour work week."

The robotic system also assures a high level of quality by automatically checking and validating test parameters. The system checks and records medium temperature - and waits until specified temperature conditions exist. Before introducing sample tablets, the system checks blank medium from each vessel. If any blank absorbance falls outside the predetermined limit, the system will rewash and refill the vessels before proceeding. The Pfizer example illustrates how the quality of analytical results is assured by automatically checking critical test parameters prior to running actual samples. Automation permits continuous validation to assure and document specified test conditions.

Richard B. Anderson and Ronald F. Quadrell of Glaxo, Inc. -Quality Directorate in Zebulon, NC design their laboratory robotics systems using continuous validation to gain accountability and security.[6] Two systems have been implemented using quantitative liquid transfers confirmed by self-calibrating, gravimetric methods. Maximum accountability for all other critical parameters and a simple, effective approach to system security are incorporated in these systems. For example, in an HPLC Tablet Assay procedure, large volumes of methanol are gravimetrically dispensed. They report "This technique compensates for the gradual heating of methanol continually pumped and recirculated through the reservoir. The precision achieved reduces the error in this dispensing to less than one part-per-thousand." Internal standards are also introduced gravimetrically. The error reported "...measured against a theoretical ratio of aliquot-to-internal standard, ranges less than one percent."

Similar validation tests are performed by their automated tablet dissolution system. All test results are permanently documented with a flag to indicate any parameter which lies outside acceptable ranges. Continuous validation combined with permanent documentation (Data Base) assures improved quality of and accountability for results.

Stanley P. Kovell, special assistant to the director of the Environmental Protection Agency's Office of Remedial Response, describes the role of the agency's Contract Laboratory Program (CLP).[7] CLP uses private laboratories to furnish the EPA with "state-of-the-art chemical analysis on a high volume basis" and provide "legally defensible" analytical results. The analytical results exhibit a high level of quality assurance, extensive documentation, maintenance of chain-of-custody information on samples, and a high degree of intra-and interlaboratory consistency.

SUCCEEDING WITH LABORATORY ROBOTICS

Implementing laboratory robotics is a project requiring goals, planning, resources, milestones and leadership. Experience shows that all successful implementation projects include the following five steps:

1. Manual Validation of Automated Techniques
2. System Configuration and Functional Test
3. Method Programs for Single Sample
4. Laboratory Validation of the Automated Method
5. Method Programs for Multiple Samples (Serialized)

While it is important to begin with a proven manual method, it should be adapted, when necessary, to take advantage of automation capabilities. The first step, therefore, should be Manual Validation of New Automated Techniques and Disposables.

System Configuration and Functional Test includes design of the detailed automated procedure, specification of any custom accessories, bench layout and preparation of a functional (not application) test program.

Single Sample Programming develops programs to process a single sample through the entire application ready for validation.

Laboratory Validation of the automated method must be performed by the end-user under actual laboratory conditions. The purpose of validation is to uncover problems not anticipated during initial configuration and programming and, then, revise the configuration and programs until valid results are achieved.

Multiple Sample Programming develops programs required to serialize and optimize operation for efficiently running multiple samples.

The end-user/project manager is responsible for final system operation and performance. The automation vendor's role is to provide products within an integrated system architecture, effective customer training, comprehensive documentation and offer professional technical support, as required, to complement the customer's staff.

A survey of successful laboratory robotics installations was conducted earlier this year. Responses were received from individuals representing 66 system installations. They ranked the following factors (on a subjective 0 - 100 scale) as keys to success:

FACTOR	RATING
Application Selection	85
Vendor Support	85
Management Support	80
Internal Technical Support	75
User Training	70

Some specific comments also provide insight into successful implementation:

"Having a realistic, obtainable goal for the first robotic application is extremely important."

"Most important is picking the key person to implement the technology. That one person will make or break the success of the initial application."

"The single most important factor in getting a system up and running and keep it running, in my experience, is to dedicate a person to the project."

"Don't bite off more than can be achieved quickly. Add to a system rather than trying to do everything at once. The more you get running, the more your mind and imagination will naturally lead you to improved approaches."

"Certainly the benefits of lab robotics are not free. They result from an initial investment in time, effort and creativity."

"We must change the way we look at procedures, Now we look how to adapt a human procedure to a robotic procedure when the human way may not be best. Machines have distinct advantages over humans in repetitive task performance .... they don't get tired or bored and are content doing the 1000th sample the same way as sample 1."
"Morale is up! It is a challenge and exciting not a threat."

Laboratory robotics is a powerful tool. As with any such tool, knowledge gained through education and experience is the key to success. This knowledge permits us to gain control over our environment. As tools and systems become more complex, we need more knowledge to maintain control.

TRENDS

The trends in laboratory robotics presented at prior meetings[3,8,9] continue to be valid today. A few points, however, are worth specific emphasis.

In critical applications, laboratory robotics must be an integral part of a higher level information system. Permanent, legally defensible data and data analysis is essential. The need for audits and accountability is increasing. Information interfaces must match common industry standards.

System reliability must continue to increase. This requires improved equipment reliability and more valid and consistent techniques. This area offers outstanding opportunities to develop innovative, new laboratory techniques which take advantage of laboratory robotic's unique capabilities.

Automated, robotic workstations will be developed for well defined combinations of laboratory unit operations (LUOs) which are common to many procedures. Within this capability, workstation will be very flexible and offer large sample capacity to minimize human intervention.

CONCLUSION

We now stand on a higher platform from which to move forward. I recommend three principles to guide our way.

Education: Successful technologies have always been built on a foundation of proficient professionals. To gain the potential strategic advantage of laboratory robotics is worth the investment in knowledge and experience.

Standardization: Consistency is the route to quality. Only through standardization can we identify the critical technique factors required for excellent laboratory results and then incorporate these techniques permanently into improved products. This standardization will permit less skilled people to achieve quality results using laboratory robotics.

Innovation: Achieving better results than current methods requires new methodology and processes which builds on the unique strengths of laboratory robotics. We must demand creative thinking which challenges conventional practice.

These continue to be exciting times to be a chemist. The laboratory robotics revolution is gaining momentum and its strategic role in our organizations is becoming clear.

REFERENCES

1. "Automation: The Boss Should Be Involved,": Business Week, October 12, 1987, p190.

2. "Clearing a Bottleneck in the Laboratory," Industrial Chemist, July 1987, p. 29.

3. F.H. Zenie, "Trends in Laboratory Automation - Technology and Economics", Advances in Laboratory Automation, Robotics - 1984, pp 1-16.

4. J. E. Curley, in Advances in Laboratory Automation - Robotics 1984, G. L. Hawk and J. R. Strimaitis, eds (Zymark Corporation, Hopkinton, MA) p 299.

5. L. J. Kostek, B. A. Brown, J. E. Curley, "Fully Automated Dissolution Testing" in Advances in Laboratory Automation -Robotics 1985, G. L. Hawk and J. R. Strimaitis, eds (Zymark Corporation, Hopkinton, MA) pp 701-720.

6. Richard B. Anderson and Ronald F. Quadrell, "Continuous Validation and System Security for Robotics in the Pharmaceutical Laboratory" in Advances in Laboratory Automation -Robotics 1986, G. L. Hawk and J. R. Strimaitis, eds (Zymark Corporation, Hopkinton, MA) pp 113-123.

7. Contract Labs Respond to Growing Demand for Analytical Testing, Chemical and Engineering News, September 7, 1987 p 33.

8. F.H. Zenie, "Strategic Trends in Laboratory Automation - 1985", Advances in Laboratory Automation, Robotics - 1985, pp 43-59.

9. F.H. Zenie, "Strategic Trends in Laboratory Automation - 1986", Advances in Laboratory Automation, Robotics - 1986, pp 571-580.

MAKING LABORATORY ROBOTS SMART

R. D. Jones, H. R. Pinnick, Jr., and J. B. Cross
Phillips Petroleum Company
Bartlesville, OK 74005

ABSTRACT

Valuable quantities of "intelligence" can be captured in languages as simple as BASIC and loaded into the minds of today's laboratory robots. The result is not just clever programming but robotic systems equipped to deal with the unexpected, the unintended, and the undesired- in other words, operational failures. This paper examines some of the building blocks of machine intelligence, and uses numerous, real world examples to illustrate their applicability to problems in laboratory robotics.

INTRODUCTION

Failure (of some sort) is a persistent phenomenon in sustained robotic operation. However, it will be the premise of this paper that a given failure may, of itself, be less significant than the robot's reaction to it.

"Stupid" robots ignore trouble. When it comes, they bumble blissfully on, wreaking havoc throughout their environment. "Dumb" robots simply recognize a problem exists, and cease operation until human intervention corrects it. "Smart" robots, as they will be defined here, go beyond the simple problem detection/system shutdown mode of operation. Strategically embedded throughout their programming are decision-making, problem handling subroutines which often lie dormant during normal operation. The nature of these subroutines can be loosely categorized as either failure preventative or failure reactive. The former strives to avoid trouble; the latter confronts it head on.

Obviously, no amount of programming can render any robot fail safe, but carefully crafted programming can make many systems decidedly more failure resistant. This translates into greater reliability, less downtime, and higher productivity. Developing "smart" programming requires not only a through understanding of a given robot's assigned duties but, equally important, a knowledge of the many ways in which it might conceivably fail to execute them. Then comes the formidable task of analyzing potential problems and determining what -- if anything -- a machine that is slow, clumsy, stupid, and practically blind can do to avoid or resolve them.

HOW IT WORKS

The essence of smart programming is coding which causes a robot's controller to do one of the things computers do best - make YES or NO decisions. Three steps are involved. First, the computer must ask the right question (*does problem "x" exist?*). Second, it must be able to answer that question (*yes or no*). Last of all, the robot's programming must include appropriate responses for either answer.

Framing the right question is simply a matter of writing code (for example, IF *such and such is true* THEN *do so and so*). Answering it is a bit more complicated. Basically, the robot's controller needs information. It can come from two sources which, in practice, often merge- external input (like sensors and user supplied data) and internal "reasoning" (such as counters, calculations, and the automatic initialization of key variables to predetermined values).

A robot may use this information to answer questions directly (as through the closure of a microswitch that signals the presence of a pipette tip) or indirectly (by inferring the answer from other data -- i.e. there was no change between the "dirty" weight of a sieve being cleaned and the "clean" weight, therefore the cleaning system is malfunctioning). Once the question has been answered, the robot's next move is automatically decided.

This then is the mind of a machine: rigidly logical, painfully unimaginative, ruthlessly consistent, but also quite capable of dealing with the simple, orderly world of a robotic workcell. Now let's look at some of the basic building blocks of "machine intelligence," as well as examples of how to use them.

COMPUTER "SWITCHES"

Computer switches are user defined variables, symbols whose assigned value can change during the execution of a computer program. In the Zymate^{tm} EasyLab^{tm} programming language, variables can be given practically any name (X, VAR, Z10, Charley, etc.), so long as that name does not begin with an integer. Typically, the value residing in a computer switch is either "1" or "0." "1" often indicates a specified event has occurred; "0" says it has not occurred.

Suppose a robot is working with two hands ("A" and "B"). For it to "remember" which (if either) hand is loaded, as well as be smart enough not to try loading (or unloading) one hand while the other is mounted, the robot's programming might use two computer switches. Let's call them **A.HAND** and **B.HAND**. When hand "A" is loaded onto the arm, **A.HAND** will have a value of "1." When it is unloaded, **A.HAND** will automatically be reset to "0." Likewise for hand "B" and its switch, **B.HAND**. The program to load hand "A" might look like this:

10 IF A.HAND=1 THEN 50

OTHERWISE EXECUTE THE STEPS NECESSARY TO

LOAD HAND "A"

50 A.HAND=1

The program begins at line 10. The first thing the robot's controller does is ask the question, "Does **A.HAND** equal 1?" If the answer is NO, it proceeds to load the hand. The last step, line 50, sets A.HAND equal to 1. If hand "A" was already in place, **A.HAND** would equal "1," and there would be no need to load it. Indeed, a serious mishap would result should the robot try. So the computer is directed to bypass the hand loading instructions and proceed directly to line 50, where it exits the program, after once again setting the value of **A.HAND** to "1."

Now suppose we want to protect the system from a situation where hand "A" is not loaded, but hand "B" is, and the robot is commanded to load hand "A." The example program just given for loading hand "A" could be modified to look like this:

10 IF B.HAND=0 THEN 12

11 UNLOAD.B.HAND

12 IF A.HAND=1 THEN 50

OTHERWISE EXECUTE THE STEPS NECESSARY TO

LOAD HAND "A"

50 A.HAND=1

When the computer enters this program, it first checks to see if hand "B" is loaded. If so, the robot automatically unloads it. If not, the computer jumps to line 12 and executes as in the above example.

Similar logic can be built into the subroutines used to unload a robot's hands -- for example, hand "A":

    10 IF B.HAND=0 THEN 12

    11 UNLOAD.B.HAND

      GOTO 50

    12 IF A.HAND=0 THEN 50

     OTHERWISE UNLOAD HAND A

    50 A.HAND=0

Note that the program not only verifies the presence of hand "A," it also checks to see if -- by some mishap -- hand "B" is loaded. If "B" is indeed on the arm, it unloads "B," reasons hand "A" must already be unloaded, then proceeds to line 50, where it exits the program.

In a similar fashion, computer switches can radically alter a robot's operation in response to a perceived problem. For example, one of Phillips Petroleum Company's robots presides over an unattended, automated polymer sieving operation.[1] To speed this operation two stacks of eight inch diameter sieves are involved. While one stack is undergoing 30 minutes of vigorous shaking, the robot is busily weighing and cleaning the second stack.

Sieve cleaning is a complex process involving an air jet and two vacuum cleaner nozzles, one of which the robot manipulates. Unfortunately, the cleaning process can fail, but such a failure does not automatically shut the robot down. It merely alters its pattern of operation. Embedded at strategic points throughout the polymer sieving program is the statement **IF CLEANING.FAILURE=0 THEN** *go to the the next step in the program.* The italicized words in the actual program are, of course, a line number indicating the next step to be executed, providing the sieves are properly cleaned. If they aren't, this fact will be noted by an electronic balance, and the computer switch CLEANING.FAILURE is given a value of "1" (by causing the computer to execute the statement **CLEANING.FAILURE=1**).

Once this happens, the robot's operation changes radically. It will set the uncleaned stack aside and attempt to complete its assigned samples using the remaining stack. The robot is able to do this because there is a point in the dual stack mode of operation where, having loaded and secured a sieve stack on the workcell's shaker, the robot is free to begin cleaning the previous stack -- assuming, of course, a previous stack exists.

In the single stack mode of operation it does not. By noting the value of the switch **CLEANING.FAILURE,** the robot "remembers" it is only working with one stack, and simply waits for the shaker to finish.   (In reality, the problem is somewhat more complex than this. The robot's routine, which in the dual mode runs about 38 minutes per sample, changes in many ways. Among other things, it must know where to place the improperly cleaned sieve stack, and how to re-arrange the handling sequence for the remaining samples. These operating changes are triggered simply by setting the value of **CLEANING.FAILURE** equal to "1" and then -- at the appropriate points in the program -- asking the question *has the sieve stack been properly cleaned?*)

COUNTERS

Using a variable in the format **X** = **X** ± *some value* creates what is commonly referred to as a "counter." A counter's value increments (or decrements) in a controlled manner, based upon recurring events, or programmed instructions. In the process, it can flag problems, alter a robot's operation, or shut the system down.

For example, to prevent a robot from tackling an operation requiring more expendables (disposable pipette tips, vial caps, empty vials, etc.) than it has on hand, the opening lines of its program might look like this:

10 IF NUMBER.OF.VIALS+1<NUMBER.OF.SAMPLES THEN 990

20 IF NUMBER.OF.CAPS+1<NUMBER.OF.SAMPLES THEN 991

30 IF NUMBER.OF.TIPS+1<NUMBER.OF.SAMPLES THEN 992

OTHERWISE BEGIN THE PROGRAM

When the robot's operator restocks the workcell's expendables, the variable representing each expendable is reset to whatever value represents "full," simply by entering, for example, **NUMBER.OF.TIPS**= *whatever number of tips the pipette tip rack holds.* Every time the robot loads a tip, there is a line in the program which reads **NUMBER.OF.TIPS**= **NUMBER.OF.TIPS**-1, so the number of tips remaining in the rack is always known, and can be referred to at any time.

Note that in this example a safety factor of "1" was included in each statement, just in case the robot failed to load a tip, or rejected a vial. Also note that if the **NUMBER.OF.VIALS+1** proves to be less than the **NUMBER.OF.SAMPLES**, the computer jumps to line 990, where it might find:

990 INSUFFICIENT.NUMBER.OF.VIALS

If **INSUFFICIENT.NUMBER.OF.VIALS** has never been defined (i.e. given a value), the Zymate computer will simply abort, leaving line 990 as the last statement on the CRT. Of course, in this example, line 991 would read **INSUFFICIENT.NUMBER.OF.CAPS**, etc. This system is particularly useful for keeping track of a robot's solvents, which tend to be out of sight, and out of mind.

For another example, assume a robot fails to uncap a vial. It might detect this through a verification sensor (like a microswitch), or, if the robot is a Zymate II, through tactile feedback from the grippers. Either way, the robot has failed, and now "knows" it.

If the programming strategy calls for the robot to make a second attempt at removing the cap, the program might take this form:

10 UNCAP.FAILURE=0

GET NEXT SAMPLE

ATTEMPT TO UNCAP SAMPLE

TEST FOR CAP REMOVAL

IF CAP IS SUCCESSFULLY REMOVED, SET FAILURE=0

THEN PROCEED WITH THE INTENDED OPERATION

BUT IF THE ATTEMPT TO UNCAP THE SAMPLE FAILED

20 UNCAP.FAILURE=UNCAP.FAILURE+1

30 IF UNCAP.FAILURE>2 THEN 50

MAKE A SECOND ATTEMPT AT UNCAPPING THE VIAL

TEST FOR REMOVAL

IF THE REMOVAL IS SUCCESSFUL, SET   FAILURE=0

THEN PROCEED WITH OPERATION

BUT IF THE SECOND ATTEMPT FAILS

50 FAILURE=FAILURE+1

IF FAILURE>3 THEN SHUT THE ROBOT DOWN

OTHERWISE, RETURN FAILED VIAL TO SAMPLE RACK

GET NEXT SAMPLE

GOTO LINE 10 AND REPEAT ABOVE PROGRAM

Two counters are used in this example. **UNCAP.FAILURE** monitors failures related to a given sample. **FAILURE** monitors the number of consecutive vials the robot fails to uncap. **UNCAP.FAILURE** assures the robot makes two attempts to uncap each problem vial. It's automatically reset to "0" everytime a new sample is positioned for uncapping.

FAILURE is a counter looking for problems more serious than overly tight vial caps. Three consecutive uncapping failures suggests a "dead" capping station, or a malfunctioning hand; problems calling for a system shutdown. **FAILURE** is automatically reset to "0" everytime the robot successfully uncaps a vial. This way its value represents a consecutive, not a cumulative total.

COMPARISONS

"Comparisons" result when a computer compares one value to another, then takes some action based upon the results. These values may be user supplied, sensor derived, calculated, programmed, or any combination of the above.

For example, to verify the stability of an electronic balance reading, a robot's computer might take two readings, then compare one against the other like this:

```
10  FIRST.WEIGHT=WEIGH

20  SET TIMER 1 2 SECONDS

30  WAIT FOR TIMER 1

40  SECOND.WEIGHT=WEIGH

50  DIFFERENCE=FIRST.WEIGHT-SECOND.WEIGHT

60  IF DIFFERENCE<0 THEN DIFFERENCE=DIFFERENCE*(-1)

70  IF DIFFERENCE<.002 THEN CONTINUE WITH PROGRAM
```

OTHERWISE

    80 WEIGH.FAILURE=WEIGH.FAILURE+1

    90 IF WEIGH.FAILURE>50 THEN SHUT THE ROBOT DOWN

OTHERWISE

    100 GOTO 10

In this example **WEIGH** is the command which causes a balance reading to be taken. This reading becomes the value stored in **FIRST.WEIGHT**. The first comparison occurs in line 60, where the difference between the readings is compared to "0." If the difference is less than zero (i.e., negative), the program multiples this value by a minus one to make it positive (greater than zero).

A second, and crucial, comparison occurs in line 70, where the difference is compared to the target value, .002. If it is less, the computer jumps over the remaining statements in the the example and continues with the main program. But if the difference is greater than .002, the computer returns to line 10 and repeats the weighing procedure.

But note that a counter (**WEIGH.FAILURE**) is also activated and will shut the system down after 50 attempts to secure a stable reading (another comparison). Of course, **WEIGH.FAILURE** will be reset to "0" if the reweighing is successful.

Comparisons can be particularly useful for detecting and flagging (or, in some situations, automatically correcting) operator input errors. Like entering too many samples, or too high a dilution factor.

CALCULATIONS

Let's say a robot is pipetting a measured amount of sample into an empty vial, then diluting it (via a Master Laboratory Station) with solvent, the ratio of which is determined by a user inputted dilution factor.[2] The maximum "safe" fill level for the empty vial is determined to be 20 mL.

To assure the robot never overfills a vial, regardless of the inputted dilution factor or the sample weight, the robot should, before dispensing solvent, first calculate the estimated final volume, then compare that value to 20. Like this:

10 EST.FILL.VOLUME=SAMPLE.WEIGHT*DILUTION.FACTOR*DENSITY

20 IF EST.FILL.VOLUME<20 THEN CALCULATE AND DISPENSE SOLVENT

OTHERWISE FOLLOW A DIFFERENT COURSE OF ACTION

Which might mean diluting the sample to a total volume of 20 ml, rejecting it and trying again (perhaps too much sample was transferred), or shutting the system down. (Note that in the above example, the solvent's density was included in the calculation.)

INITIALIZATION OF VARIABLES

Sometimes in order to satisfy the user, or to respond to a problem, a large program must be modified automatically. One way to accomplish this is through the initialization of strategically located variables.

For example, suppose a robot needs to dilute some hydrocarbon samples in xylene and others in toleune but, other than that, the overall program is identical.   Let's call this program **HYDROCARBON.DILUTION**. We shall create two new programs, **XYLENE.DILUTION** and **TOLUENE.DILUTION**.

XYLENE.DILUTION might look like this:

> 10 DISPENSE.SOLVENT=500
>
> 20 HYDROCARBON.DILUTION

And **TOLUENE.DILUTION** might read:

> 10 DISPENSE.SOLVENT=600
>
> 20 HYDROCARBON.DILUTION

In each case a variable, **DISPENSE.SOLVENT**, is "initialized" to a certain (and different) value, then the main dilution program, **HYDROCARBON.DILUTION**, is activated.

Somewhere in **HYDROCARBON.DILUTION** is the statement **GOTO DISPENSE. SOLVENT**, which, in this example, has a value of either 500 or 600. The robot's controller interprets this to mean line number, and it promptly jumps to that particular line in the program, where, of course, will be found the instructions necessary to perform the desired dilution.

Obviously this approach can modify a program in many ways.[3] It can, for example, cause a robot to prepare duplicate preparations, manipulate different sizes of vials, load (and unload) specialized vial holders on an electronic balance, as well as enable the system to get back to where it was in a complex program, should the robot be forced to exit prior to its completion.

An example of the latter might be a robot engaged simultaneously in two tasks, one lengthy (like polymer sieving which, in our case, takes 38 minutes per sample) and one that is short (like loading samples into an automated analytical instrument). Let's say the simple task requires about two minutes of the robot's time, and must be performed every 10 minutes. At convenient "break points" throughout the longer task's program there might be statements like this:

100 IF TIMER (8)>0 THEN 130

110 LINE.NUMBER=130

120 GOTO 999

130 *CONTINUE WITH THE LONGER TASK'S PROGRAM*

TIMER (8) is an internal timer set periodically to 10 minutes. Line 100 is simply asking if 10 minutes has elapsed since the timer was last set- i.e., is it time to interrupt the longer task and perform the shorter one? If the answer is "no," then the robot continues on. But if the answer is "yes," two things happen: the variable **LINE.NUMBER** is set to 130, and then the computer is directed to line number 999, which, in this case, represents the end of the program.

In this example the longer task is actually a subroutine of the shorter one. Exiting the subroutine causes the robot to perform the shorter task, after which it resets TIMER (8) to 10 minutes, then it resumes the longer task.

Upon entering the longer task's subroutine, the first statement the computer encounters is: **GOTO LINE.NUMBER** which, in the example just given, will be line number 130. But, in fact, it could be any of the line numbers associated with designated break points scattered through the longer task's programming. Of course, the actual programming associated with the above example is somewhat more complicated than shown. One must keep track of the robot's progress in both tasks and recognize when each is finished. Since this is not likely to occur simultaneously, provisions must be made for a smooth exit from the dual task mode of operation to a single task mode to, a graceful system shutdown when both tasks are completed.

SENSORY INPUT

Robots can receive sensory inputs from a variety of sources; like photo detectors, microswitches, external computers, tactile feedback, and electronic balances.[4] But in many ways balance readings provide some of the richest and most useful feedback.[5]

A key part of the action in robotic laboratory operations often involves manipulations where weights (or weight changes) must be observed and recorded. The values associated with those operations are known to the robot's programmer. The magnitude and direction of any deviations suggest both the presence of a problem, and its probable cause.

A balance reading can confirm the robot has successfully transported an empty vial (or beaker or test tube or whatever) to the balance pan at the beginning of a dilution cycle. A weight increase, following sample pipetting, of less than specified in the program can, after a comparison with the target value, send the robot back to the sample for another try (but a counter can prevent it from being trapped in an endless loop, should there be insufficient sample to meet the targeted goal.) A weight increase noticeably greater than specified (or expected) indicates that the disposable pipette tip has probably fallen into the dilution vial, in which case the robot can discard the vial, replace it with a new vial, load a new tip, and begin the dilution process once more.

Zero weight increase suggests that (1) the sample (if it's a hydrocarbon) may not be liquid at room temperature (which translates into operator error -- the sample should have been in a heated rack); (2) the pipette tip has been lost; or (3) the robotic syringe is defective. Since (1) and (2) are the most likely candidates, a robot might discard the dilution vial (to flag the problem sample), then return the sample, uncapped, to its position in the rack.

If the pipette tip has been lost (possibility 2) and the vial is small, part of the tip may be protruding above the vial's mouth, making capping impossible. If, on the other hand, the problem is the sample's viscosity (1) -- i.e., it's a solid at room temperature -- leaving the vial uncapped briefly poses no serious problem. But since (3) is also a possibility, consecutive occurrences of this problem -- monitored by a counter -- should shut the system down.)

CONCLUSION

Imaginatively used, simple programming tools can impart a minimal but also very useful amount of "intelligence" into a laboratory robot's programming. These tools enable the robot to avoid potential problems, detect mishaps, and either shut itself down gracefully, or take steps aimed at resolving a difficulty. The key to crafting robot intelligence is: (1) program the system to ask questions; (2) provide it with the means to answer those questions: and (3) encode appropriate responses for each answer.

BIBLIOGRAPHY

1.   Jones, R. D., Cross, J. B., and Pinnick, H. R., Jr.,"Robotic Automation of Polymer Sieving (Screen Test)," Advances in Laboratory Automation - Robotics 1986, G. L. Hawk and J. R. Strimaitis, eds., Zymark Corp.

2.   Jones, R. D., and Cross, J. B., "Automating Sample Preparation (And Disposal) With A Robotic Workcell," Advances in Laboratory Automation - Robotics 1985, G. L. Hawk and J. R. Strimaitis, eds., Zymark Corp., 1985, p. 293.

3.   Jones, R. D., "The Chemistry is Right for Robots at Phillips Petroleum," Robotics Engineering, August 1986.

4.   Jones, R. D., and Cross, J. B., "Developing Tools for a Tool Using Machine," Third International Service Robot Congress,   Chicago, ILL, April 28-29, 1987.

5.   Jones, R. D., Cross, J. B., and Pinnick, H. R., Jr., "Developing Robotic Systems for the Laboratory Environment," ROBOTS 11 Conference, Chicago, ILL, April 26-30, 1987,Conference Proceedings, p. 16-1

6.   General Reference: Zymate Operator's Manual, Zymark Corporation

EXPERT SYSTEMS AND LABORATORY ROBOTICS

Vance V. Kershner
E.I. DuPont de Nemours & Company
Chemicals & Pigments Department
Jackson Laboratory
Wilmington, DE 19898

ABSTRACT

One of the most exciting topics in artificial intelligence is the use of expert systems. Expert Systems are computer programs that capture human expertise about a particular subject area. Facts and "rules-of-thumb" are input to a knowledge base, from which inferences can be made about a particular problem's solution.

Many chemical companies, like DuPont, have formal programs to exploit this technology for competitive advantage. Expert systems are being developed for use in almost all areas of the business, including the laboratory.

Until recently, the development of an expert system was an arduous task that required specialized programming skills using languages like LISP or PROLOG. Now there are many so-called "Expert System Shells" available that permit expert systems to be developed without any programming. In an expert system shell the knowledge is separate from the control structure of the program, similar to the way in which a financial model in a spreadsheet is separate from the details of how the computer performs the calculations.

The integration of these expert system shells with laboratory robotics systems will be presented. The focus will be on low cost solutions that can be easily developed using "off-the-shelf" programs. Results from the solution of a sample scheduling problem with two different shells will be discussed in detail, to exemplify the value of this approach to intelligent experimentation.

INTRODUCTION

Artificial Intelligence (AI) has received a lot of press lately. Many people are proclaiming that AI is going to change every aspect of the way we do business, as we move further toward a service economy whose raw material is information and knowledge. Let's briefly review this technology to see why there has been such a resurgence of interest in AI and examine some of the ways that it might be useful to the field of laboratory robotics.

AI/Expert Systems Overview

Unfortunately, we can't begin the discussion with a universally accepted description of AI and Expert Systems, because every researcher seems to have their own definition. But, most share one common theme: AI involves making machines do things that seem intelligent. Also, most people agree that AI encompasses the following areas: Natural Language Processing, Vision Systems, Robotics, and Expert Systems.

Natural Language Processing and Vision Systems will not be discussed in this paper; however, they clearly have an important role to play in the future of Laboratory Robotics. The interest here is on Robotics and Expert Systems and, more specifically, the synergistic relationship between the two disciplines, as they are applied to problems in the laboratory.

Expert Systems, or "Knowledge-Based Systems", are computer programs that capture human expertise about a particular subject area. The knowledge domain that can be captured must be very narrow, but it can be deep. The reason for this is that there is presently no way to program a computer to have shallow knowledge or "common sense". For example, expert systems have been developed that can diagnose specific blood diseases as well as a human expert, but the system would not be able to tell you how to treat a cut finger.

In order to capture knowledge for use in an expert system, it must be codified or represented in a systematic way. This process is known as Knowledge Engineering. The vast majority of today's expert systems represent knowledge in terms of "rules" of the form: IF (condition) THEN (conclusion); i.e., IF the pH < 7 THEN acid. Rule conditions can have multiple clauses using AND, OR, and NOT operators; and rule conclusions may include ELSE. For example, IF liquid is clear AND precipitates at bottom THEN decant liquid ELSE centrifuge again. In this example, both of the clauses (liquid is clear & precipitates at bottom) must be true for the conclusion (decant liquid) to be reached; otherwise, the ELSE conclusion (centrifuge again) is reached.

Some expert systems have confidence factors (CF) assigned to the rules; i.e., IF the barometer is falling THEN take an umbrella, CF = 0.40. The notion here is that if multiple conditions support a conclusion, then their confidence factors can be combined in a way that indicates an increased confidence in the conclusion. When enough conditions combine and the overall confidence reaches a threshold, then the conclusion is reached. While the concept of confidence factors is appealing, they are frequently not used because of the difficulty of establishing the appropriate values, and because CF's are only consistent with probability theory if the rules are independent.

Once all of the knowledge about a particular domain has been represented by rules, the task at hand is to utilize the "knowledge base" to solve problems. This process is known as "inferencing". A "forward-chaining inference engine" solves problems by matching all the rules against the starting conditions to see what conclusions can be reached. These conclusions then become new conditions and the matching process is repeated. When no further conclusions can be reached, the inferencing stops and the final conclusion is stated as the solution to the problem.

In a "backward-chaining inference engine", a proposed solution (conclusion) is matched against the conclusions in the rule-set until a rule that concludes the same thing as the proposed solution is found. Then the conditions for this rule become new conclusions and the matching process continues. Inferencing stops when no more rules can be found that have conclusions matching the conditions from the last "matched" rule, and all of the now unmatched conditions agree with the initial conditions for the problem. If the unmatched conditions do not agree with the initial conditions, then the proposed solution is discarded and another tried. Although this seems rather complex when compared with forward chaining, it more closely models the way humans solve problems.

Expert System Shells

Until recently, the implementation of an expert system was an arduous task that required specialized programming skills using languages like LISP or PROLOG. This is because conventional procedural languages are not well-suited for representing knowledge symbolically or carrying out the required search strategies (inferencing). The upshot was that creating even simple expert systems was difficult.

Now there are many so-called "Expert System Shells" available that permit expert systems to be developed without any programming. These shells, coupled with the increased amount of computational power available per dollar of investment; particularly in PC's, has been a major reason for the resurgence of interest in AI in recent years. The fact that it is now possible to build small expert systems without a lot of computer expertise or investment has excited many companies, including DuPont.

Shells function in a manner that is analogous to a spreadsheet program. In a spreadsheet, data and formulas are input by the user and the program takes care of the display, interpreting the formulas, etc. Likewise, in an expert system shell, the knowledge base (rules) are separate from the control structure of the program. The user inputs the rules, and the program does the inferencing and takes care of the displaying questions and conclusions.

Commercial shells are available for under $500 that implement either forward or backward chaining inference engines, and provide varying degrees of interfacing to other programs and databases. The rules are written using keywords, like: IF, THEN, AND, OR, and NOT. Most of the programs include a text editor to input the rule-set. Once entered, the rule-set is usually compiled into an executable file.

Some shells add a different twist, by automatically deducing the rule-set from examples. The user simply tells the program what possible factor and result values could exist, and then inputs examples relating different combinations. The examples are either compiled into rules, or a decision tree.

Shells and Laboratory Robots

In a typical laboratory robotics application, complex tasks are broken down into many small subtasks. Each subtask is coded separately, and then they are combined in a hierarchical fashion to form "low level" programs. Finally, these low level program elements are then combined into a "top level" program to accomplish the desired laboratory analysis. Certainly, this is the way programming is handled in a Zymate System using EasyLab. This is a very powerful approach if the automation task is clearly defined, and not prone to errors.

Difficulty arises when control of the robot needs to deviate from the predetermined sequence of actions. This can happen if something goes wrong (an error) in a low level program that cannot be dealt with at the low level. Suppose that during execution of a low level EasyLab program a balance will not return a stable weight, and you would like to have the robot use another analysis technique that does not require a weight. Programming this sort of error handling in EasyLab is difficult when there are a lot of program levels, because EasyLab will not permit branching from a low level program to a top level program. Instead you must "back out" of the current program, all the way to the top level. This requires setting and checking a lot of flags, and is very cumbersome if there are many program levels and a large number of error traps.

One solution to this problem is to reduce the number of levels of program nesting, and have a more encompassing top level program that includes a lot of decisions and logic. The problem with this approach is that the top level program can get to be very complex and hard to understand.

Since this type of logic and decision making is the strong suit of expert system shells, an investigation was made to see if it is practical to shift some "control expertise" outside of the robot controller, to an expert system.

DISCUSSION

A Zymate II robot was interfaced to an IBM PC/XT^{tm} for the purpose of exploring the interaction between Expert Systems and robot control programs. The interfacing was accomplished using a Z845 remote computer interface, to allow external control of the robot.

The Problem

The task of scheduling sample processing steps was chosen for this investigation, because it represents a common "real world" problem and because it can be difficult. Specifically, the problem involves telling the robot how to serially process samples through a system that has one analyzer, which is the rate limiting step.

The state of the system is defined by variables, that are redefined as processing takes place. For the problem at hand, three "state variables" define the status of the system. They are SAMP.WAIT$, SAMP.PREP$, and ANAL.BUSY$, and they can take on the values of 'YES' or 'NO'. SAMP.WAIT$ refers to whether or not there are samples waiting to be processed. The value for this variable is determined by a switch on the sample rack. SAMP.PREP$ refers to whether or not a sample has been prepared and is waiting for the analyzer. And ANAL.BUSY$ indicates whether or not the analyzer is busy with a sample. The values for the last two variables are set during the different processing steps.

Outlines of the low level programs are shown in TABLE 1. These programs could be used to process samples sequentially by a simple top level program like:

```
10    PREPARE
      ANALYZE
      GET.RESULTS
      WAIT
      GOTO 10
```

TABLE 1. EasyLab Program Outlines.

```
PREPARE
      GET.SAMPLE
      PREPARE.SAMPLE
      SAMP.PREP$ = 'YES'
      IF SAMP.SWITCH = 1 THEN SAMP.WAIT$ = 'YES'
      IF SAMP.SWITCH = 0 THEN SAMP.WAIT$ = 'NO'

ANALYZE
      LOAD.ANALYZER
      START.ANALYZER
      TIMER(1) = ANALYSIS.TIME
      SAMP.PREP$ = 'NO'
      ANAL.BUSY$ = 'YES'
      IF SAMP.SWITCH = 1 THEN SAMP.WAIT$ = 'YES'
      IF SAMP.SWITCH = 0 THEN SAMP.WAIT$ = 'NO'

GET.RESULTS
      WAIT FOR TIMER(1)
      UNLOAD.ANALYZER
      PRINT.RESULTS
      ANAL.BUSY$ = 'NO'
      IF SAMP.SWITCH = 1 THEN SAMP.WAIT$ = 'YES'
      IF SAMP.SWITCH = 0 THEN SAMP.WAIT$ = 'NO'

WAIT
10    IF SAMP.SWITCH = 1 THEN SAMP.WAIT$ = 'YES'
      IF SAMP.SWITCH = 0 THEN SAMP.WAIT$ = 'NO'
      IF SAMP.WAIT$ = 'NO' THEN GOTO 10
```

However, this would not be very efficient if more than one sample was to be analyzed, because the analyzer would be doing nothing while the sample was being prepared. In order to "serialize" the program, a sample should be prepared while the analyzer is busy. The top level program now becomes much more complex, because the first sample has to be processed differently than the intermediate samples, and the last sample is also different. The sequence of events for the samples is shown in Table 2.

TABLE 2. Sample Analysis Sequence For Serial Processing.

For the first sample:

> PREPARE
> ANALYZE

Then for the intermediate samples:

> PREPARE
> GET.RESULTS "For previous sample"
> ANALYZE

And for the last sample:

> GET.RESULTS
> WAIT

This program flow can be incorporated into a top level program, as shown in Table 3. Unfortunately, you have to scrutinize the program to convince yourself that it does what is expected. If another analyzer were added to the system, or some other decisions had to be made, the top level program would quickly become exceedingly difficult to understand and maintain.

FIGURE 3. Top Level Program For Serial Processing.

```
10    IF ANAL.BUSY$ = 'NO' THEN GOTO 20
      IF SAMP.WAIT$ = 'NO' THEN GOTO 30
      IF SAMP.PREP$ = 'YES' THEN GOTO 30
      GOTO 40
20    IF SAMP.PREP$ = 'YES' THEN GOTO 50
      IF SAMP.WAIT$ = 'YES' THEN GOTO 40
      GOTO 60
30    GET.RESULTS
      GOTO 10
40    PREPARE
      GOTO 10
50    ANALYZE
      GOTO 10
60    WAIT
      GOTO 10
```

Interfacing Expert Systems

Any external program that is interfaced to the robot must support the Zymate Controller's communication protocol. Since none of the commercially available expert system shells have communications support, a BASIC^{tm} program was written for this purpose. The program, which is shown in Table 4, is based on the example given in the remote computer interface documentation. The associated BASIC subprograms are listed in Appendix 1.

The BASIC program obtains the values of the three "state variables" from the Zymate's dictionary, calls an expert system shell for advice, and then runs the recommended program in the controller. State variable information, and program names are transferred between the BASIC program and the Shell via files. An answer file (SCHDLR.ANS) provides the state variable information for the expert system, and a report file (EXPERT.RPT) contains the results of the expert system (name of the Zymate program to run).

The expert systems were executed from the BASIC program by running batch files as spawned processes. This is necessary in order to maintain the control signals between the PC's serial communication port and the Z845 remote computer interface. If the basic program had been started and stopped, the communication port would have been opened and closed, causing problems with the Z845 interface.

TABLE 4. BASIC Program For Communicating Between Zymate & Shells.

```
        CLS
                                            'open comm port
        OPEN "COM1:1200,E,7,1,RS,DS0,LF" AS #1

        OK$ = "OK" + CHR$(13)               'define some
        NOTOK$ = "NOTOK" + CHR$(13)         'variables

        PROGNAME$ = "VERBOSE3"              'set verbose level
        GOSUB 26000

10  VARNAME$ = "SAMP.WAIT$"                 'get current value
        GOSUB 27500                         'of SAMP.WAIT$ from
        SAMPWAIT$ = VARSTRING$              'Zymate dictionary

        VARNAME$ = "SAMP.PREP$"             'get current value
        GOSUB 27500                         'of SAMP.PREP$ from
        SAMPPREP$ = VARSTRING$              'Zymate dictionary

        VARNAME$ = "ANAL.BUSY$"             'get current value
        GOSUB 27500                         'of ANAL.BUSY$ from
        ANALBUSY$ = VARSTRING$              'Zymate dictionary

        SHELL "DEL EXPERT.RPT"             'delete old result

        OPEN "C:SCHDLR.ANS" FOR OUTPUT AS #2
        PRINT #2,SAMPWAIT$                  'create answer file
        PRINT #2,SAMPPREP$                  'for the expert
        PRINT #2,ANALBUSY$                  'system
        CLOSE #2                            '(1st-Class format)

        ON ERROR GOTO 20                    'enable error trap
        SHELL "EXPERT.BAT"                  'and call expert
        ON ERROR GOTO 0                     'system

        OPEN "EXPERT.RPT" FOR INPUT AS #3
        INPUT #3,PROGNAME$                  'read result from
        CLOSE #3                            'expert system and
        GOSUB 26000                         'send to Zymate

        GOTO 10                             're-check dictionary

20  RESUME NEXT

        END
```

Two different expert system shells were tested. One, Insight 2+ (Level Five Research, Indiatlantic, FL), is a backward-chaining rule based system, and the other, 1st-Class (Programs in Motion, Wayland, MA), is a forward chaining example based program. Both of these programs meet the requirements for any shell that could be used; that is, they can communicate via files, and they can run "hidden". In addition, both of these programs only cost about $500.

Insight 2+

Version 1.3 of the development system was used to create the knowledge base, and it was run using version 1.3B ROLM of the run-only system. Insight 2+ was designed to be an interactive system with user displays. However, the version of the run-only system that was used supports "hidden" execution, where no user displays are generated and control is automatically returned to the operating system when execution is complete.

The knowledge base for the Insight 2+ expert system is shown in Table 5. Words typed in capital letters are keywords for the compiler, and words typed after an exclamation point are comments. The knowledge base begins with a TITLE statement and continues until the END statement. The STRING statement defines the data type for the three "state variables" whose values are read from the SCHDLR.ANS file. FILE defines the EXPERT.RPT file for data output. The knowledge in the system is contained in the IF...THEN rules. Rules begin with a RULE statement to define a rule name.

The knowledge representation approach taken for this application began with the definition of first, intermediate, last, and no samples in terms of the state variables. These sample types were then used in conjunction with the state variables to determine which robot program to run next. Defining sample types resulted in eleven rules, compared to a minimum of five rules that could have been used. More rules were used to increase the readability of the knowledge base.

A statement of the problem that the expert system is to solve is defined by the goal statements. These are the statements at the beginning of the knowledge base that start with a number. Here the inference engine is told to first pursue the goal of reading the input data from a file. Once that goal has been satisfied, the inference engine will start pursuing each one of the sub-goals until it finds one that can be satisfied (sub-goals are indicated by the integer corresponding to the higher level goal, followed by a decimal point and another integer). The order of the subgoals does not matter, since only one of them can be satisfied. Upon satisfying a sub-goal the inference engine stops the search, writes the solution to the output file, and returns control to the batch file. The batch file executes an EXIT command, and control is returned to the BASIC program.

The resulting knowledge base involves a lot more "programming statements" than the corresponding EasyLab program, but it is much easier to understand. Each rule stands alone as an intelligible piece of information about the problem. In the EasyLab program, you must consider the interaction between many logic statements in order to understand what the program does.

Maintenance should also be considered. Changing the knowledge base is very easy, since the order of the sub-goals, or the rules, does not affect the solution that the expert system provides. Furthermore, testing and debugging of systems developed using shells is much easier than for systems implemented in EasyLab. This is because the expert system can easily run separate from the robot in an interactive mode. Therefore, effects of all the different combinations of state variables can be tried very quickly.

TABLE 5. Insight 2+ Knowledge Base.

TITLE Sample Scheduling Advisor

STRING samp.wait$! Define state variables
AND samp.prep$! as strings
AND anal.busy$!

FILE EXPERT.RPT   ! Define file for output

1. read data   ! Define the goals of the
1.1. wait for samples   ! program. First read data,
1.2. analyze sample   ! then each subgoal will
1.3. get results   ! be checked to see if it
1.4. prepare sample   ! is valid.

RULE For Reading Data   ! Read in the value of each
READ SCHDLR.ANS   ! state variable from the
DATA samp.wait$! SCHDLR.ANS file, that has
DATA samp.prep$! been provided by the
DATA anal.busy$! BASIC program.
THEN read data   !

RULE For First Sample   ! Definition of a first
IF samp.wait$ = YES   ! sample as being when a
AND samp.prep$ = NO   ! sample is waiting to be
AND anal.busy$ = NO   ! processed, and none are
THEN first sample   ! prepared or in the
AND NOT intermediate sample   ! analyzer.
ELSE NOT first sample   !

RULE For Last Sample   ! Definition of a last
IF samp.wait$ = NO   ! sample as being when no
AND samp.prep$ = NO   ! samples are waiting to be
AND anal.busy$ = YES   ! prepared, and the analyzer
AND NOT intermediate sample   ! is still busy.
ELSE NOT last sample   !

RULE For Intermediate Sample   ! Definition of an
IF NOT first sample   ! intermediate sample as
AND NOT last sample   ! being other than a first
AND samp.wait$ = YES   ! or last sample, and when
THEN intermediate sample   ! samples are waiting.

RULE For No Sample   ! Definition of when
IF NOT first sample   ! there is no sample.
AND NOT last sample   !
AND NOT intermediate sample   !
THEN no sample   !

TABLE 5. continued.

RULE For Preparing First Sample IF first sample THEN prepare sample AND FILE PREPARE	! Start by preparing ! the first sample. ! ! Run PREPARE.
RULE For Analyzing a Sample IF samp.prep$ = YES AND anal.busy$ = NO THEN analyze sample AND FILE ANALYZE	! Analyze a sample ! whenever there is ! one prepared and ! the analyzer is not ! busy. Run ANALYZE.
RULE Get Results - Last Sample IF last sample THEN get results AND FILE GET.RESULTS	! Get results when ! last sample is ! in the analyzer. ! Run GET.RESULTS.
RULE For Getting Results IF samp.prep$ = YES AND anal.busy$ = YES THEN get results AND FILE GET.RESULTS	! Get results before ! proceeding when a ! sample is prepared and ! the analyzer is busy. ! Run GET.RESULTS.
RULE For Preparing Samples IF intermediate sample AND samp.prep$ = NO AND anal.busy$ = YES THEN prepare sample AND FILE PREPARE	! Prepare a sample ! whenever the analyzer ! is busy and no sample ! is already prepared. ! ! Run PREPARE.
RULE For Waiting For Samples IF no sample AND samp.prep$ = NO AND anal.busy$ = NO THEN wait for samples AND FILE WAIT	! Wait for more samples ! when there are none ! available to prepare ! or analyze. ! ! Run WAIT.
END	! The end

Only a small fraction of the capacity of Insight 2+ was used for this simple expert system. Knowledge bases with several hundred rules are feasible. It is also possible to chain knowledge bases, so system capacity would not be a constraining factor for most applications.

Insight 2+ demonstrated reasonable performance for this type of application. Only a few seconds were required to get the current values of the state variables from the controller, run the expert system, and return a program name to the Zymate, using an IBM PC/XT. Execution speed could be substantially increased with an IBM PC/AT using a RAM disk for communicating between the BASIC program and Insight 2+.

1st-Class

Version 3.54M of the 1st-Class development and run-time programs were used for this investigation. 1st-Class is very different from Insight 2+, in that it is an example based expert system shell. Another difference is that 1st-Class provides a "spreadsheet" like environment for developing the knowledge base, compared with the more traditional "word processor" like approach used by Insight 2+.

The examples that were input to 1st-Class to generate a decision tree are shown in Table 6, and the decision tree is shown in Table 7. An asterisk in the examples indicates that the value for the state variable does not matter. Several options are available for generating the decision tree from the examples. The decision tree for this application was generated with the state variables appearing in the same order as in the examples, so that it would be easy to understand. This results in a slightly more complex tree than would have been obtained if the tree had been generated with the optimize option. The optimized tree is shown in Table 8 for comparison purposes.

TABLE 6. 1st-Class Examples For Scheduling Problem.

SAMP.WAIT	SAMP.PREP	ANAL.BUSY	RESULT
YES	NO	NO	PREPARE
*	YES	NO	ANALYZE
NO	NO	YES	GET.RESULTS
*	YES	YES	GET.RESULTS
NO	NO	NO	WAIT
YES	NO	YES	PREPARE

TABLE 7. 1st-Class Decision Tree For Scheduling Problem

```
 1: SAMP.WAIT??
 2: YES:SAMP.PREP??
 3:     YES:ANAL.BUSY??
 4:         YES:--------------------------GET.RESULTS
 5:         NO:---------------------------ANALYZE
 6:     NO:-------------------------------PREPARE
 7: NO:SAMP.PREP??
 8:     YES:ANAL.BUSY??
 9:         YES:--------------------------GET.RESULTS
10:         NO:---------------------------ANALYZE
11:     NO:ANAL.BUSY??
12:         YES:--------------------------GET.RESULTS
13:         NO:---------------------------WAIT
```

TABLE 8. Optimized 1st-Class Decision Tree

```
 1: ANAL.BUSY??
 2: YES:SAMP.WAIT??
 3:     YES:SAMP.PREP??
 4:         YES:--------------------------GET.RESULTS
 5:         NO:---------------------------PREPARE
 6:     NO:-------------------------------GET.RESULTS
 7: NO:SAMP.PREP??
 8:     YES:-------------------------------ANALYZE
 9:     NO:SAMP.WAIT??
10:         YES:--------------------------PREPARE
11:         NO:---------------------------WAIT
```

Up to 31 state variables, 32 state variable values, and 32 results can be included in a single knowledge base. However, like with Insight 2+, knowledge bases can be chained, so there is no practical limit to the magnitude of the problem that can be handled. While it would appear that a huge number of examples would be required to define a decision tree with many state variables and results, all that is really needed is an example for each physically possible scenario. This greatly reduce the number of examples required for most applications.

Compared with the EasyLab program, the 1st-Class knowledge base was actually easier to program, and is much easier to understand and maintain. Interactive testing of the knowledge base does not require making any changes, because 1st-Class automatically looks for an answer file at run time. If it does not find one, it simply queries the user for the state variable values; input screens are automatically generated.

Another useful feature of 1st-Class is that it can output a file that contains the state variables (in 1st-Class these are called factors) and their possible values. This file is formatted in a way that allows the state variables to be easily passed out as input for the BASIC program. Consequently, it is possible to write a generic communication program that is independent of the state variables.

Because there is no search involved at run time, the execution speed of the knowledge base is very fast. When running the system, most of the time is taken up by the BASIC program communicating with the controller.

CONCLUSION

Several conclusions can be drawn from this investigation:

1. EasyLab programs can be difficult to write and maintain if the application involves a large amount of error handling, or logical decision making as characterized by "intelligent experimentation."

2. The concept of "state variables" can effectively describe the status of a robotics system.

3. Expert system shells can represent the type of knowledge necessary for robot control applications, as long as a lot of numerical analysis is not required.

4. Low cost expert system shells can be interfaced to the Zymate controller with a minimum of custom coding.

5. 1st-Class provides a truly "user friendly" environment for developing example based expert systems. In addition, the example based paradigm appears to be perfectly suited for robot control applications; it is quite natural to describe the desired robot control scheme in terms of examples.

Insight 2+ is a trademark of Level Five Research Inc.

1st-Class is a trademark of Programs in Motion Inc.

IBM PC/XT is a trademark of International Business Machines Corporation.

APPENDIX 1
BASIC Subprograms For Communicating With The Zymate

```
25000 '* RECEIVE AND PROCESS TEXT MESSAGES FROM ZYMATE SYSTEM
      '* UNTIL AN OK OR NOTOK REPLY IS RECEIVED
      '* INPUTS: NONE
      '* OUTPUTS: NONE

      MESSAGES$=""
      WHILE (MESSAGES$ <> OK$) AND (MESSAGE$ <> NOTOK$)
      GOSUB 29000        'PROCESS TEXT MESSAGES
      WEND
      RETURN

26000 '* START AN EASYLAB PROGRAM
      '* INPUTS: PROGNAME$ = NAME OF EASYLAB PROGRAM
      '* OUTPUTS: NONE

      PRINT #1,PROGNAME$+CHR$(13)
      GOSUB 25000
      RETURN

27000 '* RETRIEVE A VALUE OF A NUMERIC VARIABLE IN THE ZYMATE
SYSTEM
      '* INPUTS: VARNAME$ = NAME OF VARIABLE TO RETRIEVE
      '* OUTPUTS: VARVALUE = VALUE OF VARNAME$

      PRINT #1,"? "+VARNAME$+CHR$(13)
      GOSUB 29000        'RETRIEVE THE VALUE
      VARVALUE = VAL(MID$(MESSAGE$,3,LEN(MESSAGE$)-1))
      GOSUB 25000        'RETRIEVE THE REPLY
      RETURN

27500 '* RETRIEVE A VALUE OF A STRING VARIABLE IN THE ZYMATE
SYSTEM
      '* INPUTS: VARNAME$ = NAME OF VARIABLE TO RETRIEVE
      '* OUTPUTS: VARSTRING$ = VALUE OF VARNAME$

      PRINT #1,"? "+VARNAME$+CHR$(13)
      GOSUB 29000        'RETRIEVE THE VALUE
      VARSTRING$ = MID$(MESSAGE$,3,LEN(MESSAGE$)-1)
      GOSUB 25000        'RETRIEVE THE REPLY
      RETURN

28000 '* ASSIGN A VALUE TO A NUMERIC VARIABLE IN THE ZYMATE
SYSTEM
      '* INPUTS:  VARNAME$ = NAME OF VARIABLE TO ASSIGN
      '*                   VARVALUE  =  VALUE  TO  ASSIGN  TO
VARNAME$
      '* OUTPUTS: NONE

      PRINT #1,VARNAME$+"= "+STR$(VARVALUE)+CHR$(13)
      GOSUB 25000        'RETRIEVE REPLY
```

```
        RETURN

29000 '* RETRIEVE A LINE FROM THE ZYMATE SYSTEM
        '* INPUTS: NONE
        '* OUTPUTS: MESSAGE$ = MESSAGE RECEIVED FROM ZYMATE
SYSTEM

        MESSAGE$ = ""   'BUILD AN INPUT LINE
29110 CHARIN$ = INPUT$(1,#1)
        IF CHARIN$ = CHR$(10) THEN RETURN
        MESSAGE$ = MESSAGE$ + CHARIN$
        GOTO 29110
```

CONTROLLING ROBOTS WITH SPOKEN COMMANDS

Tony Beugelsdijk and Patrick Phelan
Los Alamos National Laboratory
P.O. Box 1663
Los Alamos, NM 87544

ABSTRACT

A robotic system for handling radioactive materials has been developed at Los Alamos National Laboratory. Because of safety considerations, the robot must be under the control of a human operator continuously. In this paper we describe the implementation of a voice-recognition system that makes such control possible, yet permits the robot to perform pre-programmed manipulations without the operator's intervention. We also describe the training given both the operator and the voice-recognition system, as well as practical problems encountered during routine operation.

A speech synthesis unit connected to the robot's control computer provides audible feedback to the operator. Thus, when a task is completed or if an emergency develops, the computer provides an appropriate spoken message. Implementation and operation of this commercially available hardware are discussed.

INTRODUCTION

At our laboratory, we find it desirable to use robots for numerous processes involving remote manipulation of materials. However, many of the processes are not repetitive or they treat hazardous material, so a human operator must be in control at all times. Accordingly, it is extremely useful to let the operator control the robot by speaking commands into a microphone. The commands initiate pre-programmed procedures as soon as they are spoken.

Speaking the commands is more convenient than entering them at the keyboard because the operator's hands remain free for other tasks, and he or she may walk about. Speaking commands is also more convenient than using a "teach pendant", because the pre-programmed movements are executed faster and more accurately. Finally, because the operator needs little knowledge of how the robot works or of its programming language, he or she can operate it successfully with little training.

EXPERIMENTAL

Components

The major parts of our system are depicted in Figure 1. The laboratory robot (Model 9000 MasterLab[tm] system, Perkin-Elmer Corp., Ridgefield, CT) is under direct control of a microcomputer (Personal Computer XT[tm], International Business Machines, Boca Raton, FL) linked to a control unit. A voice-recognition system interprets commands spoken into the microphone and passes them on to the computer. The voice-recognition system is either a special keyboard with built-in electronics (Model KB 5152V, KeyTronic Corp., Spokane, WA) or an interface card installed in the computer chassis (Vocalink[tm] model SRB-LC, Interstate Voice Products, Orange, CA). The speech-synthesis unit (Echo-PC[tm], Street Electronics Corp., Carpinteria, CA) is connected to an RS-232 serial port as if it were a printer.

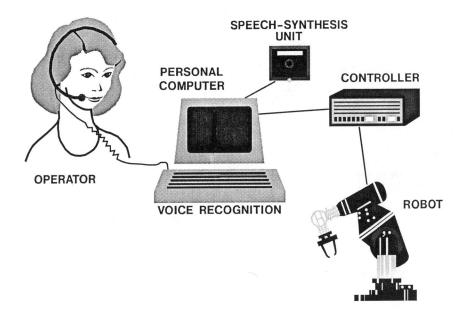

FIGURE 1. Schematic of Robotic System Being Controlled by Spoken Commands.

Installing the Voice-Recognition System

The first step is to develop the desired robotic procedures, storing each sequence of robot moves as a computer program that can be initiated by entering the program's name at the keyboard. Each procedure must be tested thoroughly before being put into use.

The second step is to install the voice-recognition system in the computer and connect the microphone. For a keyboard system with built-in electronics, installation means simply plugging its cable into the personal computer. If the system is an interface card, however, some care must be taken to ensure that its I/O bus address does not conflict with the addresses of other interface cards that are already present. If there is a conflict, the address can be changed by switches mounted on the card.

The third step is to enter a list of commands into the computer. Using software supplied by the manufacturer of the voice-recognition system, the user assigns each command a character string that is the name of one pre-programmed procedure.

Finally, each operator must train the voice-recognition system to recognize his or her voice. Software provided by the manufacturer is again used. To do the training, the operator speaks each command into the microphone when prompted by the computer. The words are repeated three to five times until the voice-recognition system has a pattern it considers typical of the individual's voice.

Installing the Speech-Synthesis Unit

All the necessary electronics and programming already reside in this type of speech-synthesis unit. Dip switches on the bottom of the unit permit the user to select the baud rate over the range 75 to 9600.

How the Voice-Recognition System Works

First, each word spoken into the microphone is compared with those in the operator's previously stored vocabulary list. The voice-recognition system compares the spoken word's digitized pattern with the patterns of the vocabulary words.

When a satisfactory match is found between the spoken command and a vocabulary word, the computer recalls the character string associated with the vocabulary word and sends the string to the robot controller as if the string had been entered at the keyboard. The robot acts on the string by performing the pre-programmed procedure in the usual manner.

How the Speech-Synthesis Unit Works

PRINT commands included in each pre-programmed robotic procedure send selected character strings to the unit as if it were a printer. When the speech-synthesis unit receives a character string, the unit processes it according to nearly 400 rules of English pronunciation, then provides an audible word or words through its built-in speaker.

RESULTS

Voice-Recognition System

After their initial training, operators found the robot easy to operate by speaking commands. The voice-recognition system correctly recognized 90 percent of the words the first time they were spoken. Usually, whenever the command was not recognized the first time, the system and the robot did not respond at all; but they did respond correctly when the command was spoken a second time. With proper adjustment of the pattern-recognition criteria (as discussed below), the frequency with which the system misinterpreted commands was reduced to less than 1 percent.

The systems we used are so sensitive to subtle differences in pronunciation that it was necessary for each operator to record a vocabulary of commands and train the system to recognize his or her unique way of pronouncing them. In general, when an operator tried to use the vocabulary that had been recorded by another, the recognition frequency was less than 25 percent.

Speech-Synthesis Unit

Users must exercise care in selecting the words to be output through the speech-synthesis unit. We did much trial-and-error testing to ensure that the words would be readily intelligible. Even so, about 25 percent of the words were unintelligible to inexperienced listeners the first time they heard them. Listeners' recognition rate grew to over 90 percent once they became accustomed to the unit's accent.

DISCUSSION

Our experience is limited to commercially available voice I/O hardware designed for use in an IBM personal computer. Therefore, we used spoken commands only with robotic systems that can be controlled by such a computer. Moreover, we used only systems that are among the least expensive. There are more-sophisticated systems available that have fewer limitations than the ones we employed.

Training Needed by Operators

It is helpful, of course, if the operators have some basic knowledge about how a personal computer works; for example, how to enter commands at the keyboard and how to check for loose cables. It is more important, however, that the operators be familiar with the robotic system. They need to know what manipulations it has been programmed to carry out, and the command words used to initiate those manipulations.

Operators also need to be trained to use the voice-recognition system. For example, they need to know how to position the microphone, and they must practice saying the commands distinctly and with a noticeable pause between each command.

Choosing the Vocabulary of Commands

Perhaps the most difficult task involved in installing a voice-recognition system is preparing the vocabulary of command words. The commands must be easy for the operator to remember, of course, so they should be few in number. It also helps if the words describe the task the robot will perform. For example, the command "arm-up" is more suggestive of a procedure than "move".

Usually it is important to avoid words that sound similar, but the software provided with the system can often alleviate this problem. For example, after a vocabulary of commands has been recorded during the training period, the computer can test the digitized patterns and measure how similar they are. If two words are quite similar, the chance for confusion can be reduced by requiring the system to make a more stringent comparison between the pattern of the incoming word and the patterns of the problem words. However, there is a disadvantage to doing this; the system may fail to recognize one of the vocabulary words if there is a slight variation in its pronunciation.

It is also a good idea to avoid one-syllable words, because the word's digitized pattern may be so simple that the system has trouble recognizing it. But, again, the software can alleviate this problem. The computer can test the digitized patterns in the vocabulary and predict how easily each command will be recognized. The computer can be instructed to be more lenient when comparing the incoming word with the simple words, if the user wishes. However, this will increase the chance that non-vocabulary words (and even extraneous noises) will be interpreted as commands..

The software provided by the manufacturer allows the vocabulary words to be grouped so that only a few words will be active at one time. This approach makes it easier for the system to recognize the commands successfully. An example of such a grouping is shown in Figure 2. The words in the first group are activated when the operator speaks the command "move". Thus, the system will recognize only the words, "up", "down", "right" and "left" until the word "revolve" is spoken. Then only the words "around", "right" and "half" will be recognized. As illustrated by this example, the same word can appear in two different groups and can have different meanings depending upon which group is active.

Move

Up
Down
Right
Left

Revolve

Around
Right
Half

FIGURE 2. Command Words Grouped to Improve Recognition Accuracy.

SUMMARY

We successfully used commercially available hardware and software to control a robot by giving it spoken commands. Such control was augmented by audible responses from the robot through a speech-synthesis unit.

ACKNOWLEDGMENTS

The authors appreciate the assistance provided by their coworker, Chris Keddy, whose efforts contributed significantly to this study.

MasterLab is a registered trademark of Perkin-Elmer Corp.

Personal Computer XT is a registered trademark of International Business Machines Corp.

Vocalink is a registered trademark of Interstate Voice Products Corp.

Echo-PC is a registered trademark of Street Electronics Corp.

CAPPING AND OTHER OPPORTUNITIES FOR CUSTOM ROBOTIC FIXTURING

W. A. Schmidt, J. J. Rollheiser
D. P. McCampbell, and K. M. Stelting
Midwest Research Institute
425 Volker Boulevard
Kansas City, Missouri 64110

ABSTRACT

As laboratory robotic technology matures, more complex applications are being developed. These applications require more sophisticated peripheral hardware (i.e., custom fixturing) to provide or enhance capabilities which are not available in off-the-shelf hardware.

Two approaches in developing custom robotic fixturing are modification of the off-the-shelf hardware to extend or augment its capabilities and design and fabrication of unique components. Examples from a variety of applications will be discussed. These include pneumatic devices to improve reliability of a commercially available capping station, an automatic test tube feeder, a high-capacity custom Erlenmeyer flask sample rack, and a combination vortexer solvent addition station.

INTRODUCTION

Midwest Research Institute (MRI) is an independent research organization providing

services in a wide variety of disciplines, including the development of laboratory robotics

systems. Over the past three years, we have set up and enhanced an in-house robotic system to analyze rodent feed dosed with potentially toxic chemicals in support of studies for the National Toxicology Program. In addition, we have provided third-party automation development of a variety of applications for a number of industrial clients. The automated systems we have developed perform tasks such as microtiter plate assays and sample preparation for colorimetric analysis.

During the three years we have been developing robotic systems, we have witnessed a steady increase in the number and complexity of the procedures our clients wish to automate. Initially, inquiries for automation development involved relatively simple robotic applications consisting of the most elemental operations such as solvent handling, weighing, mixing, and injection. Today, our clients wish to use laboratory robotics to automate more sophisticated applications such as organic synthesis, ELISA assays, ICP sample preparation, nutritional analyses, and analyses involving radioactive materials. This expanded utilization of robotics illustrates the maturation of this technology in the chemistry laboratory.

As increasingly complex robotic systems are assembled, custom robotic fixturing is becoming more prevalent and is critical to the success of many specific applications . For instance, Bruce Kropscott (Dow Chemical Company) has stated that "there is often a void between hardware needs for a specific application and what is commercially available."[1] At the Fourth International Symposium on Laboratory Robotics - 1986, more than 75% of the papers included descriptions of custom or modified devices developed to fill that void. Custom hands, pneumatic ancillary devices, special racks, and even custom designed laboratories were just some of items described at the 1986 symposium. This year's symposium will no doubt contain many presentations which describe additional custom devices that have been incorporated into automated systems.

CUSTOM FIXTURING ISSUES

Custom fixturing can have a significant impact on robotic issues such as sample throughput, cost savings, reliability, flexibility, space constraints, and safety. How each of these issues affects successful automation is an important consideration when developing custom robotic fixturing.

Sample Throughput: When the maximum sample throughput estimated for a robotic system is not adequate for the application, custom hardware can improve the efficiency of the operation. Creating stations that perform laboratory unit operations independently of the robotic arm, such as a reagent addition/vortex station that will be described later, can greatly improve sample throughput.

Cost Savings: More efficient use of automation dollars can often be obtained by creating custom devices rather than purchasing standard off-the-shelf equipment . For example, if applications do not require programmability of reagent volumes to be dispensed, we construct pneumatic reagent dispensers. These dispensers can be fabricated for about one-third the cost of programmable reagent dispensers by attaching a pneumatic cylinder to the dispenser barrel.

Reliability: A key factor in determining the success of an automated system is its reliability. All too often, the robotic arm is used for tasks other than sample transport and simple manipulations. Another approach is off-loading task execution to workstations that can perform the required operations more reliably, with minimal robotic involvement. For example, we have created a workstation for acid digestion of samples as part of an elemental analysis procedure. In this application, the robot arm is only required to transport the sample to and from the station. This example will be described further in a later section. Employing several workstations of this sort, serviced by a single robotic arm, can significantly increase the overall reliability of an automated system.

Flexibility: Laboratory robotic technology will become more flexible as custom hardware is designed to automate additional laboratory unit operations. This increased flexibility will allow robots to be used in a wider variety of applications. For example, in the colorimetric assay procedure mentioned earlier, we fabricated a workstation that drew sample solutions through the spectrophotometer flow cell and then purged the flow cell before drawing the next sample. This workstation could be used in a wide variety of applications requiring spectrophotometric determinations.

Space Constraints: Table space is often at a premium when complex laboratory robotic systems are being developed. Various approaches including tracks, turntables, and additional robots have been used to attain larger work envelopes. Another approach for solving this problem of limited work space is creating custom devices having single robotic access points. A test tube dispenser is a classic example, since the bulk of the tube dispenser can be placed well outside the reach of the robot, freeing space for additional equipment.

Safety: One advantage of laboratory robotics is that it can minimize exposure of staff to potentially hazardous situations. Extremely hazardous applications often require custom hardware development because of their uniqueness. When developing custom robotic fixturing for these types of applications, special attention must be placed on the safety aspects of the design. For example, in the digestion station mentioned earlier, sample flasks containing concentrated sulfuric acid were secured on the hot plate with a pneumatic gripper. Maintaining positive placement of the flask with the gripper during the digestion routine prevented the flask from being accidentally overturned.

METHODS OF DEVELOPING CUSTOM ROBOTIC FIXTURING

When MRI develops an automated system, we begin by examining the laboratory unit operations to determine if commercially available peripherals can perform the tasks. We also examine the design of custom equipment reported by other laboratories for its potential usefulness in the system being developed. If this investigation indicates the hardware or design does not exist or is expected to perform inadequately in that application, we develop custom fixtures. When developing custom fixtures we use the following approaches: (1) modifying off-the-shelf hardware or (2) designing and fabricating unique components.

Modification of Off-the-Shelf Hardware

When properly modified, the capabilities of much commercially available equipment can be extended or augmented for use in a laboratory robotic system. In doing this, innovation and creativity are essential in adapting equipment for successful interfacing with a robot. Generally, a combination of pneumatic and electronic devices, such as that pictured in Figure 1, is sufficient to produce such a modified module or station.

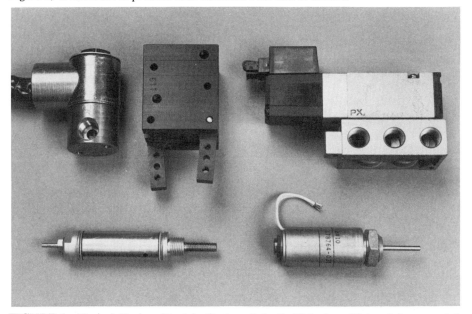

FIGURE 1. Typical Devices Used in Custom Robotic Fixturing. Pictured from top left (clockwise): solenoid valve, pneumatic gripper, 3-way solenoid valve, pneumatic cylinder and solenoid.

A simple example of this approach is the modification of a commercially available bottle dispenser for transition from manual to automated reagent dispensing, described by Markelov.[2] By attaching a pneumatic cylinder to the dispenser, a wide variety of reagents can be dispensed. Raising and lowering the dispenser barrel are achieved by activating a solenoid valve which controls the airflow into the cylinder.

Zymark robotic hands are often modified for particular operations by attaching various devices to the hand. An interesting example of a hand modified for a dissolution-testing application was presented by Wolfshütz.[3] In this application, a robotic hand was equipped with a custom designed sample probe to withdraw test solutions from 4-L dissolution vessels that were located well outside the robot's normal work cell. The sample probe consisted of three solenoid valves, a needle extended by a rod for accessing the vessels, a glass capillary fitted with a depth filter, and a temperature probe.

In MRI's dosed feed analysis system, the capping station has been modified for more reliable operation (Figure 2). A set of custom jaws was mounted on the standard Zymark capper jaws. The custom jaws can pivot around test tubes of different sizes and provide greater contact surface area for holding the tubes during the capping routines. For reliably capping larger test tubes, a guide, which extends pneumatically, is used to position the tube properly in the station as well as prevent it from precessing while spinning in the capper. Extension of the guide over the capping station is executed by activating a solenoid valve which controls the airflow into the cylinder. A second guide is located on the base of the capper to help position round bottom vessels on the capping station. These modifications significantly increased system reliability by decreasing capping failures due to improper tube positioning and tube slippage in the capper jaws.

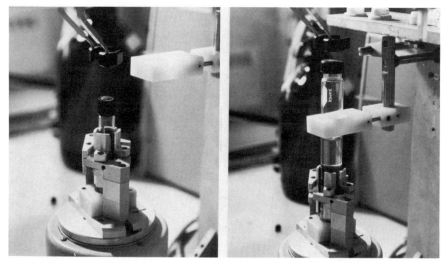

FIGURE 2. Modified Capping Station. Left - configuration for capping small test tubes (16 X 100 mm). Right - configuration for capping large test tubes (25 X 200 mm).

Another system developed by MRI includes a single workstation to perform the two laboratory unit operations of sample mixing and reagent addition. In this case, we modified a Zymark Vortex station, as shown in Figure 3, by mounting a dispensing head from a Zymark Master Laboratory station over the vortex cup. To complete the station, an air cylinder with a small pneumatic gripper attached is mounted to the base of the vortex station. The air cylinder and gripper are used to move a test tube between the vortex cup and reagent dispensing head. The robotic arm is used only to transfer the sample tubes to and from the station. The motions of the cylinder and gripper are controlled by energizing and de-energizing 12-VDC solenoid valves which direct the flow of pressurized air into the pneumatic devices. This station can add several reagents successively to a test tube, mixing between each addition. Since these laboratory unit operations can take place independently of the robot arm, other functions that require the robot can be performed concurrently. The end result of this type of custom fixturing is an increase in sample throughput.

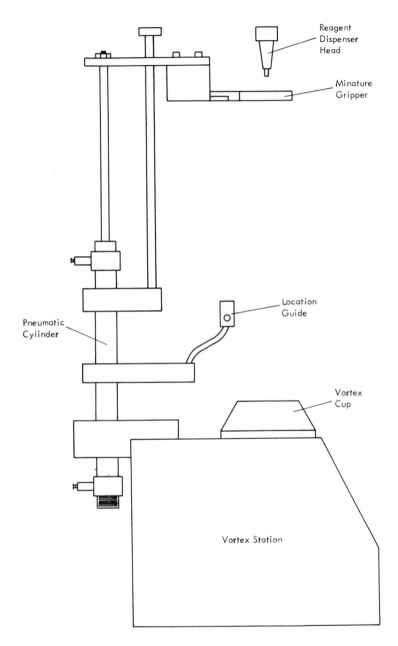

FIGURE 3. Vortex/Reagent Addition Station.

Design and Fabrication of Custom Components

Often, existing laboratory equipment cannot be modified to achieve a desired operation within a laboratory robotic system. In this case, the design and fabrication of unique components are required. In the same way that equipment is constructed for use by humans in laboratory operations, equipment must be specifically designed and fabricated for utilization in robotic operations. Because of the unique capabilities and limitations of robots, custom devices interfaced with them may be unlike conventional human-operated equipment in appearance or operation. Robot vendors have been and continue to be leaders in developing hardware for use with laboratory robotic systems. Their innovative ideas have created a large volume of robotic peripherals and have been fundamental in the growth of laboratory automation technology. However, because of the large number and diversity of procedures being automated, applications frequently require the end-user to design and fabricate custom equipment.

A test tube dispenser described by Hamilton[4] is a good example of a custom device fabricated specifically for use with a laboratory robot. This dispenser incorporates a slotted wheel that is pneumatically actuated to pick up a test tube and present it to the robot for removal. We have developed a similar pneumatic tube feeder using a custom tray that slides in and out of the tube bin. Each time the tray is retracted into the bin a single test tube is retrieved. Returning the slide to its home position places the test tube into position for robotic access. An electric vibrator is attached to the bin and is used to dislodge tubes in the unlikely event they become jammed. Our device will dispense up to 300 test tubes (16 X 125 mm).

Another interesting example, a sieve cleaning station used in particle size distribution studies, was described by Jones[5]. The station, located inside a small Plexiglas hood, consists of a vacuum cleaner and several pneumatic devices for manipulation of the sieves. An air jet/vacuum nozzle mounted on a pneumatic cylinder is raised under the sieve and a vacuum applied to remove polymer particles from the sieve. The sieve is then placed on a turntable and rotated while the robot positions the vacuum nozzle against the inner and outer walls, removing additional residue.

We have also developed a sipper station for use in robotic systems incorporating spectrophotometers (Figure 4). This station is designed to draw sample test solutions from test tubes (16 X 125 mm) through the flow cell assembly. A peristaltic pump connected to the sipper tube is used to draw the sample through the cell. A rotary actuator is used to locate the sipper tube above a sample test tube or the station's purge reservoir. A pneumatic cylinder is mounted on the rotary actuator for vertical movement of the sipper tube. Solenoid valves are again used to direct airflow into the pneumatic devices. After the robot places a tube in the station and initiates the sampling sequence, other tasks can be performed by the arm. When the sampling is complete, the robot retrieves the tube from the station and disposes of the tube while the flow cell is purged.

A final example is a workstation we recently developed for the digestion of samples using concentrated sulfuric acid and hydrogen peroxide. To perform this laboratory unit operation, the robotic workstation (Figure 5) incorporates a rapid digestion technique reported by Hach.[6] After a sample is placed in a 125-mL Erlenmeyer flask along with concentrated sulfuric acid, the robot transports the flask to the workstation where a pneumatic gripper secures the flask on a small hot plate. A glass condenser/manifold is then lowered onto the flask using a pneumatic cylinder. The condenser/manifold is used to aspirate evolving fumes as well as provide a port for hydrogen peroxide addition during the digestion process. The entire digestion procedure can be performed without any assistance from the robotic arm.

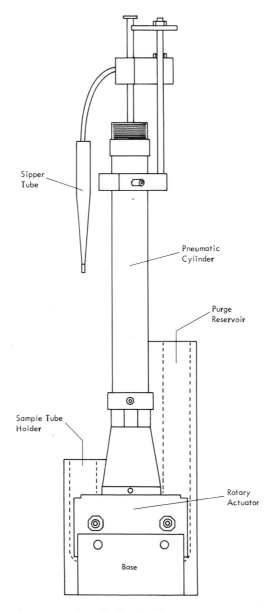

FIGURE 4. Spectrophotometer Sample Sipping Station.

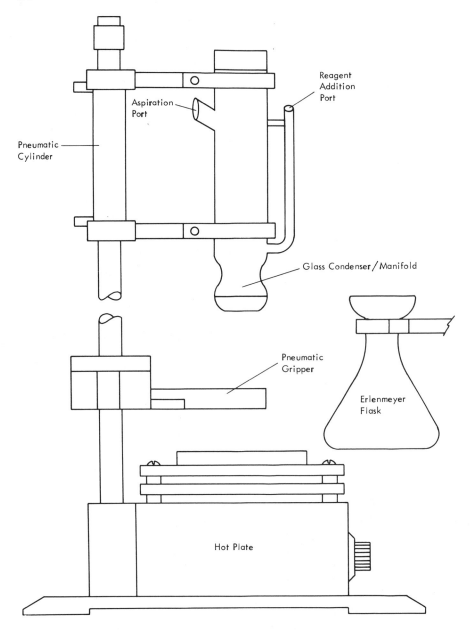

FIGURE 5. Sample Digestion Station.

CONCLUSION

Custom robotic fixturing allows a broad range of operations to be automated when the necessary hardware is not commercially available or off-the-shelf equipment is unsuitable. Two approaches can be used in the development of custom robotic fixturing: (1) modifying off-the-shelf hardware or (2) designing and fabricating unique components. Using these approaches, laboratory robotics can be employed to its fullest potential. In specific cases, custom fixturing can provide a way to improve sample throughput, reliability, and flexibility while reducing costs, table space constraints, and safety hazards.

REFERENCES

1. B.E. Kropscott, L.B. Coyne, R.R. Dunlap and P.W. Langvardt, "Alternative Task Performance in Robotics," American Laboratory, 70-75, June 1987.

2. M. Markelov, M. Antloga and S.A. Schmidt, "Automation of Multiple Analytical Procedures in an Industrial Laboratory (Trace Organics in Water & Soil, Residual Monomers, Anionic Surfactants, Preparation of Standards for GC, LC & IC, etc.)" in Advances in Laboratory Automation, Robotics - 1985, G.L. Hawk and J.R. Strimaitis, eds, (Zymark Corporation, Hopkinton, MA) pp 209-230.

3. R. Wolfschütz, H. Gänshirt and H.G. Tessun, "Automation of Dissolution Testing of Tablets and Capsules by Laboratory Robotics," in Advances in Laboratory Automation, Robotics-1986, G.L. Hawk and J.R. Strimaitis, eds, (Zymark Corporation, Hopkinton, MA) pp 139-152.

4. S. Hamilton, "Robotic Assays for Fermentation Products," ibid pp 1-21.

5. R.D. Jones, J.B. Cross, and H.R. Pinnick, "Robotic Automation of Polymer Sieving (Screen Test)," ibid pp 387- 405.

6. C.C. Hach, S.V. Brayton and A.B. Kopelove, "A Powerful Kjeldahl Nitrogen Method Using Peroxymonosulfuric Acid," Journal of Agricultural and Food Chemistry, 1117, 33, 1985.

INTERFACING ROBOTS TO LABORATORY PERSONAL COMPUTERS:

A MULTI-TASKING APPROACH

H. R. Pinnick, Jr., R. D. Jones and J. B. Cross
Phillips Petroleum Company, Research and Development
Bartlesville, OK 74004

ABSTRACT

Robots such as the Zymate Laboratory Automation System are finding wide usage for routine analysis in analytical and quality control laboratories. These robots often require (1) integration to instrumentation which will be used for the analysis; (2) integration to laboratory information management systems (LIMS) which provide information about the sample to be analyzed; and (3) integration to laboratory computers which are often used for data analysis and/or instrument control. Also important to using robots in the laboratory is a means for the operator to interact with and control this diverse collection of hardware and software.

The integration of a Zymate robot, a personal computer (PC), and a LIMS to provide a system where the operator can schedule the robot to perform a series of operations will be presented. For example, one operation may be elemental analysis of oil samples, and another the cleaning of NMR tubes. The presentation will emphasize the design of an operation scheduler software package for the PC and how it interacts with the operator, a LIMS, and controls a laboratory robot. The PC software uses a run-time library which provides a multi-tasking environment with inter-task communication and synchronization.

INTRODUCTION

The robotic automation of polymer sieving was our first project using an IBM[tm] personal computer (PC) clone as the master controller.[1] The Zymate[tm] robot was controlled from the PC via a Z845 computer interface card (Zymark, Hopkinton, MA). This interface enabled the PC software to request information and set variables on the robot as well as start programs.

A major design objective of the polymer sieving PC software was to provide for user interaction with the PC while the robot was active. This objective was needed so that the user could change samples for rush jobs and add samples prior to leaving work without stopping the robot. Thus, once a robot program was started, the PC software had to be able to receive and process input from both the user and the robot controller.

Our first approach was to use a software polling technique to test for keyboard input and for input from the robot (via a serial port). We had some success with this technique, but there were random times when the PC would not recognize user input. We tested our software and it appeared the problem was in the commercially supplied run-time libraries. It was decided to scrap the polling technique and explore possible alternatives.

DISCUSSION

In order to evaluate possible alternatives, the objectives listed below were used. The software package would:

1. Require the functional aspects of a robot operation to be separate

2. Provide for serialization of robot operations on the PC

3. Isolate the user from the robot controller

In general, each robotic operation is divided into three functional parts: initialization, action, and reporting. Initialization is the setting of parameter (variable) values in the robot controller. Action is the execution of the robotic program. Reporting is the retrieving of parameter values from the robot controller for report generation. All of these parts can be controlled by the PC software. If one were to view an operation in this manner, initialization usually requires user input; whereas action and reporting do not require user input. This structure provides a possible approach to the design of the PC application software which will be discussed later.

If we were to end our discussion at this point, PC software could be written for each separate application. It would ask the user for the values of the parameters, set the parameters in the robot, start the robot program, wait for completion, retrieve the appropriate parameters, and print the report. The question is, why is the PC needed? For this simple case, it is not. However, when another computer is involved which has information necessary for the initialization of the robot or preparation of the reports, the PC is needed.

For example, in the development of the PC-robot system for polymer sieving, the hardware was configured as shown in Figure 1. The AB/LMS (Analysis Branch / Laboratory Management System) contains information necessary for the preparation of reports.[2,3]

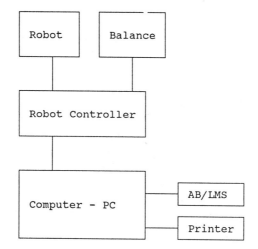

FIGURE 1. Computer Connections.

The AB/LMS is designed to store and retrieve information, but not to control instrumentation. Thus, the PC provides for user control of the system as shown in Figure 1. When the user starts the PC application program, data are requested from the user and the AB/LMS, parameters are set in the robot controller, and the robot program is started. When this program is completed, the PC reads data from the robot, and prints reports using these data and data from the AB/LMS. In the above example, the robot's operation was separated into the three parts: initialization, action and reporting.

The next objective is to provide serialization of robot operations. Some desirable features for a serial operations scheduler are as follows:

1. Allow any order for the operations

2. Allow initialization of one operation while another is active

3. Delete an operation

4. Reschedule an operation

5. Resume an operation if it is paused

6. Provide screens that direct the user

Let us assume two operations (A and B) are to be run consecutively. The initial screen for the operation scheduler is shown in Figure 2. The active operation window displays the order of scheduled operations. The possible operations window lists those operations which can be done. The softkeys window lists those softkeys which are currently active. The softkeys change as operations are started, paused or completed.

Softkey F1 displays a help window with information about the operation scheduler. Softkey F9 provides the programmer with an on-line debugging tool. Softkey F10 allows the user to exit to MS-DOS. Softkey F2 asks which possible operation is to be activated. Selection of either A or B will cause the initialization part of that operation to be executed.

```
 ┌════ Active Operations ════╗ ╔════ Possible Operations ════┐
 │                           ║ ║ 1.   Operation A             │
 │                           ║ ║ 2.   Operation B             │
 └───────────────────────────╝ ╚─────────────────────────────┘


 ════════════════════════════════ Softkeys ════════════════════════════════
 F1    Help                       F2   Activate an Operation
 F3                               F4
 F5                               F6
 F7                               F8
 F9    System Services            F10  Exit
```

FIGURE 2. Initial Operation Scheduler Screen.

When the initiation of operation A is complete, the operation scheduler will modify the screen as shown in Figure 3. Three new softkeys are displayed. Softkey F3 allows the user to delete an operation. The operation will not be deleted until the action part receives a program completion from the robot controller, then an orderly termination can be done. Softkey F4 allows the user to modify the initial data within certain boundaries. For example, to expedite unexpected priority samples, the user can alter previously inputted sample identifications. Softkey F5 allows the user to rearrange the order of the operations.

The action part of operation A will begin execution. Should there be any problem with the action part of operation A, the screen in Figure 4 will be displayed. The action can be resumed within the boundaries of the application code of operation A or it can be deleted.

```
┌══════ Active Operations ═══════╗ ┌══════ Possible Operations ═══════╗
│ 1. Operation A                 ║ │                                  ║
│                                ║ │   2.   Operation B               ║
└════════════════════════════════╝ └══════════════════════════════════╝
```

```
╞══════════════════════════════ Softkeys ══════════════════════════════╡
F1    Help                          F2   Activate an Operation
F3    Delete an Operation           F4   Service an Operation
F5    Reschedule an Operation       F6
F7                                  F8
F9    System Services               F10  Exit
```

FIGURE 3. Operation Scheduler Screen with at Least One Active Operation.

```
┌══════ Active Operations ═══════╗ ┌══════ Possible Operations ═══════╗
│ 1. Operation A                 ║ │                                  ║
│   ┌─────── Operation Paused ───────┐ │   2. Operation B            ║
│   │ Message from paused operation  │ └──────────────────────────────╝
│   │                                │
│   │                                │
│   └────────────────────────────────┘
```

```
╞══════════════════════════════ Softkeys ══════════════════════════════╡
F1    Help                          F2
F3    Delete an Operation           F4
F5                                  F6   Resume Operation
F7                                  F8
F9    System Services               F10  Exit
```

FIGURE 4. Operation Scheduler Screen With an Operation Paused.

Assuming that the action part of operation A is running successfully, the user can activate operation B. As before, the operation is activated via softkey F2. When the initialization part of operation B is completed, the action part is placed in the operations list to be executed after operation A is complete. The screen in Figure 5 is displayed.

```
╔═══ Active Operations ════╗ ╔═══ Possible Operations ═══╗
║ 1. Operation A           ║ ║                           ║
║ 2. Operation B           ║ ║                           ║
╚══════════════════════════╝ ╚═══════════════════════════╝

══════════════════════ Softkeys ══════════════════════════
F1    Help                       F2  Activate an Operation
F3    Delete an Operation        F4  Service an Operation
F5    Reschedule an Operation    F6
F7                               F8
F9    System Services            F10 Exit
```

FIGURE 5. Operation Scheduler Screen With Both Operations Active.

```
┌══════ Active Operations ══════╗┌══ Possible Operations ═══════┐
│  1. Operation B               ║│  1. Operation A              │
│                               ║│                              │
└───────────────────────────────╝└──────────────────────────────┘

  ══════════════════════════════ Softkeys ═══════════════════════════
  F1   Help                       F2   Activate an Operation
  F3   Delete an Operation        F4   Service an Operation
  F5   Reschedule an Operation    F6
  F7                              F8
  F9   System Services            F10  Exit
```

FIGURE 6. Operation Scheduler Screen After Operation is Complete.

When operation A is complete, the screen in Figure 6 will be displayed. When operation B
is complete, the screen in Figure 2 is displayed.

To accomplish such objectives, one needs a multi-tasking environment with inter-task
communication and synchronization. The serial ports must also be supported in this same
environment. MS-DOS[tm] is not a multi-tasking environment, but there are commercial
run-time libraries which provide a multi-tasking environment layered on top of MS-DOS.
Several such products are available, but only two were considered: a preemptive multi-
tasking executive from KADAK Products, Ltd. (Vancouver, British Columbia) and a non-
preemptive multi-tasking executive from Cytek, Inc. (North Andover, MA) The non-
preemptive executive was chosen because it better suited our application programming
requirements. Also, Cytek markets Multi-Comm (a serial data communication library) that
is compatible with Multi-C (non-preemptive multi-tasking executive), Multi-Windows (a
window display library), and Multi-Forms (a data entry library).

Using the Cytek multi-tasking run-time libraries, a serial operation scheduler was developed which has the screens shown in Figures 2 through 6. This scheduler has three tasks: (1) service the softkey input and call the appropriate initialization function of an operation, (2) execute the action/reporting function of an operation, and (3) display the operation scheduler's softkeys. The operation scheduler is connected to the application programs via a table. Thus, the scheduler needs no knowledge of any specific operation.

CONCLUSIONS

The polymer sieving PC software was rewritten to work with the operation scheduler. The multi-tasking approach made the software much easier to design, modify, and enhance. We no longer experience keyboard lockup that was found in the polling approach.

ACKNOWLEDGEMENTS

The authors wish to thank Michael Stevens, Alan Finger and Katherine Young of Cytek, Incorporated for the insight and suggestions on the use of Multi-C and associated products.

REFERENCES

1.   R. D. Jones, J. B. Cross and H. R. Pinnick, Jr., "Robotic Automation of Polymer Sieving (Screen Test)" in Advances in Laboratory Automation Robotics 1986, J. R. Strimaitis and G. L. Hawks eds. (Zymark Corporation, Hopkinton, MA, 1985) pp. 387.

2.   T. V. Iorns, R. C. Loyd, and P. R. Gray, "Phillips' Laboratory Management System - History, Function and Benefits", paper presented at the 1984 Pittsburgh Conference in Atlantic City, New Jersey, March 5-9, 1984.

3.   T. V. Iorns, P. R. Gray, and R. C. Loyd, "LIMS: A Managers Perspective", paper presented at the 1984 Eastern Analytical Symposium, New York, New York, November 13-16, 1984.

IBM is a registered trademark of International Business Machines Corporation.

MS-DOS is a registered trademark of Microsoft Corporation.

Multi-C, Multi-Comm, Multi-Windows and Multi-Forms are products of Cytek, Incorporated.

INTERFACING A ZYMARK ROBOT TO AN IBM PC-AT AND A DEC LABORATORY INFORMATION MANAGEMENT SYSTEM

Dante J. Rutstrom, Charles N. Kettler
and Stephen D. Forrester
Tennessee Eastman Company
P.O. Box 1972
Kingsport, Tennessee 37662

ABSTRACT

A fully integrated robotic system for the purpose of performing potentiometric titrations has been developed. The system features a Zymate II robot, a Brinkmann autotitrator, an IBM personal computer and a VAX 8600 computer system. An IBM PC/AT computer serves as the host computer, accepting sample identifications from a bar code reader, sample weights from an electronic balance, and initiating the robotic titration sequence. Upon completion of the titration, the robot controller transfers the results to the personal computer. At this point, any necessary calculations are completed and the personal computer prepares a list of the results to be reviewed by the analyst. If the results are satisfactory, they are forwarded to the VAX system where they can be received by the sample submitter through the Laboratory Information Management System (LIMS). The host computer communicates with the robot, bar code reader, and the balance through BASIC programming. File transfers between the host and the VAX computer are completed through the use of KERMIT and CROSSTALK software packages. This mode of operation has substantially reduced the time involved in analyzing samples and reporting results.

INTRODUCTION

Like many analytical laboratories across the country, we have an interest in automating our routine analytical procedures in an attempt to better utilize our labor forces. The preferred approach eliminates laboratory analyses by installing process analyzers to directly monitor the anlayte of interest. However, in many cases, an appropriate process analyzer is not available, and the samples can only be analyzed by sending them to a lab separated from the process. At Tennessee Eastman we have attempted to automate the analysis of samples that fall into this latter category through the use of laboratory robotics. We have identified three important steps associated with an analytical procedure which can benefit from automation. These include; 1) the sample submission process; 2) actual analysis of the sample; and 3) the reporting and documentation of the results. Progress in laboratory automation over the past few years has made it possible to automate the sample preparation and subsequent analysis associated with the second step. However, the use of robotic sample handling by itself does not eliminate the need for the intervention of laboratory personnel for submitting samples and reporting results. The work involved in these two steps can be minimized by using an appropriate data reporting system such as a LIMS. However, such systems are not without their own short-comings and can often be more labor intensive than the more traditional means of manual bookkeeping. To fully automate the three steps listed above requires the successful integration of an appropriate LIMS software package with the sample preparation and analysis. We will describe a system for performing potentiometric titrations which we believe accomplishes this task.

EXPERIMENTAL

The hardware associated with this system is listed in Table 1. The benchtop configuration for this application is shown in Figure 1.

TABLE 1. List of Equipment.

Zymark Corporation (Hopkinton, MA)

> Zymate II Robot Arm and Controller
> Printer
> Master Laboratory Station (MLS),(2)
> Power and Event Controller (PEC)
> Modified BOD Work Station
> Modified BOD Capper/Uncapper
> Custom Racks for 250 mL Erlenmeyer Flasks
> Z-845 Remote Computer Interface
> Z-361 Brinkmann 682 Titroprocessor Interface
> General Purpose Hand

Other Hardware

> IBM PC/AT (International Business Machines)
> VAX 8600 Computer (Digital Equipment Corporation)
> METTLER AE-200 Balance (Mettler Instrument Corporation, Hightstown, NJ)
> METTLER Option 011 Data Output Device (Mettler Instrument Corporation, Hightstown, NJ)
> Symbol Technologies Model LS6500 Bar Code Reader (Concord Technolgies, Inc., Concord, MA).
> INTERMEC Model 9570AB Bar Code Wedge Reader (Intermec South, Oakridge, TN)
> Model 682 Titroprocessor (Brinkmann Instrument Company, Westbury, NY)
> Model 665 Dosimat (Brinkmann Instrument Company, Westbury, NY)
> Model 525 Baytech Multiport Controller (Baytech Associates, Bay Saint Louis, MS)
> 250-ml Erlenmeyer Flasks with 24/40 Ground Glass Joints and Stoppers
> Magnetic Stirrer (2)

Software

> CROSSTALK (Digital Communications Associates, Inc.)
> KERMIT (Public Domain)
> EASYLAB (Zymark Corporation)
> Advanced Basic (International Business Machines)
> VAX LIMS/SM (Digital Equipment Corporation

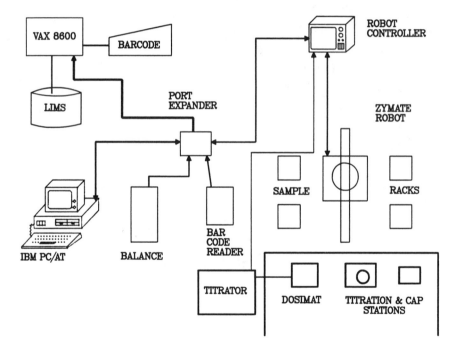

FIGURE 1. Potentiometric Titration Layout.

The procedure is initiated by the sample submitter in the plant. After the process stream is sampled, a bar code label is placed on the sample vial and the sample identification is entered into LIMS by the customer. All responses to the LIMS prompts (such as charge codes, sample identifications and method requests) are input using a Wedge Reader. No information has to be typed into the computer. This approach to entering data into LIMS substantially reduces the time required for logging samples into the system.

When the samples arrive in the analytical laboratory, the number of samples is entered into the personal computer. The sample identifications are then input to the computer with a bar code reader. Following this, the analyst weighs each sample into a titration flask. All weights are transferred directly from the balance to the personal computer using a Mettler AE200 balance, a Mettler hand key (part #42500), and a Mettler Option 011 Data Output device. After all of the samples are processed, the computer signals the robot to begin the sample preparation and titration process. The robotic steps include: removal of a ground glass stopper from the titration flask, addition of reagents, stirring, titration of the sample, and re-insertion of the ground glass stopper into the flask. Titration data for each sample is passed from the Brinkmann 672 Titroprocessor to the Zymate II Controller by using the Zymate Z-361 Titroprocessor Interface module. Upon completion of the preparation and titration of the samples, the personal computer queries the Zymate II controller for the titration volumes and completes the appropriate calculations. A report is prepared for the analyst to review; any data suspected of being in error can be removed at this stage.

By providing an interface between the personal computer controlling the sample analysis and the VAX 8600 computer running LIMS, we are able to expedite the reporting of test results to customers. The approved data file is transferred from the personal computer to the VAX computer by using CROSSTALK (Version 3.61) software and KERMIT (Version 2.29A) file transfer protocol. CROSSTALK software allows the personal computer to be connected to the VAX computer by way of a laboratory port selector. By using the appropriate CROSSTALK script file, the personal computer logs onto the VAX computer, calls up the KERMIT server, transfers the data file, and then logs off. After the data has been transferred to the VAX account, custom software within LIMS accesses the deposited information and delivers the sample results to the customer's LIMS account. All of the data transfer and reporting is acomplished with a single keystroke at the personal computer keyboard. This data reporting procedure significantly reduces the labor involved in sample reporting and allows for better sample turn-around time.

RESULTS

The performance of the sample preparation and subsequent titration was evaluated by analyzing samples with analyte concentrations of approximately 100 ("SAMPLE A") and 500 ("SAMPLE B") parts per million. Each sample was prepared and analyzed nine times. The robotic results were also compared to results obtained by manual titrations using a visual endpoint. The manual titrations were performed by a single operator. As indicated by Table 2, the results were quite favorable. The precision for the robot method was slightly better than the precision of the manual method. More significantly, the total labor involved in preparing, analyzing, and reporting results was reduced from fifteen minutes per sample to three minutes per sample.

Table 2. Comparison of Robot and Manual Titrations (n = 9).

Sample	Robot		Manual	
	[analyte],ppm	SD	[analyte],ppm	SD
A	108.4	0.7	107	3
B	508	1	504	3

CONCLUSION

The system described above provided us with several benefits. Utilizing the robot for the titrations, has reduced the labor requirements for the analysis. The errors associated with labeling samples and reporting results was also reduced by using the interface to LIMS. Sending the data to the mainframe computer provided us with immediate data storage and eliminated the need for recording large amounts of data in notebooks.

ACKNOWLEDGEMENTS

The authors would like to express their appreciation to Stewart Millen and Lester Church for providing analyses. We also wish to thank Richard Siggins and Richard Hardin for customizing the LIMS software to meet our needs. Finally, Bernice Blevins and Valecia Fillnow both assisted preparing this manuscript.

DEC, VAX, and VAX LIMS/SM are trademarks of Digital Equipment Corporation.

IBM and AT are trademarks of International Business Machines Corporation.

CROSSTALK is a trademark of Digital Communications Associates, Incorporated.

KERMIT is a trademark of Henson Associates.

Mettler is a trademark of Mettler Instrument Corporation.

INTERMEC is a trademark of Intermec Corporation.

LAL ENDOTOXIN ASSAY IN MICROTITER PLATES

Laura C. Porter
American Cyanamid Company
Medical Research Division
Lederle Laboratories
Pearl River, New York 10965

ABSTRACT

An efficient, precise robotic assay for the endotoxin content in parenteral drug solutions has been developed. It is based on the chromogenic LAL test kit procedure manufactured by Whittaker (Walkersville, MD). Robotic microtiter plate equipment used for the chromogenic reaction is combined with robotic equipment for preparing the standards and samples in test tubes. The sample preparation includes multiple vortexing and dilution steps. Samples are loaded with a syringe hand into an assay plate on a custom heating block. The reagents are then dispensed from custom storage stations with an octapipet hand. After the reaction is quenched the resulting color is measured with an ELISA reader. Automating this assay eliminates tedious manual manipulations and provides closely controlled and repeatable time, temperature and mixing conditions for the colorimetric reaction.

INTRODUCTION

Injectable drugs and medical devices are routinely tested for bacterial endotoxins which can have pathophysiological effects if administered to humans. LAL endotoxin assays have been developed as alternatives to the classic rabbit pyrogen test. All LAL tests use the Limulus Amebocyte Lysate reagent which is derived from the horseshoe crab. The initial rate of activating a proenzyme or "lysate" is affected by the concentration of gram-negative bacterial endotoxin present. There are three LAL endpoint detection methods: gel clot, turbidimetric and chromogenic. In the gel clot and turbidimetric tests the activated LAL enzyme reacts with a protein to cause coagulation. In the chromogenic test the activated enzyme is incubated with a substrate that releases p-nitroaniline which absorbs light at 405 nm.[1]

The gel clot readings are subjective and are being replaced with instrumental measurements. The turbidimetric measurements (not including any liquid handling) may be automated using instrumentation manufactured by Hitachi (distributed by Wako Chemicals USA, Inc., Dallas, TX) or by Associates of Cape Cod, Inc. (Falmouth, MA). The chromogenic assay was automated in 1984 by workers at Upjohn, Inc. using robotic test tube procedures.[2] This assay encompassed sample dilutions, incubations and absorbance measurements in a spectrophotometric flow cell. Only 9 test tubes containing standards and samples could run simultaneously (3 standards and 3 samples in duplicate). For quantitation the standards are essential because it was demonstrated in this work that the LAL reagent is unstable.

In our laboratories chromogenic LAL endotoxin assays are manually performed in microtiter plates. Microtiter plates contain 12 rows of 8 wells, each of which holds up to 300 uL of fluid. They are widely used for biological and biochemical assays because of the uniformity of sample treatment, handling convenience, reduced reagent cost, and the ease of rapid measurement and quantitation using standard ELISA plate readers.

In this work our goals are to automate both the sample preparation dilutions and the chromogenic LAL reaction using microtiter plates and the general procedure specified in the Whittaker assay kit. Upon developing the robotic assay we plan to transfer it to quality control laboratories. We hope to eliminate the tedious liquid handling manipulations, improve the reliability over the manual results and process a steadily increasing sample work load. The robotic developmental work uses the same robot table as an existing UV-Visible spectrophotometric assay[3] which must continue operating. This later constraint provides some spatial, hardware and software restrictions.

Because of the diversity of analysis needs and the requirements of the LAL assay procedure, we have developed widely applicable "generic" robotic techniques to handle both microtiter plate and test tube equipment. This work will describe how these robotic techniques are used to automate the chromogenic LAL endotoxin assay.

EXPERIMENTAL

This LAL assay follows the procedure specified in the Whittaker QCL-1000[tm] third generation pyrogen testing kit.[1] The reagents included in this kit are manually prepared and loaded into the designated reservoirs. The robotic steps are given in Table

1.TABLE 1. Steps in the Chromogenic LAL Endotoxin Assay.[1]

1) Prepare the standards (serial dilutions in test tubes #1 through 4).

2) Prepare the samples (serial dilutions in test tubes or in cover plate).

3) Pre-equilibrate the assay plate at 37°C.

4) Transfer 50 uL of each standard, sample & blank into the assay microtiter plate.

5) Add 50 uL of LAL lysate and mix.

6) Incubate for 10 minutes at 37°C (30 minutes for greater sensitivity).

7) Add 100 uL of chromogenic substrate prewarmed to 37°C and mix.

8) Incubate for 3 minutes at 37°C.

9) Add 50 (or 100) uL of 25% acetic acid or "quench" and mix.

10) Measure the absorbance of each well at 405-410 nm and process the results.

Currently a Zymate[tm] II robot with version 2.3 of the controller software is being used. A schematic representation of the robot table layout is shown in Figure 1 and an overview photograph is in Figure 2. The UV-VIS analyses[3] utilize the space contained in an arc approximately 70 degrees on both sides of the robot arm position depicted in Figure 1 (including two test tube racks). The LAL assay is compressed into the remaining 220 degrees of space. The one exception is a pyrogen-free water dispenser at the master laboratory station (MLS), used with a 2.5 mL syringe and an auxiliary valve. The line power source feeding all of the robotic components is regulated and filtered (6 amps max load).

For endotoxin assays all containers, pipet tips and other materials coming into contact with samples must be pyrogen-free. All water and reagents must also be pyrogen-free. Because the endotoxin has a great affinity for glass it is essential to vortex the vials and test tubes,

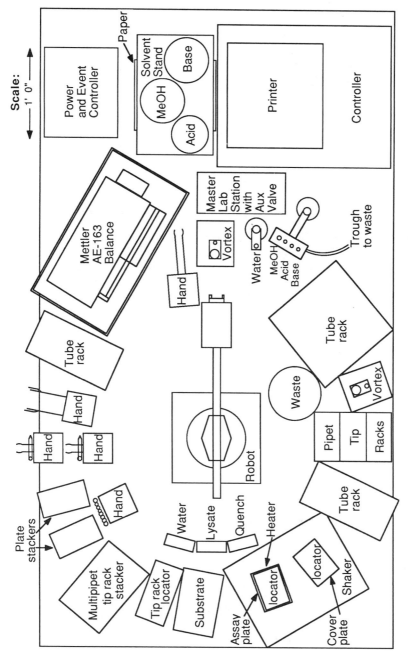

FIGURE 1. Schematic Representation of the Robot Table Layout (to scale).[4] The LAL endotoxin assay is performed on the left side and a UV-Visible spectrophotometric assay is on the right side.

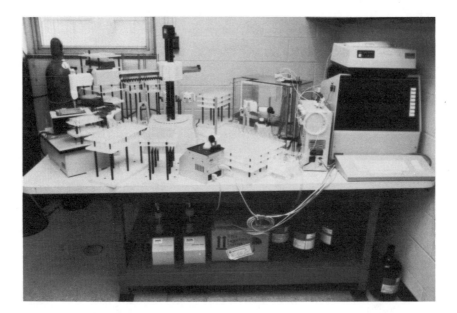

FIGURE 2. Overview of the Robot Table.

especially for the higher concentration standards. With plastic test tubes it may be possible to avoid this glass adhesion problem, depending on the preference of the user.

To minimize the environmental contamination the pyrogen-free water, lysate and substrate storage stations are covered. The acid reservoir is not covered, because when it is used the reaction is quenched. The covered reservoir stations were custom products developed by Zymark Corporation. The lids are actuated by pneumatic valves connected to power and event controller (PEC) switches. Figure 3 is a photograph showing the multipipet robot hand accessing the heated substrate reservoir (with its cover opened). This substrate reservoir is a modified Pierce Reacti-Therm[tm] Heating Module #18800 (Pierce Chemical Co., Rockford, IL). The acid, lysate and water reservoirs are shown in front, left to right in the photograph.

At the left of Figure 3 is the assay microtiter plate in a locator on a heating block (Lab Line Instruments, Inc. #2052, Melrose Park, IL) adapted by Zymark Corporation. A thermocouple inserted into the heating block reads temperature data into the power and event controller A/D control. The temperatures were calibrated with a short immersion thermometer. The entire heating block and the cover plate locator are mounted on an orbital shaker.

FIGURE 3. View of the Multipipet Robot Hand, the Custom Reagent Reservoirs and the Assay Microtiter Plate. The multipipet is accessing the heated substrate reservoir (with the cover opened). The acid, lysate and water reservoirs (left to right) are in front. The assay plate is located on the custom adapted heating block mounted on the orbital shaker.

The volumes of liquid handled in this assay range range from 50 uL to 2400 uL. To prepare the standard endotoxin solutions the amounts pipetted and dispensed are[1]: 100 uL, 500 uL, 900 uL, 1500 uL and 2000-2400 uL (variable). For accuracy, a 250 uL syringe, a 1000 uL syringe and the MLS dispenser are used (in order of increasing liquid volumes). Test tubes (12 x 75 mm) are used to handle these volumes. Both syringes are mounted on dual function hands so that the test tubes can rapidly be moved with gripper fingers in and out of the vortex. Also, for the microtiter plate manipulations a multipipet hand and a (plate/tip rack) gripper hand are needed. Shown in Figure 4 are these 6 tools on the 4 robot hands and their parking stations. The robot is holding an assay plate and cover plate with its plate/tip rack gripper hand, accessing a microtiter plate stacker rack.

FIGURE 4. View of the Robot Tools and Parking Stations. With the plate/tip rack gripper hand the robot is holding an assay plate and cover plate; it is accessing a plate stacker rack.

The microtiter plate layout to be used initially is schematically represented in Figure 5.[4] The outer wells are not used in this initial work because of our concern about providing adequate temperature control while the assay is being run. Instead the outer wells will be filled with water and prewarmed to 37°C. In the Whittaker procedure[1] "each series of determinations must include a blank plus the four endotoxin standards run in duplicate. The blank wells contain 50 uL of pyrogen-free water instead of sample." In this initial work 6 samples are run in duplicate at 3 concentrations each, for a total of 36 tests.

Once the LAL reaction is quenched with acid, its timing is stopped and the absorbance can be measured later. We do not have space on this robot table for a plate reader and are not ready to make this investment. For the initial development work we are using a plate reader in another laboratory.

		S1	S2	1a	1b	1c	4a	4b	4c	
		S1	S2	1a	1b	1c	4a	4b	4c	
		B	S3	2a	2b	2c	5a	5b	5c	
		B	S3	2a	2b	2c	5a	5b	5c	
		B	S4	3a	3b	3c	6a	6b	6c	
		B	S4	3a	3b	3c	6a	6b	6c	

FIGURE 5. Schematic Representation of the Microtiter Plate Layout to be used Initially.[4] The blanks are labeled "B"; the standards at the 4 specified concentrations are labeled "S1" through "S4"; the samples are labeled with numbers 1 through 6 followed by "a", "b" or "c" for the three dilutions of each.

DISCUSSION

Generic Robot Programming

While programming the robotic assay we have attempted to anticipate and accommodate the quality control laboratory needs which include: 1) rapid new robot start-ups; 2) "user-friendly" programs that can be interpreted and used by technicians; and 3) high versatility both in the sample dilution schemes and in the plate setup schemes. We will need the capability of varying the number of samples per run/per day, the number of replicates, and the number of dilutions for samples in varied endotoxin concentration ranges. A preliminary screening run to determine the proper number of dilutions is desired. Methods to handle product matrix interferences[1] will be needed.

Within a single run of the assay six tools are used, varied volumes are dispensed, and samples are handled in both test tubes and microtiter plates. The many ways that the robot will pipet from one container and dispense into another are summarized in Table 2.

TABLE 2. Liquid Pipetting and Dispensing Combinations Used

Pipetting From:	Dispensing Into:		
	Test tube	Cover plate	Assay plate
Master laboratory station (water)	X		
Test tube (in rack or vortex)	X	X	X
Cover plate		X	X
Water reservoir	X	X	X
Lysate reservoir			X
Substrate reservoir			X
Quench reservoir			X

To perform these manipulations "generic" programs applicable to several related tasks have been implemented.[4] The first step is to develop programming techniques based on relative positions; then a single absolute rack position is defined for each task. A spatial representation of the geometric relationships is depicted in Figure 6. The arrows show the order in which the robot would move between the relative positions (never going to the absolute position) to pick up or attach an object. For the two "HIGH" positions the object held in the robot tool is clear from the worst case obstruction. For the two "LOW" positions the empty robot tool is clear. This programming approach has several benefits - there are few named positions; a program can be used with any hand; it is easy to redefine a hand, move a rack or modify the assay.

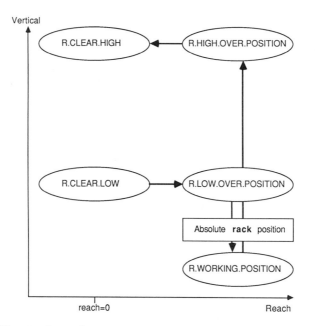

FIGURE 6. Sketch of the Geometric Programming Concepts used for Generic Robot Manipulations.[4] The y-axis represents robotic motion in the vertical direction and the x-axis represents motion in the radial "reach" direction. The names for the generic relative positions used are within the 5 ovals. They start with the letters "R". The absolute position for a particular rack is generally located just above the rack working position. The arrows show the order in which the robot would move to pick up or attach an object.

Robotic Tactile Sensing, Verification and Diagnostics Generic Techniques

The programs which pick up different objects (named with the word "GET") and replace them (named with the word "PUT") are extensively used in this LAL assay and are subject to failure. Robotic "tactile sensing" or force measurements help to detect a failure occurrance. Vertical forces are measured when attaching pipet tips and robot finger grip forces are measured when picking up an object. For both, the force while approaching the object is measured (before contact). This "null force" is subtracted from the force later measured while gripping or pushing down, and the resulting difference is compared against a variable.[4] In Figure 7 the values for these variables that are currently in use for picking up tubes, plates and racks, and attaching three types of pipet tips are summarized. The open and closed finger grip settings are also given.

"Tactile Sensing" = Force Checking

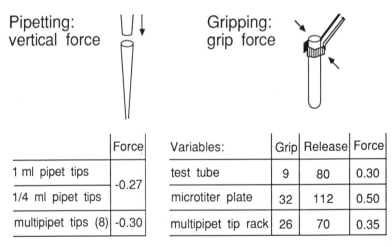

	Force
1 ml pipet tips	-0.27
1/4 ml pipet tips	
multipipet tips (8)	-0.30

Variables:	Grip	Release	Force
test tube	9	80	0.30
microtiter plate	32	112	0.50
multipipet tip rack	26	70	0.35

FIGURE 7. Sensing Variables and Their Initial Values used in the Generic "GET" Algorithms When Picking up Pipet Tips, Tubes, Plates and Racks. The process of attaching three types of pipet tips is represented on the left side. The vertical force values listed on the left are compared with the measured force difference to detect failure. The process of picking up test tubes, microtiter plates and multipipet tip racks is represented on the right side. The grip force values on the right (labeled "Force") are used to detect failure. The value for "Grip" is the finger grip setting for the first attempt at picking up the object. The value for "Release" is the grip setting used when approaching the object with the fingers empty.

If the robot correctly attached or picked up an object the measured force difference will be evaluated according to the generic "GET" algorithm represented in Figure 8. If a pipet tip failure is detected, the robot will push down further and try again 5 times. If the failure is detected a sixth time, it will shuck the pipet tip and try again with a new tip. If an object pickup failure is detected, the robot will grip harder and try again 5 times; it will hang up if the failure is detected a sixth time. The positions and the force values have been optimized so that the failure detection test is passed during cycle #2-4.

Robotic Liquid Handling Techniques

Generic pipetting and dispensing algorithms have been developed for use with all three syringes.[4] The appropriate syringe size "SYRINGE.SIZE" is set up in the robot hand attachment program. The following variables and flags are input in a liquid handling program: "VOLUME.WANTED", "NUMBER.OF.TIP.PREWETS" AND "DROP.TOUCHOFF.WANTED". Since the locations have been defined as racks the same liquid handling program is used with all three hands. This program utilizes the following generic algorithm:

TABLE 3. Robotic Liquid Pipetting Algorithm.[4]

Syringe Height	Program Statement Executed
	DO [NUMBER.OF.TIP.PREWETS + 1] TIMES
Above the liquid:	SHUCK.BAR.0 + AIR.GAP.1
Into the liquid:	+ INT [200 * VOLUME.WANTED / SYRINGE.SIZE]
Above the liquid:	Drop touchoff reach / angle
	+ AIR.GAP.2
If a tip prewet:	Dispense
	Drop touchoff reach / angle ENDDO

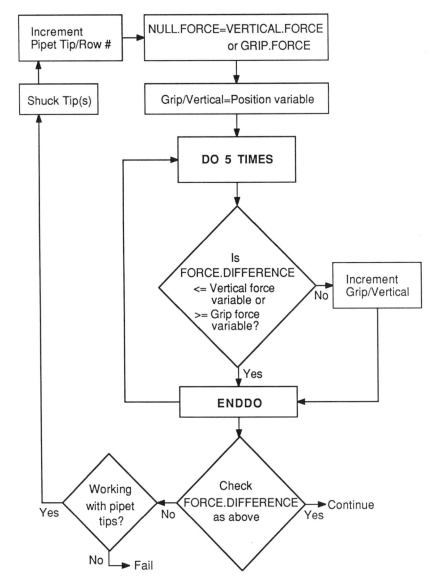

FIGURE 8. Flow Chart Representation of the Generic "GET" Verification and Diagnostics Algorithms for Picking up Objects. Vertical positions and forces are used for attaching pipet tips; finger grip positions and forces are used for picking up objects. The comparison between the measured force difference and the force value listed in Figure 7 is represented by the central diamond.

The first air gap pushes out liquid when dispensing and the second air gap prevents dripping. A drop is touched off in a test tube by moving the angle of the robot hand. At a reservoir or a plate well the robot arm reach is moved for drop touchoff. These liquid handling techniques are easily modified to achieve either increased speed or better quantitative accuracy.

High Level Algorithms

The assay is programmed by nesting the generic algorithms described previously. An example of a complex high level algorithm is depicted in Figure 9. The purpose of this algorithm is to attach a fresh row of 8 unused tips to the robot multipipet hand at any time during assay, no matter what the status of the robot is. Robot hand management routines are an integral part of this high level algorithm.

Control of Experimental Parameters

For this chromogenic LAL endotoxin assay the experimental results are very technique dependent. According to the vendor's instructions[1], the "plate wells must be treated in exactly the same manner... It is important to be consistent in the order of reagent addition from well to well or row to row, and in the rate of pipetting". When manually performed, great dexterity and mental concentration are required for good results. In general, robotic procedures are far more reproducible and more carefully timed than manual manipulations. However, they are also usually a little slower. The slower speed may be a problem for this assay, because the time between dispensing the substrate into the first row and dispensing the quench into the same row must be exactly 3 minutes. Initially, we will process only 8 rows of samples. We may later be able to speed up the liquid handling routines and process more samples.

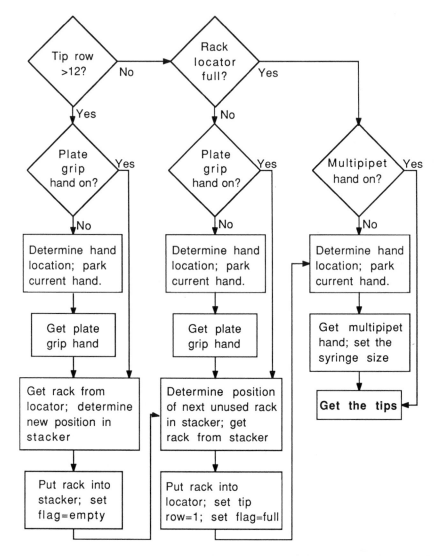

FIGURE 9. Flow Chart Representation of the Example High Level Algorithm used to Attach 8 Fresh Pipet Tips to the Robot Multipipet Hand (called "GET.MULTIPIPET.TIPS").

Sample throughput is not a major concern and we are currently planning for 1-20 samples per day (plus replicates, standards and blanks). The throughput is already much better than that reported in the Upjohn procedure, where for duplicate sample measurements only 3 samples were processed in one run.[2] In this work 18 samples are run, or 6 samples run in duplicate at 3 concentrations each. Also, in this work the standards are run in duplicate and 4 blanks are run, in comparison with only 3 data points for standards in the Upjohn procedure. The LAL reagent is unstable and a new standard curve is made for every sample run. Thus using more data for standards better quantitative results should be achieved. More samples can be processed without human intervention than in the previous work. Microtiter plate equipment can handle more samples in the same volume of space than test tubes, and plate readers are faster than spectrophotometric flow cell measurements.

Careful temperature control and good mixing are essential for this chromogenic LAL assay. We may need to modify the heating block to provide feedback from the measured thermocouple data to the thermostat. We may need to modify the mixing technique; i.e., by adjusting the orbital shaker speed and stroke, by tapping the plate to mimic the manual mixing, or by changing the liquid dispensing technique. We may also need to take further precautions to reduce the environmental contamination, such as covering the test tubes. However the robotic technique should be more aseptic than for a human technician.

CONCLUSION

Sophisticated generic programming techniques have been developed for robotic manipulations of test tubes and microtiter plates. These programs are easy to use, provide tremendous versatility and are applicable to many related assays. With these techniques we expect to rapidly implement the LAL assay in quality control laboratories, easily modify it and have the capability of integrating it with other assays on the same robot table. We should achieve greater reliability, better sample throughput and quantitative accuracy, and reduce the cost of the chemical reagents. We will eliminate the tedious manipulations currently performed manually.

ACKNOWLEDGEMENTS

Claude Hatfield, Steve Miller, Brian Lightbody and Kevin Tucker of Zymark Corporation (Hopkinton, MA) were major contributors in developing the robot techniques. At the American Cyanamid Company's Lederle Laboratories Eileen Beysel, Genevieve Rothlauf and Bob Bernardo shared information about how the chromogenic LAL assay is manually performed.

REFERENCES
1. "Third Generation Pyrogen Testing", QCL-1000[tm] Quantitative Chromogenic LAL Test Kit, Whittaker M. A. Bioproducts, Inc,. Walkersville, MD 21793.

2. P. A. Martin and K. Tsuji, "Automation of Bacterial Endotoxin Testing with a Zymate Laboratory Automation Systems", in Advances in Laboratory Automation Robotics 1984, J. R. Strimaitis and G. L. Hawk, eds. (Zymark Corporation, 1984), pp. 219.

3. L. Porter Powell and P. Mirando, "Semimicro UV-VIS Absorbance Analyses", in Advances in Laboratory Automation Robotics 1986, J. R. Strimaitis and G. L. Hawk, eds. (Zymark Corporation, 198) pp. 313.

4. These concepts and programs were developed by Zymark Corporation and were extensively modified by the author. The major contributors were Claude Hatfield, Steve Miller, Brian Lightbody and Kevin Tucker.

APPENDIX A: BENCH LAYOUTS

Schematic diagrams and photos of bench layouts are listed by application and page number:

Appendix B: Poster Abstracts

Abstracts of the video-poster sessions presented at the Fifth International Symposium on Laboratory Robotics, Boston, 1987.

ROBOTIC RESIDUE SAMPLE PURIFICATION BY
SOLID-PHASE EXTRACTION

K. H. Akkari
FMC Corporation
Princeton, NJ 08540

A Zymate II PyTechnology system was configured to automate residue sample purification by solid-phase extraction. The initial application established was for routine purification of organic solvent extracts of a synthetic pyrethroid by adsorption (Florisil[R]) chromatography prior to megabore capillary GC-ECD analysis.

The scheduled procedure comprised the following five laboratory unit operations (LUO'S): (1) Source (sample extract in non-polar solvent) ; (2) Non-robotic 1 (sample concentration, 13 mL to 1 mL) ; (3) Robotic operations (column conditioning with polar and non-polar solvent, pouring of sample on column, rinsing tube and column with non-polar solvent, and sample elution with solvent of suitable polarity; (4) Non-robotic 2 (evaporation of elution solvent, 5 mL to 0.5 mL); (5) sink (adding 5 mL of non-polar solvent for storage of purified extract).

Column efficiencies of 85% or better were achieved for amounts of the pyrethroid ranging from 5 nanograms to 100 micrograms. Methods were validated for sensitivities of 2.5 parts per trillion in water, 1 part per billion in soil, sediment, fish and mussel, and 0.05 parts per million in soil and cotton foliage.

AUTOMATED ANALYSIS OF ANTI-INFLAMMATORY AGENTS
IN BIOLOGICAL FLUIDS

L. A. Brunner and R. C. Luders
Ciba-Geigy Corporation
Development Department
Pharmaceutical Division
Ardsley, NY 10502

Fully automated procedures have been developed for the analysis of several anti-inflammatory agents in biological fluids. A laboratory robotics system which has been interfaced to high performance liquid chromatographic equipment has been designed for routine use in disposition studies involving both experimental drug candidates and marketed compounds. The robotic system performs all the necessary steps for the liquid-liquid extraction of the compounds from the biological matrix as well as introduction of the sample into the chromatographic equipment for analysis. Serial sample preparation ensures uniform sample treatment and fast turn-around time.

Application of the procedure to the analysis of CGS 10787B, CGS 15529, and Voltaren has shown accuracy and precision acceptable for unattended analysis. Overnight operation of the automated system affords fast data collection and minimal human intervention with results comparable to those obtained with manual (non-robotic) methods.

ROBOT-ASSISTED OXIDATION OF PLANT AND ANIMAL SAMPLES

**L. G. Carter, J. E. Conaway, M. T. Goetz, O. R. Hunt,
R. L. Johnson, III, M. J. Kennard and C. M. Pukalski
E. I. Dupont de Nemours and Co.
Agricultural Products Department
Wilmington, DE 19898**

The oxidation analysis of plant and animal samples using a Packard 306 Oxidizer provides the basis for location and quantitation of [^{14}C]-labeled materials in a biological test system. A custom-designed Zymark Laboratory Automation System is used to automate the labor-intensive operation of the Packard oxidizer.

This robotic system accomplishes the following tasks necessary for successful oxidation of a sample:

o Load combustion cones.

o Uncap and recap scintillation vials.

o Load and unload scintillation vials.

o Initiate oxidation.

The efficiency of the robotic system lies in its ability to run unattended including overnight. Minimal operator time (approximately 20 minutes) is needed to set up the system.

A NEW APPROACH TO AUTOMATED SAMPLE PREPARATION

G. J. Fallick
Waters Chromatography Division
Millipore Corporation,
Bedford, MA 01730

The recognition that sample preparation is often the limiting operation in analytical chemistry has generated very strong interest in automating these operations. A number of approaches based on general purpose use of robotics have been taken. However, in many instances the highly repetitive, labor intensive operations are based on certain groups of procedures. Filtration, solid phase extraction and related liquid handling tasks represents one such group with vary wide spread utility.

Waters' new MilliLab[TM] Workstatation is a self-contained system for performing automated filtration with Millex[R] Filters and automated extraction with Waters' Sep-Pak[R] Plus Cartridges. The major components of this compact, streamlined robotic system will be described and examples of how it is used in conjunction with HPLC will be presented.

RESISTIVE PULSE PARTICLE SIZE AND THE SINGLE ROBOT

R. J. Freitag
Xerox Corporation
Webster, NY 14580

Zymark has provided the means for improving day-to-day life in the analytical laboratory. With labor constraints, tight dollars, and the need for improving quality a constant pressure, robotics has changed from being a "luxury" to being a necessity.

Our necessity involved a Coulter Counter system, a technician who was "locked" to the Coulter Counter, and a workload of approximately 10,000 samples a year. An integrated system was developed incorporating master/slave controller protocol. The system consists of a Coulter Counter TA-ll multi-channel analyzer; Xerox-developed sensing unit; a Zymate I robot with MLS, vortex mixer, and external communications interface; and a Xerox 820-II micro-computer.

The 820-II acts as the master, controlling the actions of both the Zymate controller, and the Coulter Counter/sensor unit via two serial ports. It controls all activities from sample entry and identification to final data statistics output.

DERIVATIZATION OF AMINO ACID SAMPLES USING A
ZYMATE II ROBOT

C. Martin, J. Oberdier and G. Murphy
Abbott Laboratories
North Chicago, IL 60064

Until about three years ago, the analysis of amino acids in most laboratories was performed using the traditional ion exchange/ninhydrin technique. In 1984, a new method was published which can perform the assay in a fraction of the time it formerly took. This procedure, as described by Bidlingmayer, Cohen and Tarvin, consists of pre-column derivatization of the sample with phenylisothiocyanate (thereby converting the amino acids into UV visible chromophores) followed by reverse phase HPLC.

However, the derivatization portion of the analysis is quite labor intensive and automating it has significantly increased the productivity of our lab. A Zymate II Laboratory Robot has been used for this purpose. The automated (robotic) version of the assay is essentially the same as the manual version although it was necessary to have Zymark custom-design several unique pieces of equipment. A vacuum drying station, refrigeration unit, and the "mini-rack" concept of handling 6 mm test tubes are some of the new features which were incorporated into this system. The procedure has been fully validated and is now one of the routine procedures in our laboratory.

REFERENCES

B. Bidlingmeyer, S. Cohen and T. Tarvin, Journal of Chromatography, 336 (1984) 93-104.

S. Cohen, T. Tarvin and B. Bidlingmeyer, American Laboratory (August, 1984) 48-59.

ANALYSIS OF INDUSTRIAL HYGIENE FIELD SAMPLES USING A ZYMATE LABORATORY ROBOT

C. N. Peck, L. B. Coyne and D. M. Gay
The Dow Chemical Company
Analytical and Environmental Chemistry Health and
Environmental Sciences
Midland, MI 48674

Preparation of industrial hygiene field samples for analysis can be time-consuming and tedious. Sample preparation procedures for various industrial hygiene samples were developed using a Zymate laboratory robot. The steps used to extract analytes from air sampling tubes and filters were patterned after manual operations with modifications that made the procedures more amenable to automation.

The robot performed a series of tasks including solvent manipulation, linear shaking, and crimping autosampler vials. The robot's capabilities were demonstrated in the extraction of membrane and Whatman #2 filters and in the desorption of a newly designed one-gram charcoal tube. The recoveries and relative standard deviations for all sampling devices obtained by the robot were comparable to those obtained using manual desorption procedures.

These applications demonstrate that a robotic system can be a reliable and cost-effective tool for the sample preparation of industrial hygiene field samples.

ROBOT ASSISTED RADIORECEPTOR BINDING ASSAYS

A. W. Rhind II
Nova Pharmaceutical Corporation
Drug Discovery Division
Baltimore, MD 21224

Radioreceptor binding assays are utilized to quickly and reliably test thousands of compounds for their neuropharmacological effects. An automated method for assisting technicians to perform these molecular screening techniques has been developed using the Perkin-Elmer MasterLab System. Each system consists of an IBM AT, a robot, a device interface, an inverted capping station, a dual syringe, two gas controllers, a modified Rainin EDP Pipette and a 1.1 m linear transport mounted on a 4.5 x 9 ft. work surface. Many specially designed pieces were also created "in-house" to increase the throughput, productivity, and accuracy of the system. Each robot is capable of handling up to 336 sample vials, 5 different buffers, and 8 racks of test tubes with over half of the original surface area available for future development.

The robots are responsible for three steps of the binding assay: compound solubilization, compound transfer, and buffer addition. This relieves technicians from the most tedious, routine and time-consuming operations of these experiments and allows them to perform other vital operations. The programming has also been written to optimize the system. The rate-limiting step in this procedure is the uncapping and recapping of the vials. Since more than twenty assays can be performed on one group of compounds, a multiple rack dispensing procedure was chosen. In this method three robots are used to prepare from one to four assays where the only difference between each assay is the buffer which is added. Each assay usually consists of five sets of forty-two compounds. The first two robots would be responsible for pipetting two sets of compounds each and the third robot would pipette one set. This reduces the amount of uncapping and recapping by up to three-fourths and in turn reduces the total time by up to two-thirds.

THE IMPLEMENTATION OF A ZYMATE II IN ANTICANCER DRUG SCREENING

R. Willebrords[1], W. Distelmans[1], F. Vander Auwera[2],
R. Rosiers[2] and M. De Brabander[1]
[1]Laboratory of Oncology,
[2]SID Janssen Research Foundation
Beerse, Belgium

Approximately 2500 new synthetic compounds are being tested yearly *in vitro* for possible antieoplastic properties.

Aiming at reducing human interventions and extending our screening capacities, the Zymate II system has been implemented in our laboratory. The new compounds are dissolved during the preceding night and subsequently added to different cancer cells in microtest plates. The effect of each drug at 5 different concentrations is microscopically evaluated by a skill staff member. The following 5 criteria for anticancer properties are used: cytotoxicity, growth inhibition, antimicrotubular activity, interference with a tumor promotor (tetradecanoyl phorbolacetate; TPA), interference with a growth factor (epidermal growth factor; EGF).

The robot can be displaced along an X-Y axis to reach the incubators. The configuration permits automated transport of the microtest plates from the laminar flow hood to the incubators and vice versa.

The drug-exposed cancer cells are fixed, stained and washed in due time. Previous microscopical findings are macroscopically verified. It is hoped that the implementation of the Zymate II allows a more accurate and extended screening of anticancer drugs at lower costs.

ROBOT-BASED ENZYME LINKED IMMUNOSORBANT ASSAYS (ELISA) IN 96 WELL MICROTITER PLATES.

J.J. Yacobucci, D.J. Hook, J.A. Sowek and S. O'Connor
Bristol-Myers Company
Pharmaceutical Research and Development Division
Department of Screening and Biochemical Research
Wallingford, CT 06492

In our laboratories, ELISA systems are used in the selection and development of monoclonal antibodies for use in our research programs. When performed manually, ELISA-type screening is demanding, repetitive and labor-intensive. These characteristics make it an ideal candidate for robot based automation. Our method is based on the Zymark Robot upgraded to Zymate II status.

Using monoclonal antibodies, a wide range of analytes can be quantitated by ELISA techniques. The method is sensitive, selective and used depending on the analyte of interest. We describe the use of our system to screen for hybridomas producing an antibody to a modified protein. The method is as follows: A. adhere antigen to wells of 96 well plates (overnight), wash 5 times (Non-robotic operation); B. Block residual binding sites with bovine serum albumin; hold at 37 degrees for one hour. Wash 5 times (non-robotic operation); C. Add Hybridoma fluid containing monoclonal antibody. Incubate and shake one hour, wash 5 times (robotic); D. Add goat anti-mouse biotinylated antibody. Incubate and shake one hour, wash 5 times (robotic); E. Add Streptavidin-enzyme conjugate. Incubate and shake one-half hour, wash 10 times (robotic); F. Add Enzyme substrate with chromophore. Incubate and shake in darkness 20 minutes (color develops) (robotic); G. Measure color development using a microplate reader (robotic).

Some of the Zymark accessories for robotizing ELISA screening were not suitable for our purposes. Necessary modifications are described.

The procedure is programmed in a modular fashion so that ELISA assays that require different timing and sequences can be readily accommodated. Data will be presented on the accuracy and reproducibility of the system.

ROBOTS IN INDUSTRIAL LABORATORIES

M.F Antloga, J.L. Buteyn, M. Markelov, and B.R. Seitz*
BP America
4440 Warrensville Center Road
Cleveland, Ohio 44128
***Zymark Corporation**
Zymark Center
Hopkinton, MA 01748

This poster was originally written for a presentation of robotics to production laboratory management, whose justification requirements are much more stringent than that of a research facility. The emphasis of this poster is on the justification procedure, both from an economic and non-economic standpoint. Most of the justification information is a compilation of material from Zymark.

Several robotic procedures are described that perform typical routine analytical analysis of a production lab. The procedures include quality control and environmental type samples.

MICROWAVE ACID PRESSURE DISSOLUTION OF
MINERAL ORES USING ROBOTICS

R.C. Barette and J.M. Labrecque
Kidd Creek Mines
Analytical Laboratory
Timmins, Ontario, CANADA P4N 7K1

Pressure dissolution of mineral ore samples by microwave at Kidd Creek Mines is a rapid and cost effective routine method. The dissolution is conducted in sealed Teflon PFA vessels eliminating contamination and losses of volatile elements. The method involves weighing a batch of 18 samples into vessels followed by the addition of acids and capped with an air operated ratchet. The tray of samples is placed into the CEM microwave oven for a three minute digestion at 600 watts. Once the vessels are cooled and uncapped, the final volume is reached by adding water. This method of sample dissolution results in a significant time and cost reduction compared to traditional methods, however the increasing number of samples for microwave dissolution has made this procedure labor intensive and stressful to the analyst. For these reasons a flexible automated system was sought to conduct the method without human assistance. This poster presentation describes the microwave pressure dissolution of samples developed using the Zymate II system in an effort to reduce human manipulations and to improve the precision and accuracy of the final results. A layout of the system and examples of test studies describe the performance of the robotically controlled microwave pressure dissolution compared to those done manually. Advantages and limitations of the system are also discussed.

FULLY AUTOMATED, PROFILED DISSOLUTION TESTING OF IMMEDIATE RELEASE PHARMACEUTICAL PRODUCTS

D.J. Gleason, J. D. Dunkle, and Gerard C. Hokanson
Parke-Davis Pharmaceutical Research Division
Warner Lambert Company
Morris Plains, NJ 07950

Detailed studies of dissolution characteristics are an integral part of a pre-marketing stability program for new pharmaceutical products. The Zymate II Automated Dissolution Testing System[R] has been modified to accommodate the profiling of immediate release preparations at short 10 minute sampling intervals using USP Apparatus II (rotating paddles). This robotic system has the flexibility to analyze both capsule and tablet preparations using on-line HPLC and/or ultraviolet spectrophotometric sample analysis. Validation studies and examples of successful applications will be described.

FULLY AUTOMATED DISSOLUTION TESTING USING A MODIFIED USP APPARATUS I (ROTATING BASKET) ASSEMBLY

J.D. Dunkle, D.J. Gleason and G.C. Hokanson
Parke-Davis Pharmaceutical Research Division
Warner Lambert-Company
Morris Plains, NJ 07950

The Zymate II Automated Dissolution System[R] has been adapted to totally automate dissolution analysis using a modified USP Apparatus I assembly. Stainless steel shafts have been specially designed to facilitate efficient attachment/detachment of the standard USP baskets by the robot. Dissolution software has been modified to allow multiple sample sets to be analyzed using USP Apparatus I methods, employing on-line HPLC and/or ultraviolet spectrophotometric sample analysis. Illustrations of the basket attachment and detachment using the modified basket assembly will be shown.

AUTOMATED ANALYSIS OF ANTIPYRINE IN HUMAN SERUM

H.G. Fouda and R.P. Schneider
Drug Metabolism Department
Central Research
Pfizer Inc.
Groton, CT 06340

Antipyrine is a widely used marker drug to evaluate hepatic function and to assess inhibition or induction of the microsomal oxidizing system resulting from disease state,[1] Vitamin deficiency[2] or exposure to various xenobiotics.[3] Changes in its pharmacokinetic profile are directly related to changes in intrinsic drug metabolizing enzyme activity.[3] HPLC is the most popular method for the analysis of antipyrine due to the ease of automating the analytical step.[4] The other assay steps are, however, laborious and error prone.

We have integrated a Zymate[5] robot, several commercially available components and some in-house designed modules into a flexible and rapidly switchable system for the complete automation of analytical methods for drugs in biological fluids.[6] The system has been applied to the analysis of many drugs including antipyrine in human serum. It produces precise quantitative results that compare favorably with those produced by manual procedures. The robot's assay throughput is higher than the manual methods. Moreover, the robotic system requires only one hour of manual work daily, saving about 7 man-hours a day. Utilization of well-designed robotic systems increases laboratory productivity and frees skilled analysts from routine tasks, allowing more time for challenging assignments.

[1]Rimmer, M., Routledge, P.A. Tsanaclis, L.M., and Richens, A. Br. J. Clin Pharmacol. 21, 511 (1986).

[2] Khanduja, K.L., Dogra, S.C., Kaushal, S. and Sharma, R.R. Biochemical Pharmacology, 33, 3, 449 (1984).

[3]Vessel, E.S. ClinPharmacol. Ther. 26,275 (1979).

[4]Greenblatt, D.J., Abernathy, D.R. and Divoll, M. Int. J. Clin.Pharm.. Ther. Toxicol. 21,51 (1983),

[5]Zymark Corporation, Hopkinton, MA.

[6]Fouda, H.G. and Schneider, Trends Anal. Chem. 6,139 (1987).

ROBOTIC AUTOMATION OF THE INTENSIVE CARE LABORATORY

R. A. Felder, J. C. Boyd, K. Margrey,
A. Martinez and J. Savory
The University of Virginia Medical Center
Department of Pathology
Charlottesville, VA 22098

Programmable robots have the potential to improve the delivery of health care in the hospital setting at reduced labor costs. With the advent of hospital reimbursement for services according to diagnostic related groups (DRG) many hospital clinical laboratories have consolidated services into centralized facilities. Many satellite laboratories located close to critical care patient units were eliminated in favor of a centrally located clinical lab in order to reduce costs of staffing small laboratories. Programmable robotic arms in unmanned laboratories are being investigated at the University of Virginia as a method to perform clinical analyses close to the patient bedside, yet maintain reduced labor costs.

A Perkin Elmer Master Lab system was used to obtain arterial whole blood specimens from a rack equipped with an optical sensor. The robot fingers were retrofitted with additional optical sensors for determining presence of a sample syringe and locating the position of the plunger. Plunger position could be directly related to sample volume. A Corning 178 blood gas analyzer was fitted with a universal interface developed at the University of Virginia allowing complete control of instrument functions from the personal computer controlling the robot. Blood gas analyses were successfully performed by robot, after which, samples with sufficient blood volume for reanalysis were indexed into a holding rack and all other samples discarded. Sample results were passed electronically back to the host computer for verification and reporting.

Correlation of blood gas results with manual methods in a sample population of 277 specimens resulted in a high degree of correlation (r=O.993, r= 0.975 r=0.976 for p02, pH, and pCO_2 respectively). Not all specimens could be handled by the robotic arm, however. Specimen labels and/or surgical tape were found to interfere with robotic handling of 13% of syringes. The time required to perform a single blood gas analysis was 130 sec for manual manipulation by a technologists vs 215 sec for robotic handling of the specimen. In case of positional error by the robot (this was an extremely rare occurrence), a device was designed which successfully recovered the specimen for reintroduction by the robotic arm.

We conclude that the feasibility of a robotic specimen handling in a remote unmanned laboratory has been demonstrated for properly prepared specimens. Reliability of robotic specimen handling will require users to be instructed in proper specimen preparation and labelling. The reliability required for analysis of often irreplaceable human specimens can be achieved by implementing several fail-sail error detection routines, both in the mechanical hand of the robot as well as in software design.

USING LOTUS 123 TO CONTROL AND COLLECT DATA FROM YOUR LAB ROBOTIC SYSTEM

A. Martin and James Tung*
Source for Automation, Inc.
Holliston, MA 01746
***Lotus Development Corporation**
Cambridge, MA 02140

The flexibility of a laboratory robotic system should not be limited to the task of preparing samples for off-line analysis. The cost of a typical robotic system prohibits the simple preparation of samples as justification and tends to drive typical applications to a near impossible task.

The true benefit of a lab robotic system cannot be fully realized until it becomes an integral part of a flexible workcell architecture capable of interfacing to a wide variety of lab instruments and laboratory information management systems.

Our objective will be to present a standard architecture based on off-the-shelf products. This architecture will provide an easy-to-use programming environment for developing top level programs for instrument and robotic control. It will also provide automated data collection from a wide variety of lab instruments directly into Lotus 123 or Symphony. Once the data is present in the 123 spreadsheet, it is available immediately, and without human intervention, for subsequent analysis, reporting, and file transfer to your laboratory computer.

EVALUATION OF THE HPG ROBOT FOR GENERAL ROBOTICS APPLICATIONS

D. P. McCampbell, W.A. Schmidt, M. F. Fischer,
J. J. Rollheiser and K. M. Stelting
Midwest Research Institute
Kansas City, MO 64110

A robotic system utilizing a modified Zymark™ arm has been developed by HP Genenchem specifically to automate microtiter plate procedures. In addition to the arm, the system incorporates a Vectra™ (IBM PC AT™ compatible) computer, a modular working environment (including a platform and deck), a syringe pump module, a microplate reader, and methods development software (MDS). At the Fourth International Symposium on Laboratory Robotics-1986, a paper was presented discussing the application of the system to an ELISA assay.

MRI has evaluated the capability and suitability of the HPG system for general use in laboratory robotics. The evaluation strategy was to utilize the HPG system in automating a typical analytical chemistry application. The application involved laboratory unit operations such as weighing, diluting, and pipetting using conventional robotic hands, glassware and racks. The three areas of focus for this review were: 1) hardware, including effectiveness of the modifications and complexity of instrument interfacing; 2) software, including ease of teaching and programming; and 3) documentation, for completeness and organization. The results of our evaluation in each of these categories will be presented.

AUTOMATION OF HPLC ASSAY INJECTION AND DATA COLLECTION

C. W. Skelley, C. R. Glover, D. C. Fischer and
R. S. Castellucci
Merck, Sharp & Dohme
Elkton, VA 22827

Phase I of robot usage at Merck Sharp & Dohme Pharmaceutical Laboratories in Elkton, Virginia was semiautomation of dissolution testing. Successful implementation led to Phase II, which was automation of HPLC injections for dose uniformity and assay testing of tablet products manufactured at the Elkton facility.

The HPLC.ASSAY program works by the robot arm attaching the syringe hand and picking up a pipette tip. An aliquot of sample is drawn up by the syringe hand and injected into the injector station; the pipette tip is shucked. The integrator is signaled to start collecting data. After the integrator has generated the data, the robot repeats the program.

Communication between the Zymark controller and the Perkin Elmer integrator is the strength of the HPLC.ASSAY program. This communication allows the controller to signal the integrator when a sample has been injected, and the integrator begins collecting data. After data collection, the integrator sends a "ready" signal to the controller and the robot proceeds to inject the next sample. This communication network makes the HPLC.ASSAY program generic for any product.

After sample injection, the integrator takes over sample processing; all sample specific parameters are entered into the integrator prior to HPLC.ASSAY program start-up. (The HPLC.ASSAY program does not contain any sample specific parameters.) By conforming to testing specifications on column type, mobile phase and integrator parameters, any product/raw material requiring HPLC assay can be tested using the automated program and the Zymark robot.

Validation standard injections, performed by the syringe hand, agreed within 0.5% of manually injected standards. Validation of the method was accomplished, and the program is in place.

Automating HPLC injections reduced chemist involvement by 75%. Communications between the Zymark controller and the HPLC equipment is to be investigated for greater unattended operation. Enhancements to the present arrangement include justification and purchase of additional robotic equipment to both prepare and process samples during non-working shifts. Also, a computer program to both calculate data and generate a report package is in progress.

THE USE OF ROBOTICS FOR THE PREPARATION OF GEOLOGICAL SAMPLES

S.A. Wilson, P.H. Briggs and R.E. McGregor
U.S. Geological Survey
Denver, CO 80225

Increased sample workloads in the laboratory have stimulated interest in laboratory robotics as a means of increasing sample throughput, while maintaining established quality control guidelines. Our laboratory currently has three robotic systems used for the physical and chemical preparation of geologic samples. One robotic system is dedicated to the grinding of samples to pass 80 mesh. This system uses precrushed material (10 mesh) and a Bico vertical grinder to produce samples that pass 80 mesh. The system is capable of processing ten samples per hour for a period of four hours without major mechanical readjustments. Information will be presented on sample composition during this grinding interval and its potential impact on chemical analysis of the sample.

The second system at the laboratory utilizes a multiple-acid digestion of geologic material for inductively coupled argon plasma (ICAP) analysis. Results from the analysis of USGS standards AGV-1, GSP-1,BCR-1, and G-2, for copper, zinc, chromium, and cobalt using both the manual and robotic procedures have demonstrated no significant difference in the two procedures. The system is capable of digesting 24 samples over a 18 hour period, which is ready for direct ICAP analysis. The robotic preparation method will be discussed with regards to advantages and limitations over manual operations especially as they relate to analytical blanks, worker safety, analytical reliability, and potential sample-throughput.

The third system used at the USGS is for the determination of gold in geologic samples, collected as part of our Mineral Resource Assessment Programs. This procedure utilizes a hydrobromic acid digestion procedure. This is followed by an extraction of the gold into methyl isobutyl ketone (MIBK) followed by analysis by flame atomic absorption spectroscopy (AAS) . The robotic procedure is capable of preparing 24 samples in an eight hour interval with an average relative standard deviation (RSD) of ten percent, for replicate samples. The robotic method will be discussed with regards to problems encountered in the analysis of carbonate and sulfide material, and the potential advantages of the robotic approach in comparison to manual methods.

AUTOMATED SYSTEM FOR SIMULTANEOUS DETERMINATION OF SEVERAL INGREDIENTS IN PHARMACEUTICAL PREPARATIONS USING HPLC AND A LABORATORY ROBOT

T. Yoshida, Y. Ito, M. Handa, O. Kasai and H. Yamaguchi
Dept.of Analytical Chemistry Research Center
Taisho Pharmaceutical Co.,LTD.
Saitama 330, Japan

An automation system for the preparation of solutions from solid samples for HPLC analysis has been developed and applied to the simultaneous determination of nine ingredients in cold remedy tablets, capsules and granules. Powdered samples are weighed, added to the extraction solvent containing internal standard substances, extracted by supersonic wave irradiation and vortexing, centrifuged and injected into two HPLCs using a laboratory robot. Two HPLCs and a electronic balance are interfaced with a PC-9801 personal computer (NEC).

The analytical data are automatically calculated and recorded on floppy disks and the final reports are generated.

MAKING LABORATORY ROBOTS MORE PRODUCTIVE BY EXPANDING THEIR EFFECTIVE WORK ENVELOPE

R.D. Jones, J.B. Cross and H.R. Pinnick, Jr.
Phillips Petroleum Company
Bartlesville, OK 74004

Limited reach severely restricts the volume of space accessible to a laboratory robot. Sample racks, specialized workstations, and analytical instrumentation can quickly fill this "work envelope," but the associated workload may not fill the robot's time. As a result, laboratory robots all too often end up dedicated to only one or two tasks, and idle many hours each day.

Of course 100% utilization of any machine is difficult to achieve, but many laboratory robots are capable of being far more productive, given the opportunity. That means figuring out how to get additional work to them, or vice versa; in other words, devising ways to expand a robot's effective work envelope so that it encompasses the racks, support equipment, etc. necessary for performing additional duties.

At Phillips we have found two ways to accomplish this. The first involves adding what might be thought of as "drawers" around the outer perimeter of a robot's reach. These "drawers" are actually sample racks mounted on wheeled carts. The carts roll on rails running parallel to, and slightly above, sample racks positioned on the workcell's floor. They remain beyond the robot's reach until needed, at which time the robot grasps a handle on the desired cart's front (the only part of it extending into the work envelope) and pulls the cart into reach.

A second (and far more useful) way to expand a robot's work envelope is to mount the arm on a motorized cart, and give it the ability to commute, as part of its programming, between adjoining workcells. In our case this cart runs on rails, and has a pneumatic latching system to lock it into place once the desired workcell is reached. The cart/track/latching system was built in house for less than $2,000.

UNI-LAB; REGULATED WORK AREAS FOR LABORATORY ROBOTICS

R.E. Hill
HEMCO Corporation
Independence, MO 64050

The importance of controlled isolation containment of critical laboratory procedures and robotics operations give assurance of the quality of the end results.

The UniLab is a new concept in Flexible/Regulated laboratory work areas that can provide a class clean work area combined with temperature and humidity controlled environments; thus providing for an effective Quality Control Program.

When equipped with explosion proof services and filtered exhaust systems, the UniLab can effectively contain and control hazardous laboratory procedures and maintain a higher level of laboratory safety.

The pre-engineered modular design allows for fast installation in existing or new laboratory facilities. The flexible design permits for ease of expansion to accommodate future needs. The UniLab is equipped to desired configuration and can also be set up under a leasing program.